Graphical Analysis

Understanding Graphs and Curves in Technology

Hayden Series In Applied Mathematics

Graphical Analysis
Understanding Graphs and Curves in Technology

PHILIP STEIN, B.S.

Head, Physics Department,
RCA Institutes

Lecturer in Electronics, Physics Department,
Adelphi University

HAYDEN BOOK COMPANY, INC., NEW YORK

to Frieda, my wife

Preface

In 1786, an English statistician wrote, "I have succeeded in proposing a new and useful mode of stating accounts. . . . As much information may be obtained in five minutes as would require whole days to imprint on the memory . . . by a table of figures." This was William Playfair, reputedly the first man to apply charts and graphs to finance. Since that time the rapidly developing worlds of business, science, and technology have far more extensively and intensively applied the principles of graphs first set forth by René Descartes in 1637. In October, 1962, newspaper columnist Richard Slawsky reported,* "The average flight of a missile . . . lasts only about 15 minutes but, in that time more than 1,000,000 bits of information are compiled on the performance of each of the vehicle's components. . . . A single . . . test . . . might generate more than 20,000 pages of pertinent data. . . . Thus threatened with a complete deluge of numbers and endless reams of paper . . . engineers . . . sought relief. . . . The solution was simply a matter of converting the numbers . . . into graphical form. . . . Within half an hour, a determination could be made as to how each particular system functioned and what, if anything, went wrong. . . . 'We thought for a while we would have to rent a warehouse to keep all the paperwork in; now we can carry the results of a test in a briefcase.' "

In recognition of the needs of science and technology, a course on graphs and their analysis was incorporated into the program of study at RCA Institutes. Because of my interest in this area and of my agreement on the desirability for such a course, I was asked to write the course outline and to select a text. The objectives were the following:

1. To teach the student scientist, engineer, or technician how to plot data correctly and effectively on the various types of graph grids, useful in information display
2. To develop the student's ability to read significant information from curves and graphs and to make predictions from them
3. To teach the student to think in terms of rates of change, curve bounded areas, and limiting values
4. To discuss the properties of curves and waveshapes common in science and technology
5. To show the student that graphs are an effective tool in the study and understanding of laws and phenomena in science and technology.

With the course outline completed, the quest for an appropriate text began. Although many references for various parts of the course were found, no one volume covered even a substantial portion of the required material. After several terms of giving the course without a text, I undertook the writing of one. The following volume is the result.

I wish to thank the many people whose efforts and suggestions were of considerable aid to me. In particular, these include my colleagues at RCA Institutes: Mr. Jacob Brody, Head of the Audio Department, for his review of the chapter on polar coordinates; Mr. Henry Warner, Head of the Communications Systems Department, for his review of the discussion of the hyperbola and the hyperbolic functions; Mr. Harry Abelew, Head of Technical Editing, for his review of Chapter 7; Dean Harry Silverstein for his suggestions on normalized curves; Director Harold Fezer and Instructor Paul Gerhart for their problem suggestions; and Mr. Abe Schwartz, Head of the Computer Programming Department, for his suggestions and discussions on applicable terminology. My very special thanks go to the many engineers and industry and government personnel throughout the country who gave of their time and effort to send me the illustrations and information I needed and to the many who, in addition, sent me best wishes by telephone and mail.

Most of all I thank my wife and four children for their cooperation and understanding when on the many weekends and evenings the lights were on in the study and the door closed.

September, 1964
Merrick, New York   *Philip Stein*

---

* Reprinted by permission from the New York *World-Telegram and Sun.*

Contents

CONTENTS

List of Illustrations

Chapter 5

Chapter 8

1 - GRAPHICAL REPRESENTATION OF TECHNICAL DATA

In the past several years the use of graphs and charts to represent technical information has increased so rapidly that present day science and technology are very heavily dependent on information displayed by them. Medical diagnostic information (Fig. 1-1), a radar screen display (Fig. 1-2), mechanical vibration pickup (Fig. 1-3), a bar graph of business activity (Fig. 1-4), the characteristic curves of a transistor (Fig. 1-5), and radiation energy measurements (Fig. 1-6) are but a minute portion of the extensive list of applications of graphs in all technologies. The wealth of data related to elaborate systems would become a meaningless deluge unless graphically represented, as for example, mis-

EEG (electroencephalograph)

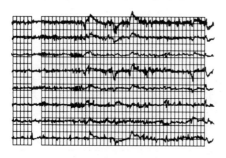

EKG (electrocardiograph)

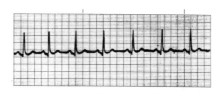

Heart sound

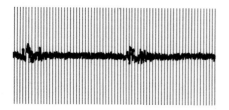

Respiration volume

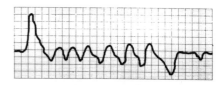

(EKG, Courtesy, FORTUNE)

Fig. 1-1. Measurement of typical body functions

1

Fig. 1-2. Radar screen display

Fig. 1-3. Mechanical vibration pickup

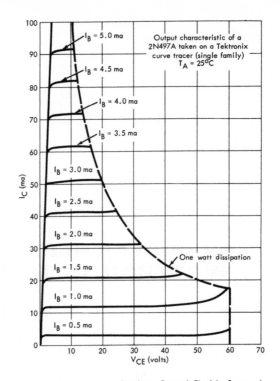

(Courtesy, General Electric Company)
Fig. 1-5. Characteristic curve of a transistor

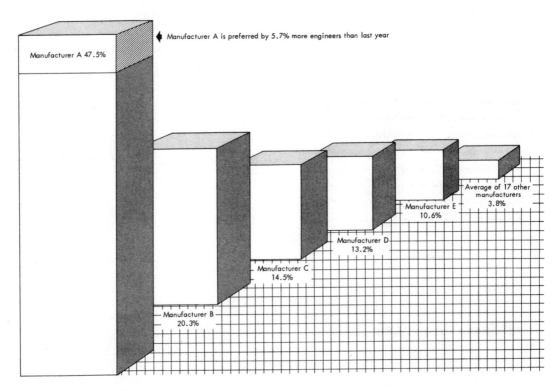

(Courtesy, Lambda Electronics Corp.)
Fig. 1-4. Bar graph of relative sales

sile and satellite launching systems.

As a further indication of the present widespread and ever-expanding use of graphs and charts, an entire industry has developed in this area. There are presently, in the United States alone, over fifty manufacturers of mechanical chart recorders of all types. The products of two of these are shown in Figs.

1-7 and 1-8, and many others are discussed in Chapter 8 of this volume. To them must be added the many producers throughout the world of electronic display equipment using cathode-ray tubes (see Figs. 1-9, 1-10, and Chapter 8) and, of course, the producers of the many types of graph and chart papers used for mechanically and manually produced

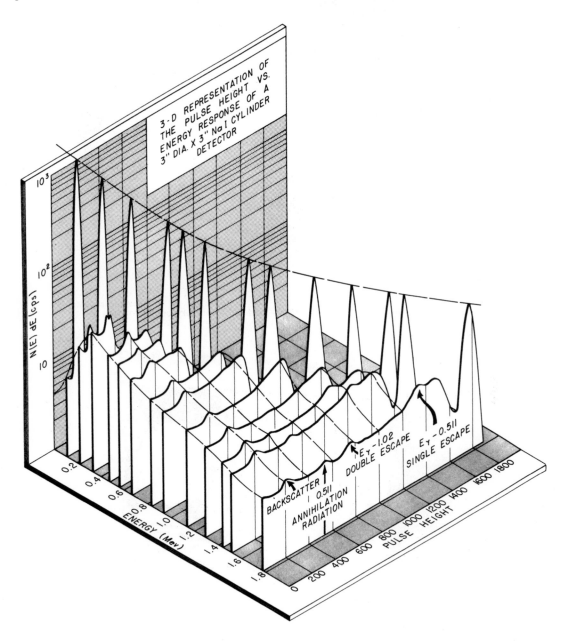

Fig. 1-6. Plotted surface representing radiation energy measurements

(Courtesy, Varian Associates)

Fig. 1-7. Automatic chart recorder designed for laboratory bench top use

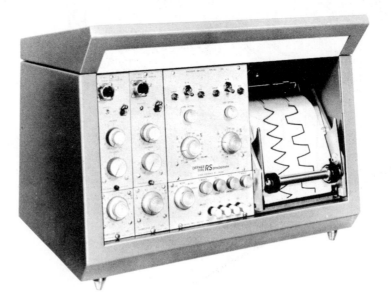

(Courtesy, Beckman Instruments, Inc.)

Fig. 1-8. Two-channel Dynograph recorder (produced as rack-mounted, table-top, or portable unit)

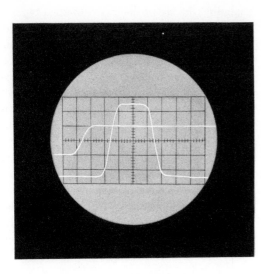

Fig. 1-9. Two graphs simultaneously displayed on screen similar to TV screen

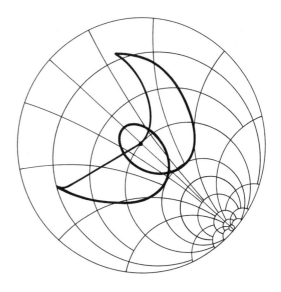

Fig. 1-10. Graph electronically produced on tube screen with special reference lines and curves on its face

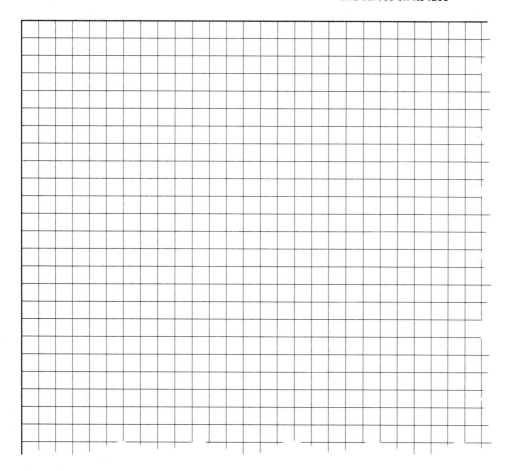

Fig. 1-11. Uniform rectangular-coordinate graph paper, five calibration lines to the inch

graphs. A small sampling of the different types of papers commonly used is shown in Figs. 1-11 through 1-15. At this point the papers are merely named. But these and others will be referred to again later in the text and their applications discussed.

However, unless "graphical language" can be readily understood by the technician, equipment operator, and professional man, this important aspect of technology is useless. Understanding graphical language means being able to interpret the information completely, whether manually, mechanically, or electronically plotted. It means being able to present information efficiently and effectively in the form of a graph. This, in turn, requires under-

standing the use of the many different types of graph papers, knowledge of accepted standards and practice for graphical display, a familiarity with the advantages and disadvantages of the different types of graphs, and a knowledge of the available means for automatic display.

The purpose of the following chapters is to provide just such knowledge and information. The first portion of the book is directed toward the novice, the beginning student in technology. The material is then developed, chapter by chapter, so that from Chapter 4 onward, it will be of value to the engineering or technical student who has completed his basic work as well as to the practicing engineer and technician.

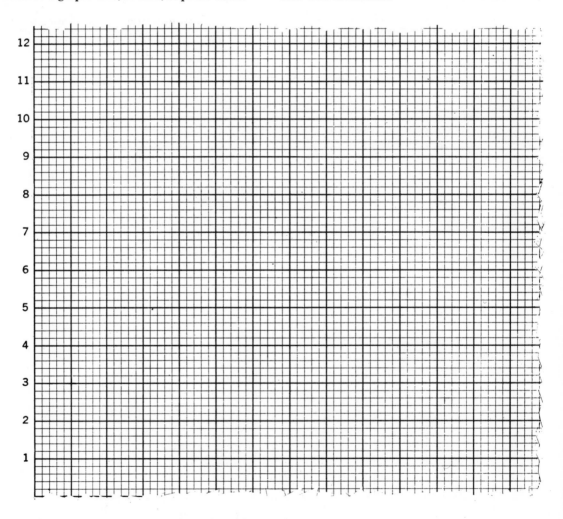

Fig. 1-12. Pre-numbered, uniform rectangular-coordinate graph paper, five calibration lines to the centimeter

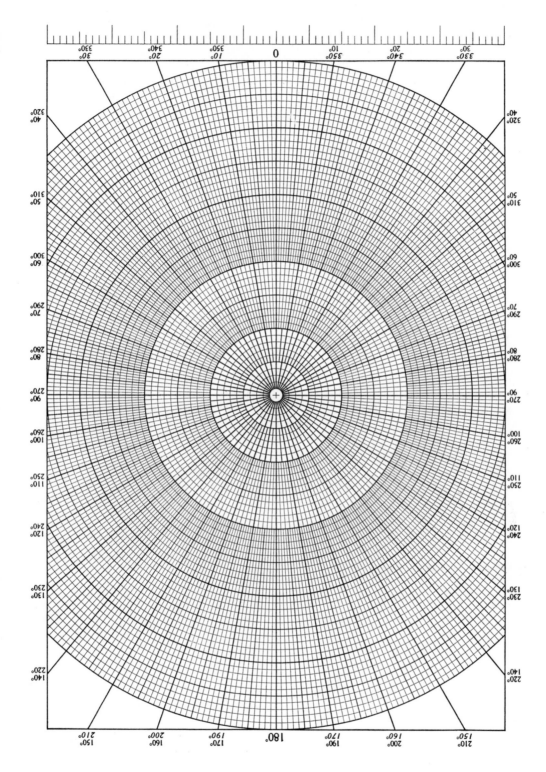

Fig. 1-13. Polar coordinate paper uses concentric circles as well as radial lines

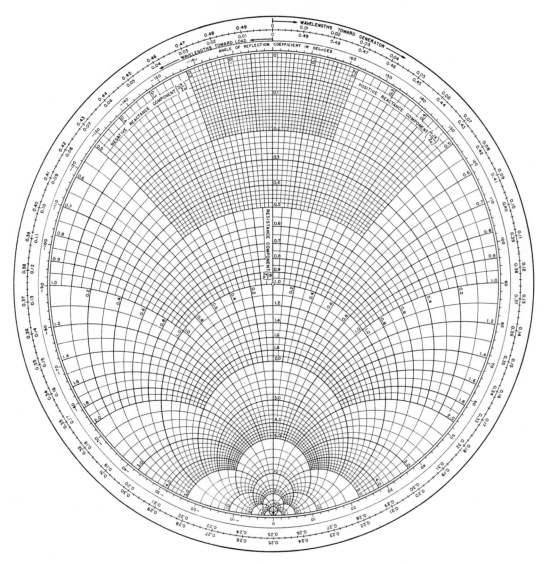

(Courtesy, Emeloid Co., Inc.)
Fig. 1-14. Smith chart paper, used to facilitate "transmission line" calculations in electronics technology

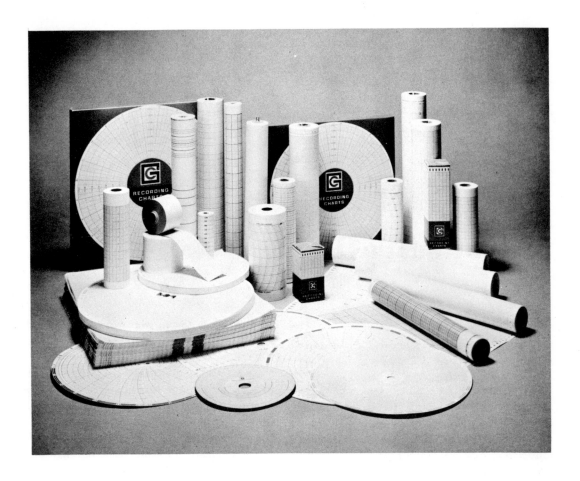

Fig. 1-15. A sampling of graph papers for graphical recorders

2 - BASIC GRAPHS

2.1. What is a graph?

A graph is a means of *pictorially* showing *numerical information* by keying it to one, two, or more *reference* lines. Notice that the important words of this definition are in italics. Since the numerical information is not shown on a graph by using the digits 1, 2, 3, etc., we say it is *pictorially* represented. *Numerical information* has two parts. First of all, each piece of numerical information or data gives information on size, value, amount, quantity, or magnitude as it is referred to in technology. The second part of this numerical information is direction. In most technical applications a number has no meaning at all until a direction is assigned to it. For instance, if you were asked to travel 2 miles from your starting point to arrive at a given location, this number would be absolutely useless unless you were also told in which direction to travel the 2 miles. Direction is omitted only if the direction is obvious to any observer or if only one possible direction exists. For instance, if you were told that it takes about 30 seconds for a vacuum tube to heat up to the point of normal operation, you would expect no direction information with this number, because there is only one direction in which time moves, and that is forward, or in an *increasing direction* from any starting point, never decreasing. Since only one direction exists (or, if you will, the direction in this case is obvious), no information on direction is needed or given. On a graph both the magnitude and the direction of a piece of data are keyed to or related to the reference lines or "axes" as they are technically called. Now that the key words have been clarified, let's try out the definition.

2.2. Applying the definition

The preceding section tells us that a graph is a pictorial representation of technical data keyed to reference lines. On the basis of this definition, is a road map a graph? For convenience, a portion of a road map is shown in Fig. 2-1. To answer the question, use the significant words of the definition. First of all, is the road map a pictorial representation? Yes, it is. It certainly is not a column of figures. Is magnitude and direction information given? Yes, if you were at any one point on the map and wanted to get to another, the map would yield distance (magnitude) information and show the proper direction to take. Finally, is

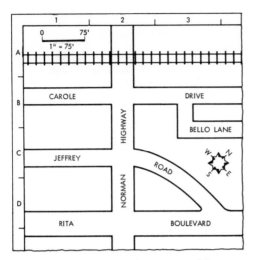

Fig. 2-1. Is a road map a graph?

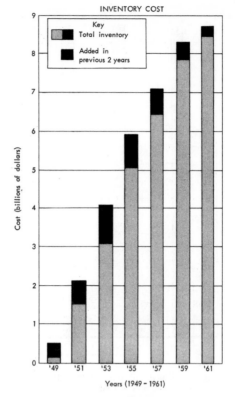

Fig. 2-2. Bar graph using the two most
important bar properties—length
and shading

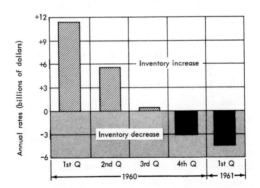

Fig. 2-3. Bar graph using direction and
shading as important properties

all this information keyed to a set of reference axes? Certainly. Notice the horizontal line of numbers along the top and the vertical line of letters along the left side of the map. These lines of numbers and letters represent the axes. Thus, a road map satisfies all parts of our definition of a graph and is therefore a true graph.

2.3. The bar graph

We all know, of course, that the road map is not the only type of graph. As indicated in Chapter 1, many different varieties of graphs exist, each with its own particular advantages, applications, and limitations. One family of basic graphs that finds wide application is the bar graph. Of course, our general definition of Section 2.1 applies to this kind of graph, but how can this all-purpose definition be expanded to explain what is meant by a bar graph? Reference to Figs. 2-2, 2-3, and 2-4 will help provide the answer. A bar graph is one that employs horizontal or vertical bars to picture the required numerical information. The significant properties of the bars, listed in the order of their importance are:

Length	Fig. 2-2
Shading	Figs. 2-2 and 2-3
Direction	Fig. 2-3
Width	Fig. 2-4
Color	

2.4. Advantages and disadvantages of the bar graph

The bar graph is used primarily when it is desired to show comparison. Notice how obvious it is from Fig. 2-5 that a drastic difference exists in the size of the copper stock as com-

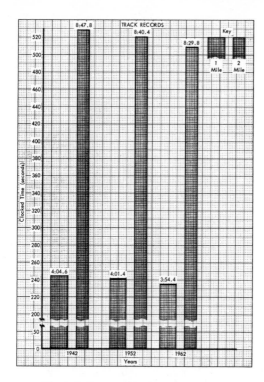

Fig. 2-4. Bar graph using bar width for classification

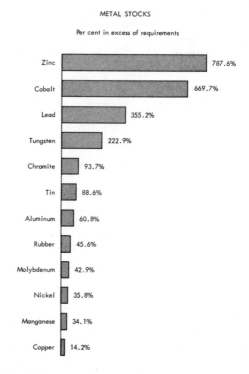

METAL STOCKS

Per cent in excess of requirements

Zinc	787.6%
Cobalt	669.7%
Lead	355.2%
Tungsten	222.9%
Chromite	93.7%
Tin	88.6%
Aluminum	60.8%
Rubber	45.6%
Molybdenum	42.9%
Nickel	35.8%
Manganese	34.1%
Copper	14.2%

(Copyright by the New York TIMES. Reprinted by permission.)
Fig. 2-5. Bar graph using horizontal bars. To compensate for graph's limited accuracy, exact numerical values are often shown at end of bars

pared to the stock of zinc. This ready comparison is by far the most important advantage of the bar graph. The bar graph is easily read and is therefore just as useful in the form of a large poster that is to be viewed by a group as it is on a small sheet designed for an individual reader. In addition, the bar graph is attractive to the eye and is readily produced.

The bar graph, however, has limitations. The first of these is limited accuracy, that is, the difficulty of providing numerical information accurate to one or two decimal places. For example, referring to Fig. 2-2, we can see that the cost shown by the 1961 bar is higher than that of the 1959 bar. But by how much? This can be only roughly estimated from the graph. By examining the two bar heights closely, we can approximate that they differ by about one-third of a division of the vertical scale shown at the left. This amounts to about one-third of a billion dollars. Not very accurate, is it? Notice how this problem was overcome in the graph of Fig. 2-5. Here the exact value for each bar is given. This is additional

information that is not truly a part of the bar graph, but it is a technique often used. The very fact that it is used accents the limited accuracy of the bar graph.

In addition to its lack of accuracy, the bar graph is easily misused. Since only the five characteristics of length, shading, direction, width, and color can be used to distinguish between bars, any attempt to show more than five changing quantities on one bar graph leads to confusion. Even the use of four or all five characteristics on one graph is very poor practice. Notice the bar graph of Fig. 2-6. An attempt was made here to crowd too much information into one graph. The result was to defeat the purpose of a graph, which is to provide information readily. Notice the amount of written numerical information necessary in this example. Thus, a bar graph is easily overcrowded. In Fig. 2-7, for example, an attempt was made to show four different pieces of information (projected student enrollment, minimum gap to be met, present capacity, and year) using 12 bars and three

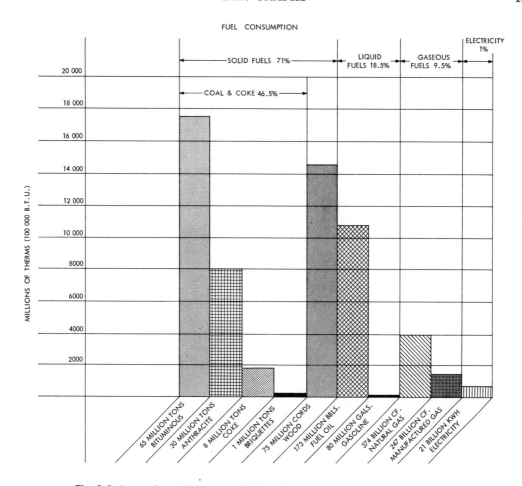

Fig. 2-6. A poor format because of attempt to convey too much information

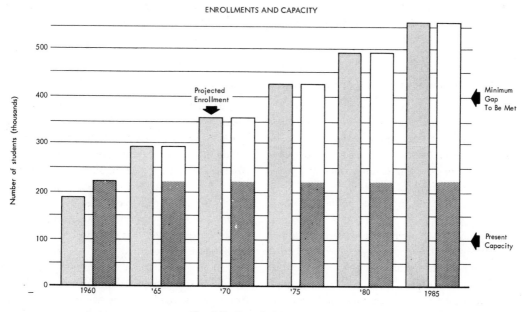

Fig. 2-7. Crowded bar graph

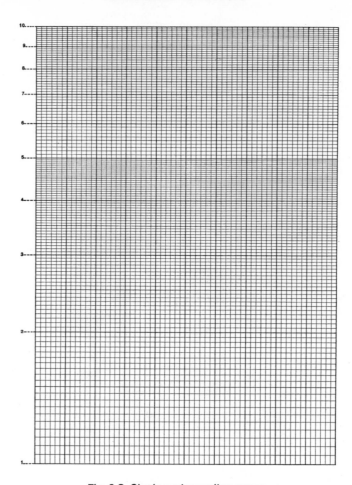

Fig. 2-8. Single-cycle semilog paper

different shadings. For this type of presentation, no more than four bars should appear on the graph. As it is, the graph is cluttered and its purpose defeated.

2.5. How to make an effective bar graph

In general, the procedure for making an effective graph of any type is the same. A listing and discussion of the steps follows:
1. Choose the correct type of graph paper.
2. Draw the proper reference lines or axes.
3. Calibrate the axes properly.
4. Label the axes and all components completely.
5. Transcribe the numerical information to the graph sheet.
6. Complete the graph.
7. Name the graph.
8. Interpret the graph as a test of its effectiveness and value.

2.6. Choosing the correct type of graph paper

The small sampling of graph papers shown in Figs. 1-11 through 1-15 is sufficient to show that the choice of the correct graph paper requires some thought. For a bar graph the field is limited somewhat, since a bar graph requires the use of rectangular coordinate graph paper. This is paper in which the *grid work* is made up of horizontal and vertical straight lines. The term "rectangular" is used since the lines of the grid work meet at right angles as do the sides of a rectangle. The word "coordinate" refers to two items of equal importance or rank, and this is certainly true of the horizontal and vertical lines of graph paper. But does "rectangular coordinate" completely describe the required graph paper? Before trying to answer this question, refer to Figs. 2-8 and 2-9. Are the grid lines (coordinate

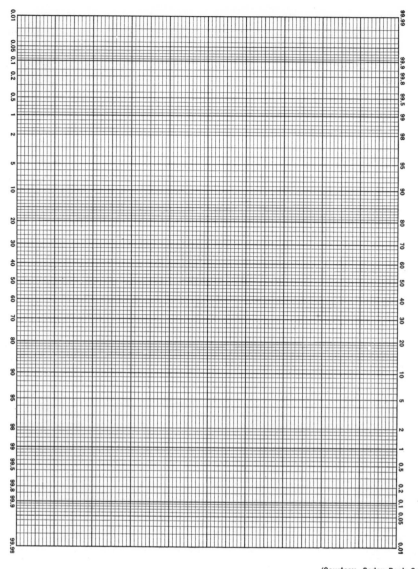

Fig. 2-9. Arithmetic probability paper

(Courtesy, Codex Book Co.)

lines) all made up of horizontal and vertical straight lines? Certainly. Then are all these papers the same? Obviously, they are not. By looking along the bottom horizontal line of Fig. 2-8, you will see that uniform spacing exists between the vertical lines. In other words, the distances between the lines drawn vertically are all the same. However, a glance up the page will verify that this uniformity of spacing does not exist between the lines drawn horizontally. That is, the spacing between the horizontal lines is nonuniform and seems to decrease as we look up the page, from bottom to top. Now note the graph paper of Fig. 2-9.

Here we have a rectangular coordinate paper that shows a uniform line spacing in one direction but nonuniform spacing in the direction in which the printed numbers appear. Note that this nonuniformity in spacing is somewhat different from that of Fig. 2-8 and is therefore intended for a different application. From this discussion, it is evident that specifying rectangular coordinate paper is insufficient. Bar graphs require rectangular coordinate paper, uniformly spaced throughout.

The terms "rectangular coordinate" and "uniformly spaced" used in the preceding paragraphs are quite descriptive and clearly specify their own meaning. However, these terms have synonyms in technology that are as often used as they are. The "rectangular coordinate graph paper" is often replaced by "Cartesian coordinate graph paper," which is taken to mean the same thing, that is, graph paper whose gridwork is made up of two sets of straight lines, perpendicular to one another.[1] The term "uniform spacing" is often referred to as "linear spacing" or "linear calibration." Thus Fig. 2-10 is an example of linearly calibrated Cartesian coordinate graph paper, a type of paper well suited for bar graphs as well as for many other graphs and curves yet to be discussed. But why all the

accent on the naming of the straight-line graph papers? Do rectilinear (straight line) graph papers exist that are not rectangular? Reference to Fig. 2-11 will answer that question. The gridwork of this paper is made up of straight lines, uniformly spaced throughout. Plainly, however, not all the lines are horizontal or vertical. Two sets of diagonal lines also exist, making this paper nonrectangular coordinate paper. Thus we see the need for completely descriptive terms for the various types of graph papers.

Figures 2-10, 2-12, and 2-13 are all examples of uniform, rectangular coordinate paper. The only difference between them is the

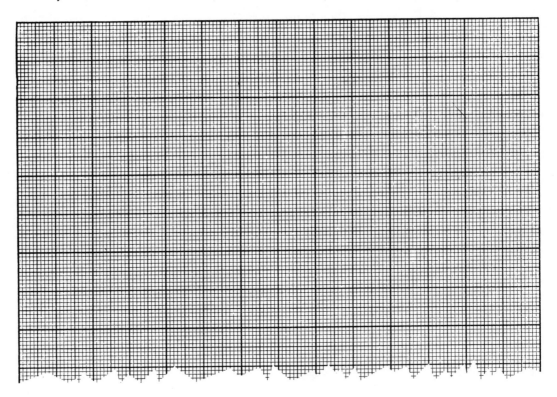

Fig. 2-10. Uniform Cartesian coordinate paper

---

[1] The coordinate reference system for locating a point in a plane or in space was developed by the French philosopher-mathematician, Rene Descartes (1596-1650), and the system is therefore known as the "Cartesian coordinate system." It should be noted, however, that the term "Cartesian coordinate" does not necessarily refer to coordinate line directions that are perpendicular to one another. In application, perpendicularity is the most convenient direction and hence the most often used. Consequently, the term "Cartesian coordinate" is often used as a synonym for rectangular coordinate. The term that refers to right angle measurement in *three directions* is "orthogonal." Here again, "Cartesian coordinate" is used as a synonym even though the term could refer to a system of reference lines making angles other than 90 degrees with one another. (See Chapter 7 for applications of "3D" coordinate systems.)

Fig. 2-11. Isometric-orthographic paper for three-dimensional plotting

number of calibration lines drawn per inch. The proper choice depends on the amount of numerical information to be included on each axis. If a great deal of information is to be included on one or both of the axes, then paper with a *fine calibration* (lines closely spaced) is required. If rather limited information or few calibration points are to be shown on the axes, then paper with coarse calibration such as four lines to the inch (4×4) is sufficient. However, if it is desired to keep a supply of one paper that will serve effectively for a wide range of applications, the 20×20 paper shown in Fig. 2-10 is recommended. The 100 calibration lines that this spacing permits in the long direction are a very convenient number to work with, and the 70 lines in the short direction are usually sufficient for most applications. An additional advantage to the graphist is the existence of a heavy calibration line every half-inch. The technical term used to designate the heavy lines is "primary calibration lines." The lighter lines of the graph

paper gridwork are called the "secondary calibration lines." Thus, the uniform, 20×20 Cartesian coordinate paper shown in Fig. 2-10 has a primary calibration line every half-inch and, as already stated, 20 calibration lines per inch.

2.7. The margins

One additional comment is necessary before we leave the discussion of graph-paper choice for our bar graph. Note the paper of Fig. 2-14. In addition to the grid-line spacing, this paper is different from the others in that it has no margins. Marginless graph paper is used for sketching rather than for final work. The margins that appear on most graph papers are not intended for any information that is at all related to the graph. The reason for this is that, since a graph is a concise presentation of a great deal of information, it is often this portion of a report or technical paper that is reproduced for wider circulation. Since a wide range of copying methods exists (blueprint,

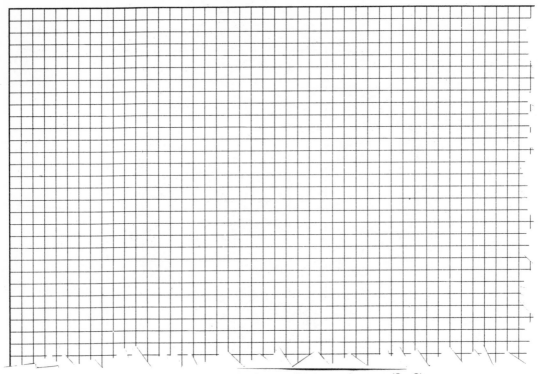

Fig. 2-12. Uniform rectangular-coordinate graph paper (8 x 8)

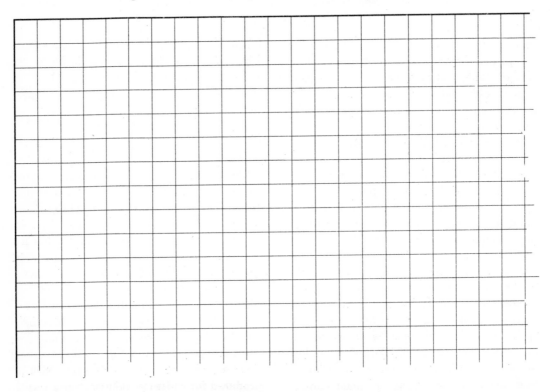

Fig. 2-13. Uniform rectangular-coordinate graph paper (4 x 4)

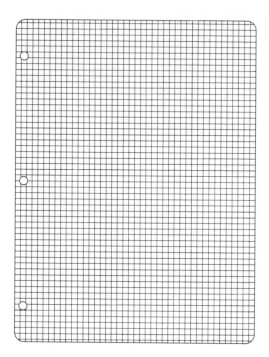

Fig. 2-14. Uniform, marginless rectangular-coordinate graph paper (5 x 5)

photostat, ozalid, etc.), the borders may be required to clamp the original into the copying machine, and no guarantee can be made that information included in the margins will be reproduced. For this reason and because one margin is often required for binding purposes (one wide binding margin is usually provided), it is considered poor practice to include any pertinent information at all outside of the gridwork of the graph paper.

2.8. The axes

Whether a bar graph or any other graph using rectangular coordinate paper is to be drawn, a pair of axes (reference lines) is required—one horizontal and one vertical. These lines should be drawn with a straight edge so that they meet at a point often located near the lower left-hand corner of the graph paper gridwork. This point is called the "origin," and it is the zero-value point (starting point) for both the horizontal axis and the vertical axis.[2] For purposes of abbreviation, the horizontal

---

[2] Later discussions will show applications in which the origin is centered on the graph sheet.

axis is often called the "X axis" and the vertical reference line is often referred to as the "Y axis." An additional designation used for the horizontal (X) reference line is "independent axis," since it is along this axis that we locate the numbers or quantities that are either self-determined or that do not depend on the other quantity of the graph for their value. For instance, if a bar graph is to be made of the average temperature reading of a given region for each season of a certain year, then the four seasons would be shown along the horizontal axis (see Fig. 2-15), since certainly the seasons are the independent quantity (they are not determined by thermometer readings). On the other hand, the average thermometer reading is determined by the seasons. The seasons are thus the *independent* quantity, and they are shown along the horizontal axis. The average temperature is the *dependent* quantity and is shown along the vertical axis, or *dependent* axis, as the Y axis is sometimes called. In general, whenever time is involved in a graph, it is plotted along the horizontal axis, since time is an independent quantity and does not depend upon anything else for its value.

Often, however, graphs are required in which it is not obvious from the mere names of the quantities which one is independent and which is dependent. The standard method of designating which is independent and which dependent is to use the term "versus" (abbreviated "vs.") between the two quantities involved. The quantity appearing *before* the word "versus" is the dependent quantity and should therefore be shown along the Y (vertical) axis. The quantity appearing *after* the word "versus" is the independent quantity and should therefore be shown along the X (horizontal) axis. Thus, Fig. 2-15 could be designated as a graph of average temperature versus the seasons. The rule is, therefore, dependent vs. independent, Y vs. X, vertical vs. horizontal. Suppose you were required to produce a graph of distance vs. time. Which quantity would appear on the vertical axis and which on the horizontal? Refer to Fig. 3-1 in Chapter 3 for a check on your answer.

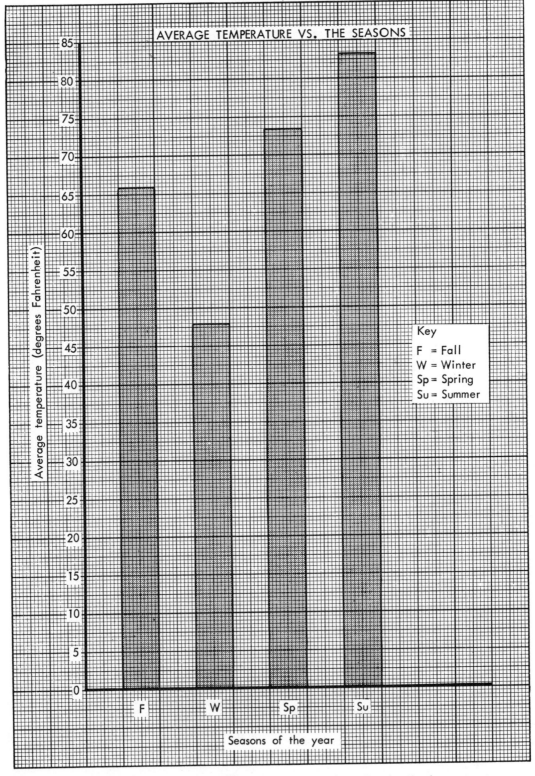

Fig. 2-15. Bar graph of average temperature of specific region for the four seasons (independent quantity, the seasons, appears on **X** axis, and dependent quantity, temperature, on **Y** axis)

Now that we know the convention, what useful purpose does it serve? Does it supply the graph reader with any pertinent information to know that for every graph he reads, the horizontal axis contains the independent quantity and the vertical axis the dependent? A glance at Fig. 2-16 may be helpful in answering this question. The variables in both diagrams "a" and "b" are pressure and volume, but pressure is shown along the horizontal axis in "a" and volume appears along the horizontal axis in "b." Are these arrangements significant in any manner? Definitely. In "a", pressure is the independent variable, meaning that the pressure was varied in order to obtain the required data, and the *resulting volume* measured and recorded. However, in "b", the independent quantity is volume, meaning that the volume was varied to obtain this data (by means of a piston or other appropriate device) and the *resulting pressure* measured and recorded. Consequently, merely by looking at the axes of a given plot we have an insight as to how the data were obtained. To supply this insight is the primary purpose of the convention.

2.9. The quadrant

It was stated earlier that when the axes are drawn on linear paper they are placed so that "they meet at a point near the lower left-hand corner of the graph-paper gridwork." Although this statement is valid and is certainly borne out by the graph of Fig. 2-16 and others throughout this volume, it tells only a part of the story—one-fourth, to be exact. Actually, the horizontal and vertical axes are a pair of perpendicular lines that serve to break up a plane surface into four equal sections, called "quadrants," as shown in Fig. 2-17. The four quadrants are referred to by number, with the first quadrant, Quadrant I, being the one in the upper right hand corner. The quadrants are numbered in a counterclockwise order. Thus, the upper left section is Quadrant II, the lower

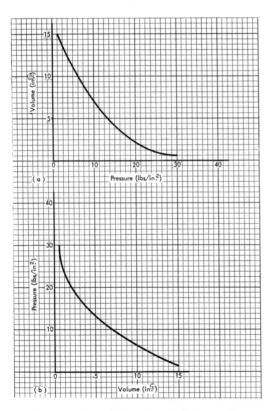

Fig. 2-16. Convention dictates that independent quantity should appear on **X** axis and dependent quantity on **Y** axis, thus providing significant information

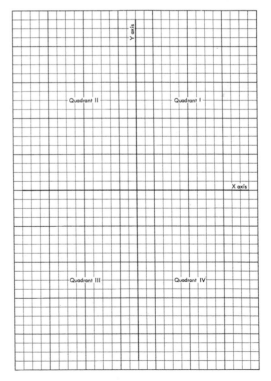

Fig. 2-17. **X** and **Y** axis divide a plane surface into four quadrants

left section is Quadrant III, and the lower right section, Quadrant IV. This counterclockwise direction of travel is standard and is referred to as the "positive" direction of travel from one quadrant to the next.

Note that the bar graph in Fig. 2-15 requires the use of only the first quadrant. Thus, when only this quadrant is drawn on a sheet of rectangular coordinate graph paper, the point of intersection of the axes (the origin) appears near the lower left-hand corner of the gridwork. We will shortly consider bar graphs that require the use of more than one quadrant and in later discussions will come across graphs that require showing all four quadrants.

2.10. Calibrating the axes

Since a graph represents numerical information, a method for incorporating numbers into the graph is necessary. This method is called the "calibration" of the axes, that is, the measuring off of specific lengths of an axis and assigning values (numbers) to these lengths. Since we are dealing with linear rectangular graph paper in the present discussion of bar graphs, equal units of length along the axis in question will have equal values, as shown in Fig. 2-15. The vertical axis of this figure is calibrated so that each primary division line represents 5 Fahrenheit degrees. Now why was this graduation decided upon? Why wasn't each primary calibration line of the graph paper made to represent 10 degrees or 1 degree? Also, why wasn't the graph paper held on its side with the binding at the top so that the shorter axis could be used for temperature and the longer one for the seasons of the year? All these are valid questions at this point and indicate the factors to be considered when planning an axis calibration.

Let's answer the last question first. Why wasn't the shorter direction used for the vertical axis (temperature) and the longer axis used for the seasons? Notice that the temperature range necessary is from 0 to 85 degrees, whereas only four seasons need be represented. Therefore the quantity with the longer list or wider range of numbers was set on the longer axis and the shorter list, of four items, on the shorter axis. The reverse arrangement would obviously produce undue crowding on one axis. The value for each calibration is also determined by the range of numbers to be represented. A count of the primary calibration lines of the graph paper in the long (vertical) direction yields 20. Since at least two of these primary spacings will be required for the worded information at the bottom of the graph, only 18 usable primary calibration lines (180 secondary calibration lines) remain. Suppose each of the primary calibration lines were given a value of 10 degrees; would this be sufficient to cover the entire range of 85 degrees? Easily—too easily, in fact. With such a calibration, the 85-degree mark would be reached before the ninth primary calibration line. Thus, the longest bar of the graph would go less than halfway up the paper, as shown in Fig. 2-18. Even though the same information is plotted in both Figs. 2-15 and 2-18, note how much wasted usable space exists in the latter.

How many degrees does each secondary calibration of Fig. 2-15 represent? One-half of a degree is the answer. Now, how many degrees does each secondary calibration of Fig. 2-18 represent? One degree. Therefore, which graph can be read more accurately? Figure 2-15, obviously, since half-degree lines are clearly shown and in Fig. 2-18 degree fractions have to be guessed at, or estimated, to use the technical word. From Fig. 2-15 what is the average temperature shown for the summer season? 83¼ degrees. Can Fig. 2-18 be read or estimated to this degree of accuracy? No. Thus, for purposes of accuracy in reading and producing the graph, *the largest possible portion of the available graph sheet should be used* for each graph drawn, and the value for each primary (and secondary) division should be chosen to accomplish this end.

2.11. The broken scale

Very often a problem in calibration arises in which the range of numbers is so great that in order to show the total range on less than 10 in. of usable axis would require assigning a very large value to each primary calibration

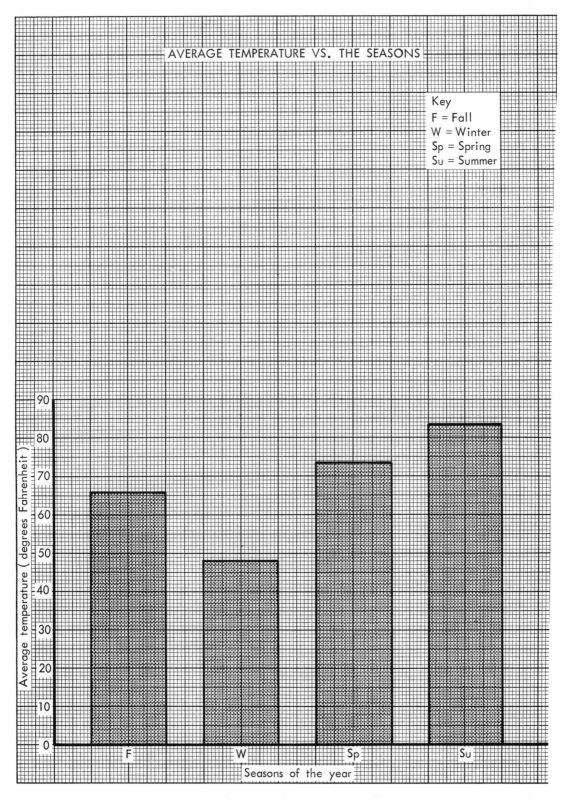

Fig. 2-18. Improper calibration results in wasted space, relative inaccuracy, and
interpretative difficulties (compare with graph of Fig. 2-15)

interval. This would severely limit the accuracy of the graph and would make it impossible to read small values or small differences in plotted values. In connection with problems like this, it is often true that only a small fraction of the wide range of values is important for plotting or for reading back. For instance, suppose we were interested in showing graphically the increase in the value of the manufactured output of the United States over a period of several years (see Table 2-1).

Table 2-1.

Year	Gross national product (billions of dollars)
1955	390
1956	420
1957	445
1958	447
1959	480
1960	505
1961	520
1962	550

Notice the range of significant numbers is actually from 390 to 550, and yet it is necessary to scale the axis from 10 to 550. Every axis showing numerical information must start at 0 rather than 390 or any other number. The origin should be shown to avoid giving the impression that any pertinent information has been omitted from the plot. Thus, whether the field is technology, economics, or any other, the origin of every set of axes must be shown.

The use of a *broken scale* will solve the problem of how to include the total range of numbers (0 to 550 for this example) and still obtain good accuracy for the significant range of numbers (390 to 550 in this example). As shown in Fig. 2-19, a broken scale is produced by starting the axis at 0 (the origin) and using a *very small length* of the axis to represent the less significant portion of the over-all range of values, 0 to 380 for this example. The balance of the range is calibrated uniformly over the entire remaining length of axis, thus permitting a much more accurate calibration for the more meaningful numbers. In Fig. 2-19, the broken-scale method permits a scale value of 20 for every primary division

line, which means a value of 2 for every secondary division line. This permits an accurate plotting and reading of the resulting graph. The name, "broken axis," is derived from the method used to show which portion of the axis has the squeezed or condensed calibration. The broken axis is indicated in Fig. 2-19 by dashes, that is, a broken line rather than a solid or continuous one. Note also that all portions of the graph affected by the break are also shown with dashes. Sometimes a jagged line rather than dashes are used to denote the condensed calibration.

The use of the broken axis does have a disadvantage, however, when used in connection with a bar graph. A comparison of the bar graph produced when the data of Table 2-1 is plotted without a broken scale (Fig. 2-20) with that obtained with the broken scale (Fig. 2-19) shows that the *relative lengths* of the bars when compared with one another are severely *distorted* on the broken scale. Note that a casual glance at Fig. 2-19 seems to show that the 1962 bar is many times the value of the 1955 bar. The true ratio between the two bars, however, is much less than 2:1 as can be seen in Fig. 2-20. It is to avoid this type of impression that the broken axis, whenever used, must be clearly marked with a broken or jagged line, and the affected portion of the graph must also be so marked.

The advantage obtained from the use of the broken axis can readily be appreciated by reading back information from Fig. 2-19 and attempting to obtain the same information from Fig. 2-20. The application to which a particular graph is put will determine whether the advantage of the broken scale outweighs the disadvantage, or vice versa. The techniques for reading out considerable information from bar graphs discussed later in this chapter will be helpful in determining whether or not a broken scale should be used in a given application.

2.12. Labelling the axes

All the time and effort involved in choosing the correct paper, drawing the proper reference axes, and carefully calibrating the axes is

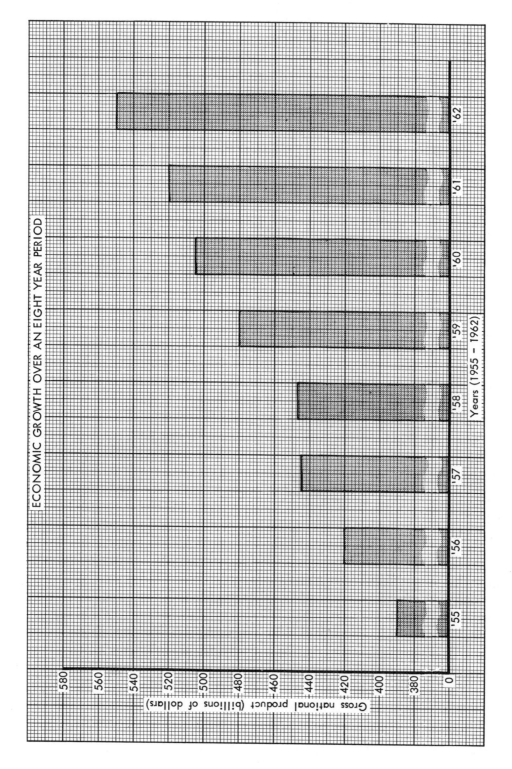

Fig. 2-19. Bar graph using broken scale to permit accurate plotting and reading of the significant portion of large range of numbers

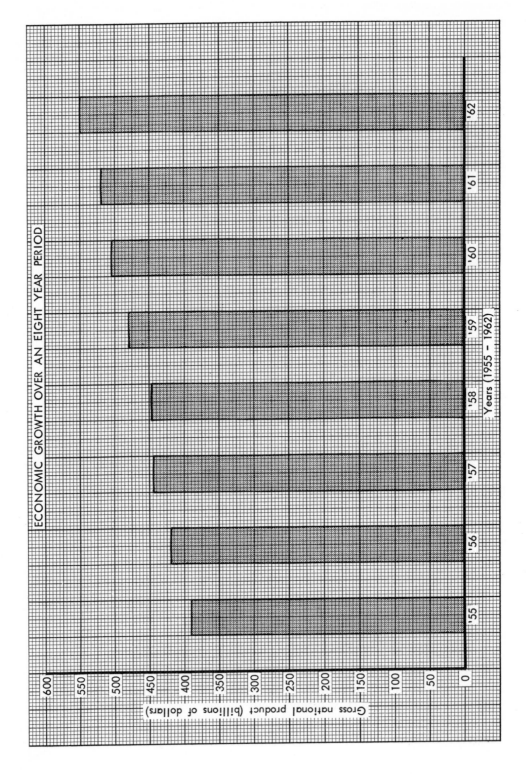

Fig. 2-20. Bar graph produced from same data as Fig. 2-19 but without use of broken scale. Comparison of two shows advantages and disadvantages of broken scale

lost if the results of this effort are not properly conveyed to the reader of the graph. To give the graph meaning, to help insure that it is properly read and understood, the axes must be fully labeled and the graph itself adequately titled. Although no one system or convention for labeling graph and axes can be said to be the very best for all applications, one format is generally used throughout technical literature. This labeling convention may be described as follows:

Each of the axes drawn on Cartesian coordinate paper requires:

1. Calibration numbers or symbols
2. The units of the calibration numbers
3. A name

As an example, refer to Fig. 2-15. Notice that the dependent axis is calibrated so that each primary division represents five units. However, to determine what these units are, it is necessary to refer to the wording alongside the axis. The *units of calibration* are shown *in parenthesis after* the name of the axis. Thus, we see by looking both at the calibration numbers and at the parenthetically enclosed units that each primary division line of the vertical axis represents 5 Fahrenheit degrees. Calibration units, it must be pointed out, are not always possible. For example, the symbols along the horizontal axis represent seasons, and no calibration units can be applied to them.

Note that both axes are completely named, without abbreviations, so that the reader of the graph is in no doubt at all about what is represented. The direction and location of the lettering for each axis is also established by convention. The wording should always appear *along* the axis it refers to and not at the top, bottom, or anywhere else. Note in Fig. 2-15 that with the page in normal position, that is, with the binding at the left (or right) the wording below the horizontal axis can be read from left to right. When Fig. 2-15 is turned so that the *binding is at the top* (or bottom), the wording for the vertical axis can be read from left to right. The calibration numbers and symbols that appear along the axes should be made short, that is, with as few digits (or letters) as possible. They can then be ar-

ranged on the axes to read normally when the graph sheet is held so that the vertical axis is at the left. As an example, note that in Fig. 2-15, calibration symbols are used on the horizontal axis to represent the seasons. As the full name of each season does not fit well under the bars, representative letters are used and an explanatory key provided. This system permits the horizontal calibration to be positioned for easy reading. Note also the vertical-axis calibration numbers of Fig. 2-19. Since the vertical axis is calibrated in billions of dollars, writing out the full number would require a different arrangement of the numbers or a large area of the graph sheet devoted to these calibration numbers. To permit the use of numbers of only a few digits, which are readily positioned on the axis, the units shown in the parenthesis for the vertical axis are billions of dollars. Thus, only three digits need appear on the division lines of the vertical axis.

By referring to the vertical axes of Figs. 2-18, 2-19, 2-20, and others, we note that the calibration numbers are set *astride* the calibration line they represent and not above or below the line. It is established practice to print the calibration numbers and symbols so that the division line to which they refer goes right through the digits. The exception to this rule is illustrated on the horizontal axis of Fig. 2-15. The symbol designating the bar is centered below the bar and does not refer to any one particular division line. This is a common arrangement in bar graphs.

Our writing is normally done horizontally. Thus, a graph would be so laid out, calibrated, and worded that it is not necessary to write in a column or at an angle. A properly arranged graph gives a professional appearance and wears the correct "attire" for the technical information being presented. Figure 2-20 is an example of a properly presented bar graph whereas Fig. 2-6 is an example of a poor one.

2.13. Putting the data on the graph

The process of transcribing numerical information from the columns of data to a graph varies somewhat with the type of graph being drawn. In the bar graphs being discussed, it is the height (or length) of the individual bar that conveys the required numerical information.[3] Compare the column of data of Table 2-1 with the corresponding bar graph of Fig. 2-20. From Table 2-1 note that 390 is the Y-axis value (the ordinate value) corresponding to 1955, the related X-axis value (the abscissa value). Therefore, on the graph the bar drawn at the 1955 position is made high enough to reach the 390 level as calibrated on the vertical axis. But, with the calibration chosen for the vertical axis, the number 390 does not appear as one of the primary calibration lines. However, since each secondary calibration line represents five units, a specific secondary calibration line does exist for 390, and the top of this bar can be accurately located two secondary division lines below the 400 position. Similarly, the 420 ordinate corresponds to the 1956 abscissa of Table 2-1, and the 445 ordinate corresponds to the 1957 abscissa, and both can be accurately located on a secondary division line. This is, however, not the case for the 447 ordinate corresponding to the 1958 abscissa. The line above the 445 secondary division line represents 450 on the Y scale. Thus, the top of the 1958 bar has to be positioned by approximation. Since each secondary division represents five units, 447 is two-fifths of the way up from the 445 position. As can be seen from the graph, it is barely possible to notice any difference in height between the 1957 and 1958 bars, and even if a difference is noted, the amount can be gauged only very approximately. As pointed out previously, this problem can be alleviated by using the broken-scale technique shown in Fig. 2-19.

2.14. Arrangement of the bars

One factor to be considered in connection with converting numerical information into a bar graph is the order in which the bars should

appear. If the independent axis represents time, then we have no choice but to arrange the bars in order of increasing time. However, when there is a choice, the bar should be arranged in the order of increasing or decreasing lengths. This arrangement permits a ready comparison among the lengths of the bars, much more so than if the bars were haphazardly arranged. Note the horizontal bar graph of Fig. 2-5. The dozen metals represented could certainly have been listed in any order as far as the names of the metals are concerned, but notice the ease with which the bar lengths can be compared because of the arrangement of increasing lengths from bottom to top of the graph. The same effect would result if the longest bar were placed at the bottom and the shortest at the top of the graph as long as the same orders of the bars were maintained.

To summarize, accuracy and order of arrangement are the two foremost considerations when transferring data onto a bar graph. The importance of accuracy will be maintained in all types of graphs, but order of arrangement as discussed here is unique to the bar graph.

2.15. Completing the graph

Completing the graph means different things for different graph types. For the bar graph it means, for one thing, shading the bars. This should be done even if all the bars have the same shading and the shading has, therefore, no special significance. Information can far more readily be obtained from shaded bars than from those that are not shaded, because the bars stand out from their background and their boundary lines are more clearly defined.

Other tasks to be accomplished during the completion stages of the graphing are putting the key or legend on the graph paper, if one is needed, and then naming the graph. In Fig. 2-15, one- and two-letter symbols were used in the horizontal axis designations. The meaning of each symbol is given in the *key* (or *legend*) shown on the grid portion of the figure. Since the location of the key is not critical, it is put on the graph paper after the graph has been drawn. It is only then that the

---

[3] In Section 2.3, the characteristics of the bars used to convey information are listed, and all will be more fully discussed in this chapter. However, the bar length is by far the most significant property for conveying numerical information.

most convenient location for this information becomes apparent. If the graph sheet is reasonably filled up by the plotted information and it is necessary to crowd the legend into a limited space, a box should be drawn around it to outline it. This separation from the rest of the information on the sheet will draw attention to it.

2.16. Naming the graph

To aid the reader of the graph, each plot should be appropriately named. If no short, descriptive title is applicable, the graph can then be named by using the Y vs. X format. To use this arrangement, we replace the Y by wording from the dependent axis and the X by wording from the independent axis. As an example, notice that this technique was used to name the graph of Fig. 2-15, thus yielding the name "Average Temperature vs. the Seasons." On the other hand, the title of Figs. 2-19 and 2-20, "Economic Growth Over an Eight-Year Period," aids considerably in conveying information to the graph reader.

The title should be the last piece of information put on the graph. Since the title should appear on the gridwork of the graph paper, it is not until the graph is otherwise complete that one can see where sufficient space is available. If at all possible, it should be put at the top or toward the top of the graph sheet. Like all wording on the graph sheet, the title should be clearly printed.

2.17. Reading the graph

The discussions of the preceding sections deal with the techniques for converting columns of data or statistics into meaningful and easily read bar graphs. Most of the methods and terminology presented will be applicable to all other types of graphs, as will be shown later. However, how can we determine how successful we have been in producing a graph? Also, just how much information can be obtained from a graph as basic as the bar graph? How much more rapidly can the desired information be obtained from the graph than from the original lists of numbers, and how much more obvious is it on the graph? You

can answer all these questions by learning how to read out information from graphs.

For example, refer to the bar graph in Fig. 2-21. From the title and the names of the axes, it is apparent that the graph deals with the number of physics Ph.D. degrees granted by U.S. universities over a range of years. The bar heights show quite clearly that there was a general increase in the number of these degrees granted per year from 1920 to 1940, that a sudden spurt took place in 1950, and that the ensuing years show a continuing increase. However, all this information is general. Can we obtain more specific information, meaning exact numerical information? What was the exact rate of increase in the 1920–1930 decade? How does this compare with the 1950–1960 decade? Is it possible to determine from the graph approximately how many degrees were granted in each decade? Is it possible to determine the total number of degrees granted over the span of time covered by the graph? Are there any bars that can be considered particularly significant? If so, how do they compare with one another? What additional numerical information is available from this graph?

To start with, let's consider the first question posed. What was the exact rate of increase in the 1950–1960 decade? First of all, what is meant by the "rate of increase"? This refers to the amount of increase per unit of time. If our unit of time is taken to be a year, the question therefore actually is, What is the *increase per year* in the number of degrees granted during the 1950–1960 period? From the information given on the graph, we can see that three pieces of information are available for the period in question. The 1920 bar height (or ordinate value) is 31 Ph.D. degrees, the 1925 ordinate is 50 degrees, and the 1930 ordinate is 106 degrees. The increase per year shown by the first bars is calculated as follows:

First increase rate

$$= \frac{\text{Ordinate for 1925 minus ordinate for 1920}}{\text{Total span of time}}$$

Substituting the values into this expression, we obtain:

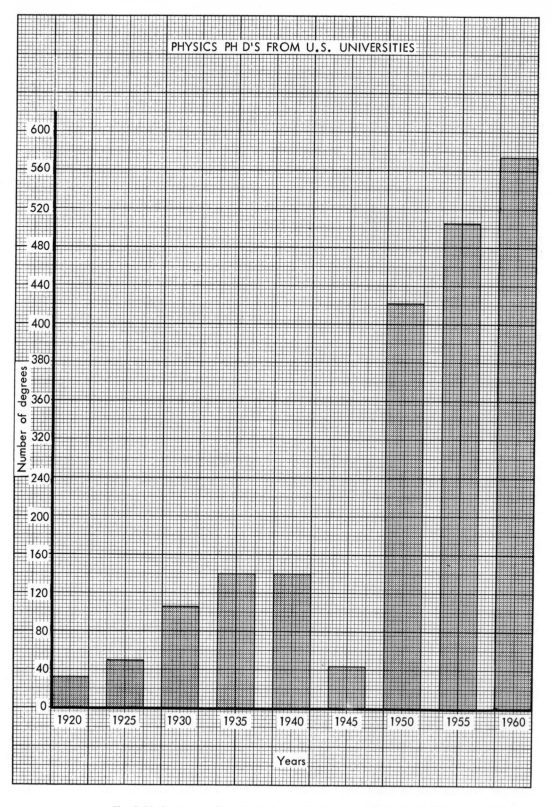

Fig. 2-21. Proper reading of graph can yield considerable information

First increase rate

$$= \frac{50 \text{ degrees} - 31 \text{ degrees}}{5 \text{ years}}$$

$$= 4 \text{ degrees per year}$$

Notice that the solution was expressed as the closest nearest integer since fractions have little meaning here. The second increase rate can now be obtained for this decade from the available information by using a similar procedure for the second and third bar heights:

Second increase rate

$$= \frac{\text{Ordinate for 1930 minus ordinate for 1925}}{\text{Total span of time}}$$

$$= \frac{106 \text{ degrees} - 50 \text{ degrees}}{5 \text{ years}}$$

$= 11$ degrees per year (expressed to the nearest whole number)

The average for the entire decade can now be obtained by averaging the two increased rates available for that 10-year span. Therefore,

Average increase rate for entire decade

$$= \frac{4 \text{ degrees per year} + 11 \text{ degrees per year}}{2}$$

$= 8$ degrees per year (approximately)

Had five bars been shown for the same period of time, then the increase rate would have been obtained for each of the four pairs of bars and these results averaged to yield the over-all average rate of increase of degrees per year. Thus we see that useful numerical information is readily obtained from this graph beyond the mere ordinate values of each of the bars drawn.

The second question posed above asks how the 1950 decade compares with the 1920 decade in terms of the increase in degrees granted year by year. The problem therefore is to determine the average increase in degrees granted per year in each decade and to compare them with one another. Comparison can be accomplished by either setting up a ratio or by the percentage difference. Both comparisons are worked out below.

For 1950 the graph shows 422 degrees granted.

For 1955 the graph shows 506 degrees granted.

For 1960 the graph shows 574 degrees granted.

The increase rate from the first and second graph values is

First increase rate

$$= \frac{506 \text{ degrees} - 422 \text{ degrees}}{5 \text{ years}}$$

$$= 17 \frac{\text{degrees}}{\text{year}} \text{ (to the nearest integer)}$$

and from the second and third graph values

Second increase rate

$$= \frac{574 \text{ degrees} - 506 \text{ degrees}}{5 \text{ years}}$$

$$= 14 \frac{\text{degrees}}{\text{year}}$$

The average of these two results is the average rate of increase of degrees granted per year over the entire 1950 decade. Thus

Average increase rate for decade

$$= \frac{17 \text{ deg/yr} + 14 \text{ deg/yr}}{2}$$

$$= 15 \frac{\text{degrees}}{\text{year}}$$

Comparing the 1920 decade average increase rate with that of the 1950 decade, we have

$$\frac{1950 \text{ decade average}}{1920 \text{ decade average}} = \frac{15 \text{ degrees per year}}{8 \text{ degrees per year}}$$

$$= 2 \text{ (approximately)}$$

Thus it is seen that during the 1950 decade the change from year to year was almost twice that of the 1920 decade.

This same information can be expressed in terms of a *percentage difference* (symbolized as $\%D$) between the increase rates of the two decades. Using the 1920 decade as reference, we have

$$\%D = \frac{\text{Difference}}{\text{Reference}} (100)$$

$$\%D = \frac{15 \text{ deg/yr} - 8 \text{ deg/yr}}{8 \text{ deg/yr}} (100)$$

$$\%D = 0.875 (100)$$

$$\%D = 87\frac{1}{2} \text{ per cent}$$

This result states that the increase in the number of degrees granted from year to year in the 1950 decade was 87½ per cent greater than during the 1920 decade. An increase of 100 per cent means that the rate was doubled. Therefore, the 87½ per cent result agrees with the ratio of almost 2 obtained above. In a case such as this, percentage difference results are preferable, because they are not limited to integral values in order to obtain meaningful results.

Additional questions raised earlier with regard to exact numerical information obtainable from the bar graph were whether it is possible to determine from the graph the total number of physics Ph.D. degrees granted in each decade and also during the entire interval covered by the graph. It is possible to obtain a good approximation of these amounts by using averages. This is necessary because the graph gives the number for the beginning, middle, and end of each decade, and not the number for each of the ten years in each decade.

The average number of degrees granted for each year of a particular decade can be found by summing up the three ordinates for each decade and dividing by three. Thus, for the 1920 decade:

Average number of degrees per year
$$= \frac{31 \text{ deg} + 50 \text{ deg} + 106 \text{ deg}}{3 \text{ yrs}}$$
$$= 62 \frac{\text{deg}}{\text{yr}}$$

for the 1930 decade:

Average number of degrees per year
$$= \frac{106 \text{ deg} + 145 \text{ deg} + 144 \text{ deg}}{3 \text{ yrs}}$$
$$= 132 \frac{\text{deg}}{\text{yr}}$$

for the 1940 decade:

Average number of degrees per year
$$= \frac{144 \text{ deg} + 43 \text{ deg} + 422 \text{ deg}}{3 \text{ yrs}}$$
$$= 203 \frac{\text{deg}}{\text{yr}}$$

for the 1950 decade:

Average number of degrees per year
$$= \frac{422 \text{ deg} + 506 \text{ deg} + 574 \text{ deg}}{3 \text{ yrs}}$$
$$= 501 \frac{\text{deg}}{\text{yr}}$$

Since the average number of degrees earned per year in each decade is now known, it is merely necessary to multiply this average by 10 years to find the total number of degrees earned during the decade. Thus, for the 1920 decade:

$$\text{Total number} = \frac{62 \text{ deg}}{\text{yr}} \times \frac{10 \text{ yrs}}{\text{decade}}$$
$$= 620 \frac{\text{deg}}{\text{decade}}$$

for the 1930 decade:

$$\text{Total number} = \frac{132 \text{ deg}}{\text{yr}} \times \frac{10 \text{ yrs}}{\text{decade}}$$
$$= 1320 \frac{\text{deg}}{\text{decade}}$$

For the 1940 decade, the same procedure yields 2,030 degrees, and for the 1950 decade, 5,010 degrees. These totals are certainly not available from a casual glance at the graph, nor would the list of data that yielded the bar graph supply the information. Thus, a store of information is available from even the fundamental bar graph, and reading a graph means obtaining from it all the useful facts it contains, both numerical and general.

Figure 2-21 permits us to go a step or two further. As indicated above, the total number of physics Ph.D. degrees earned during the entire 40-year span of the graph can also be obtained. This requires summing up the number obtained above for each decade and yields a total of 8,980 degrees. It should be borne in mind that these values are effective, useful values although the graphical source of information does not permit accuracy to the nearest integer. It certainly does, however, permit accuracy to well within 10 per cent of the absolutely correct values, and this is acceptable tolerance for most applications.

Another question raised earlier with respect to this graph asks, Are there any bars that can be considered of special significance? Values of significance are usually the maximum and minimum values of a graph and also regions where a sharp change takes place. In our graph, the 1920 bar has the minimum ordinate, and the 1960 bar shows the maximum ordinate. Ratios or percentage difference can be used to accent the differences. The two adjacent bars that show the greatest change of the entire graph are the 1945 and 1950 bars. Here again, ratios and percentages can be obtained to supplement the mere difference in ordinate values that the graph gives us directly.

Further numerical information obtainable can be the comparison between any two or more bars of particular interest in a special application. Also, comparisons of rates of increase, of percentage differences, of ratios, of totals from any one group of data with any other can readily be made. The list can be extended but it is obvious that full and correct reading of a graph requires know-how. The review problems appearing at the end of this chapter will provide some practice, but full proficiency will come only from applying these techniques to the graphs that you will find in technical, scientific, or business literature and in newspapers and magazines.

2.18. Bar graph types

In the preceding sections of this chapter, the bar graph was used as a means of illustrating general principles that apply to most graph types. The impression should not be obtained, however, that the bar graph is not effective as a graph in its own right. Quite the contrary is true, as is borne out by the development of many variations of the plain bar graph for the purpose of extending its range of application.

Basically, the variations of the fundamental bar graph accomplish two objectives. First, they permit an increase in the amount of information that can be presented on one graph and, second, they make this information more useful to the reader. Many techniques also exist for making graphs more striking in appearance. These techniques will not be considered here.

2.19. The positive and negative bar graph

This type of bar graph is used to show the relationship among quantities, some of which are above a given reference level and some of which are below. The height of the bar indicates the amount above or the amount below the zero or reference level. Figure 2-22 is an example of a positive and negative bar graph type. Here the positive bars indicate a net profit and the negative bars a net loss. In this case, the zero level is a *true* zero.

The zero reference level of the positive-negative bar graph of Fig. 2-23 is *not* a true zero. The primary purpose of this graph is to compare the economics of a particular company during the second quarter of a year to its operations during the first three months of that year. Thus, as indicated in the note on the graph sheet, the reference level for each bar is the dollar value for that item during the first quarter of the year. Since the reference value for each bar would thus be a different number

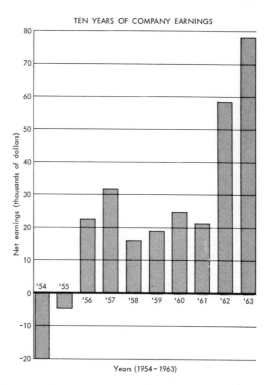

Fig. 2-22. Bar graph showing both positive and negative values, indicating profit and loss of a company

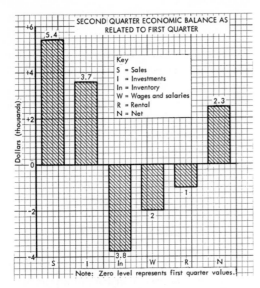

Fig. 2-23. Positive-negative bar graph offering succinct comparison of a company's first- and second-quarter economics

general rule occurs when the horizontal axis is expressed in units of time, as is the case in Fig. 2-22. Under these conditions, bars are arranged in chronological order without regard to positive and negative grouping. Note also from Fig. 2-23 that the positive bars are often distinguished from the negative ones by shading, one type of shading or crosshatching being used for the positive bars and another for the negative. This is done to accent further the difference between them. Different colors often serve as a striking substitute for the shading but serve no other purpose.

2.20. The component bar graph

It can readily be seen that the bars of Fig. 2-24 are made up of two component parts, one crosshatched and the other heavily shaded. By reading the graph we see that each bar represents tax revenue related to the trucking industry for each of the five years shown. This revenue is determined on two different bases —mileage and permits. The amount related to each basis is shown on the graph in the form of two parts to each bar. Certainly, two sepa-

of dollars, all the first quarter values were set at reference zero. The length of each bar therefore shows the second quarter value insofar as it is greater or less than the reference (first quarter) value. The lengths of the bars do not show actual dollar values for the second quarter operation.

The advantage of this type of a bar graph is that it relates all the information contained to the determined reference value. Furthermore, the significance of the reference value is accented graphically by having all other values related to it. The graph reader's attention is thus directed to this reference far more effectively than it could be on a plain bar graph in which this value is pointed out by wording or an indicating line.

This type of bar graph does take somewhat more effort to produce than a plain bar graph, since it is necessary to relate all the data to the reference value and to develop a new table of values from the given data before any information can be plotted. The additional time spent in this endeavor, however, is usually rewarded by a far more effective result.

As seen in Fig. 2-23, the positive bars of such a graph are usually grouped together and are generally presented first, that is, at the left end of the line of bars. The exception to this

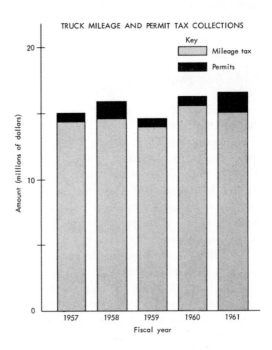

(Courtesy, New York State Department of Taxation and Finance)
Fig. 2-24. Component bar graph showing tax income from two sources

rate bar graphs could have been made for the two sets of values, but these sets are so closely related (being two component parts of one item, tax revenue) that they truly belong on one graph. The result can be characterized by saying that the permit-revenue bars are placed on top of the mileage-revenue bars. The bar that results for each year yields a ready comparison of the amounts obtained on each basis. The bars for the several years shown can readily be compared to one another from the point of view of total amount of revenue, of revenue from truck mileage, and of revenue from truck permits. Considering that ratios, percentage differences, and rates of change for the several years can also be obtained in addition to the above, it becomes apparent that a compound bar graph is a very compact way of presenting a wealth of information in a very simple manner.

Theoretically, there is no limit to the number of components one bar of such a graph can have. However, the practical limit is three or four. If more are used the results tend to produce confusion, particularly if there are several such bars on the graph. This defeats the purpose of making a graph of the numerical data in the first place. Under such conditions, more than one bar graph should be made, or a compound bar graph, discussed in a later section of this chapter, is in order.

2.21. The percentage bar graph

The percentage bar graph is a special case of the component bar graph. In this case, however, the components are different percentages of an entire quantity. Since the several components of each bar add up to 100 per cent, all the bars on such a graph are necessarily of the same length—100 per cent. Figure 2-25 is an example of this type of graph. This particular graph shows only two components for each bar, but theoretically there is no limit to the number of different components a bar may have. For practical purposes, no more than three or four components should appear per bar. Note that all the bars are of equal height, representing 100 per cent. The vertical axis may be conspicuous by its absence from the

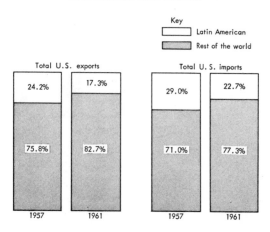

Fig. 2-25. Percentage bar graph (special case of component bar graph)

diagram. Since each of the components represents a different percentage of the whole, it is of no practical use to set up an ordinate axis starting from 0 and going to 100 per cent. Each component starts where the previous one left off, rather than starting from the zero ordinate level of the graph. Sometimes, however, a vertical axis is drawn showing equally spaced calibration lines, thus permitting, at a glance, an approximate evaluation of each of the percentage components of the bars, as shown in Fig. 2-26. However, if possible, the percentage value of each component is usually shown directly on the bar component itself, as illustrated in Fig. 2-25.

Since the percentage bar is actually a type of component bar, under what conditions is each of the forms used? The answer to this question can be obtained from a careful comparison of Figs. 2-24 and 2-25. Note that in Fig. 2-24, actual amounts are given in terms of a calibrated coordinate axis. Figure 2-25 gives no specific values, and even if a vertical axis were provided, it would merely be an aid to gauging the percentage value of each component. Thus the *percentage bar graph is used if the total amounts of each quantity are less significant than the comparisons between these quantities.* Furthermore, the components must add up to one complete **quantity** (100 per cent).

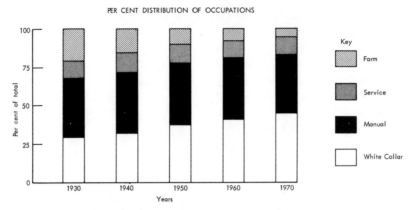

Fig. 2-26. Percentage bar graph with calibrated percentage axis to permit instant approximation of each component

It should be noted from both Figs. 2-24 and 2-25 that the smaller components are placed at the tops (or ends) of the bars. For ease of comparison, the components should appear in order of decreasing size as the reader goes up a vertical bar or from left to right on a horizontal one. Therefore, the smaller components of the bars of Figs. 2-24 and 2-25 appear at the top.

2.22. Max-min bar graph

Our discussions up to this point have dealt with the fundamental bar graph and some of its variations. In each case all the bars on any one graph started at the same zero level, and it was their maximum height (or lengths) that showed the differences between them. Up to this point the only inkling that some exceptions to this rule could exist came from the discussion of the component and percentage bar graphs. In these graphs, each component starts where the previous one ends, rather than at the zero level.

An extension of this idea leads to the bar graph type where *both* the starting level and the finishing level of the graph have significance, as well as the over-all length of the bar. Note the bar graph of Fig. 2-27. As the title

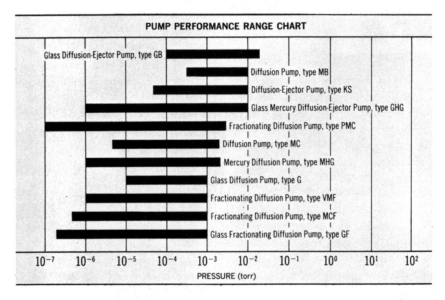

(Courtesy, Consolidated Vacuum Corp.)

Fig. 2-27. Max-min bar graph in which beginning and end position of bars as well as their over-all length is significant

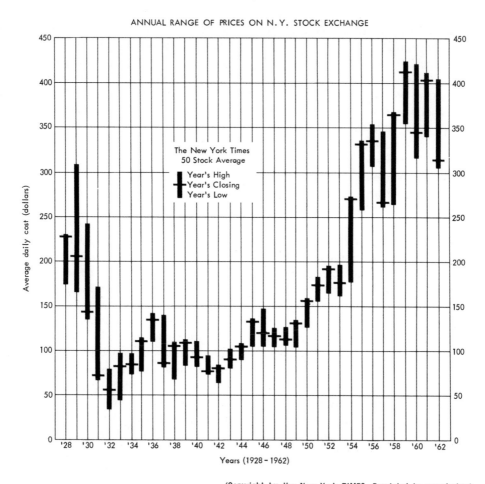

ANNUAL RANGE OF PRICES ON N.Y. STOCK EXCHANGE

The New York Times
50 Stock Average

Year's High
Year's Closing
Year's Low

Average daily cost (dollars)

Years (1928 - 1962)

Fig. 2-28. Max-min bar graph type commonly found in newspaper business periodicals

of the graph indicates, this is a range chart. The length of each bar, when compared to the calibrated horizontal axis, shows the range of pressures that the named pump can produce. In addition, however, the minimum pressure and the maximum pressure obtainable from each pump are also available from the graph. For instance, the diffusion pump, type MB, is shown to have the shortest pressure range capability whereas the fractioning diffusion pump, type PMC, has the greatest range capability. In addition, the maximum and minimum pressure values for each of these ranges can readily be obtained from the graph. For the short-range pump (type MB), the range is shown to vary from a maximum of 10^{-2} (0.01) torr units of pressure down to a minimum of about one-half of 10^{-3} (0.0005) torr

units of pressure.[4] Thus the bar neither starts nor ends at a zero level. In this particular graph, no zero is even shown on the calibrated axis, which shows pressure from one ten-millionth of a torr unit up to 100 torr units.

Figure 2-28 is another example of the max-min bar graph type. It is frequently found published in newspapers and business periodicals. In this graph, each bar represents values obtained by finding the sum of the daily stock prices for 50 key securities and multiplying it by a correction factor. However, since over the

---

[4] The term "Torr" is generally accepted as the international standard pressure term equivalent to a column of mercury 1.0 mm high. ("Torr" is in honor of Evangelista Torricelli, who invented the barometer in 1643.)

period of a day the price of any one security varies, its average price is used in the corrected summation. Thus, the vertical axis is the (corrected) average daily cost of 50 representative stocks, measured over a period of one year. Each individual bar, therefore, yields several significant pieces of information. It shows the minimum and maximum cost average for that year and thus the range of the average costs for that year. Furthermore, a *marker* appears on each bar to represent corrected total cost for the 50 securities for the last business day of that year. In addition to these four significant numerical values obtained from each bar, the over-all graph yields information obtainable from the basic bar graph. Comparison of the ranges over the entire 34-year period can be made, as well as of the maximum, minimum, and closing values. Any two bars can be compared with one another or any group with any other group to obtain further useful numerical information.

This particular example employs a reader aid that is worthy of added attention. Since the graph extends over a rather wide range along the horizontal axis, the vertical axis and its calibration is repeated at the right-hand side of the graph. In this case, the additional vertical axis is merely a convenience for the reader. Later sections will discuss cases in which more than one vertical (or horizontal) axis is used of necessity rather than convenience.

2.23. The compound bar graph

A compound bar graph is actually two or more bar graphs drawn on the same set of axes. In addition to the normal amount of information that can be gleaned from a standard bar graph, the compound graph permits a ready comparison between what are actually two separate graphs. Note the compound graph of Fig. 2-29. It is apparent that this chart is actually four separate bar graphs, one for each of four items from which state tax revenue is obtained. Each of these bar graphs drawn separately would yield considerable information. However by putting the four bar graphs on the same set of axes, we affect a ready com-

parison among them. Notice that different shading is used to emphasize the separate bar graphs and that an appropriate key is included to explain the shading code. Ratios and percentage differences between bars of a given year can now easily be obtained as well as the differences in these quantities from year to year.

Since a compound bar graph is actually several different graphs depicted together, care must be exercised to avoid overcrowding, since this would defeat the very purpose of the graph. The ideal arrangement is the incorporation of only two graphs into one compound graph. However, conditions may require comparison between three or four items and the resulting compound graph, if carefully made, can be very useful. Incorporation of four or five bar graphs into one compound graph is about the outside limit before confusion rather than clarification results. A second compound bar graph of four different items is shown in Fig. 2-30. Note that the presentation of the information is somewhat differently arranged than in Fig. 2-29. In Fig. 2-30, the shading and key are used to distinguish between the four years covered by the graph. In Fig. 2-29, the shading and key are used to distinguish the commodities from one another, and the years appear on the independent axis. The reason for the difference is the relative importance of the time element (the years) in the two different graphs. In Fig. 2-29, more accent is desired on the differences from year to year rather than the differences between the commodities. Therefore, the years appear on the axis, and the key refers to the different items. In Fig. 2-30, the reverse accent is desired. Thus the commodities are shown on one of the axes, and the years are distinguished from one another by the shading and explanatory key.

2.24. The pictograph

This graph type is a popular modification of the bar graph. Since the term "bar" does not appear in its name, it is often referred to as a separate graph type. The sole difference between the pictograph and the other types of bar graphs is that a row of representative

STATE TAX COLLECTIONS

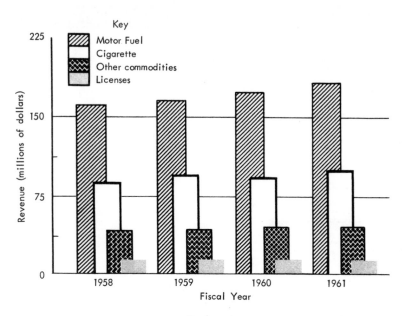

(Courtesy, New York State Department of Taxation and Finance)

Fig. 2-29. Compound bar graph in which different commodity tax revenues are compared

ACTIVE COMMODITY FUTURES

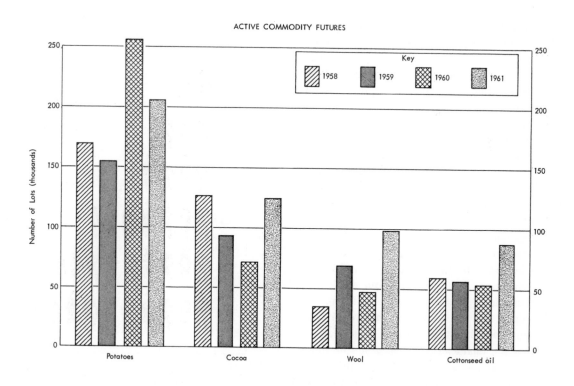

(Copyright by the New York TIMES. Reprinted by permission.)

Fig. 2-30. Compound bar graph—composite of four different bar graphs

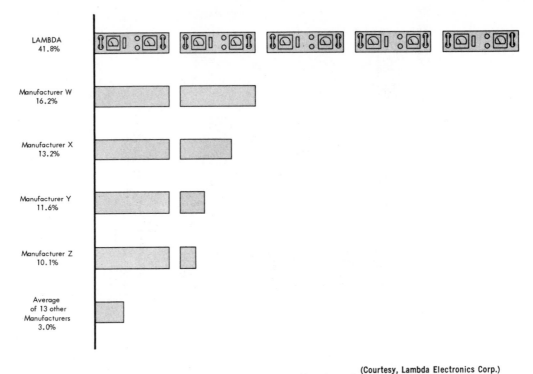

Fig. 2-31. Pictograph—a popular modification of the bar graph

symbols is used in the pictograph to make up the bar. Note, for example, the pictograph of Fig. 2-31. This is obviously a bar graph except that the bars are made up of pictures of front panels of electronic power supplies. These pictures are truly representative, since Fig. 2-31 was a part of an advertisement put out by a leading electronic power supply manufacturer. Since the pictograph is truly a bar graph, it has the limited accuracy characteristic of the bar graph. Thus Fig. 2-31 also gives numerically the percentage of the total market sales represented by each bar. Figure 2-32 is an example of a pictograph in which human figures are used as the representative symbols. Obviously, therefore, this graph deals with population. A closer look at the graph shows that the figures represent elderly men and women and the key tells us that "each symbol represents 2 million persons." Note here again that the characteristic inaccuracy of the bar graph or pictograph is offset by printing the exact value of each bar directly on the graph. Such values are omitted if the exact values are not significant. However, when such informa-

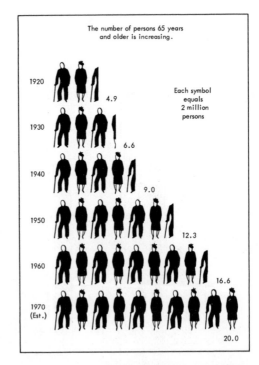

Fig. 2-32. Human figure symbol indicates this pictograph deals with population. (What license taken here is normally not permissible?)

DEPTHS TO PLANT SUMMER-FLOWERING BULBS

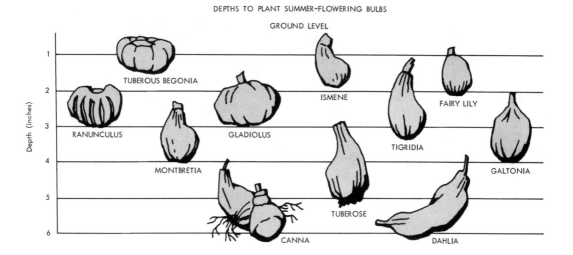

Fig. 2-33. Not every pictorial chart is a pictograph

tion is included it is of considerable aid to the reader interested in a complete analysis of the graph. For instance, Fig. 2-32 permits a reasonably valid determination of the percentage increase of the senior citizen population from decade to decade in addition to showing it pictorially. Without the given numbers, only a rough scaling of each of the bar lengths could be used to obtain numerical information, or else a count of the number of whole symbols and estimate of the fractional ones could be used to yield numerical comparisons between the several decades shown.

A pictograph is basically a bar graph, and care should be taken not to include in the category of the pictograph every chart or drawing merely because it shows comparison or pictorially presents information for ready comprehension. Refer, for example, to Fig. 2-33. This chart pictorially presents information, but the items shown are not symbols representing a specific quantity, and no attempt is made to relate the items shown by means of a scale of reference or to collect the symbols into bars or other indications of numerical value. Is the diagram of Fig. 2-34 a pictograph? Does each automobile symbol represent a large quantity of autos? Is a scale of values established that permits a comparison or relationship to be established between

the several symbols? Have the symbols been collected into bars or other form to yield numerical information? The answer to all these questions is No. Thus, the chart of Fig. 2-34 is not a pictograph or any other type of graph. Each outline shown represents a specific automobile model of given length and is not used as a symbol representing a larger quantity. The diagram effectively serves the pur-

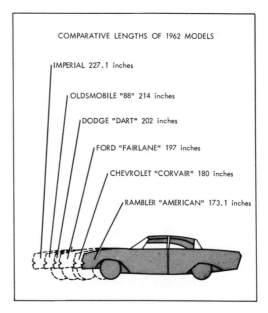

Fig. 2-34. Is this chart a pictograph?

pose for which it was made but for the reasons given is not a graph.

2.25. The histogram

Suppose you were interested in an exact measurement of your height, accurate to two decimal places. Let us assume that, to accomplish this, you took 40 individual readings (Table 2-2) and because of slight variations in the use and reading of your measuring device, differences existed in your readings. If you wanted to represent your results pictorially, you could make a bar graph in which the height of the bar would depend on the number of times a certain reading came up, using a different bar for each different number (Table 2-3). The resulting bar graph would be a *histogram*, an example of which is shown in Fig. 2-35. Notice that this bar graph is different in one important respect from any previously shown. The bars have no spacing between them, that is, they are put together in a block form. Thus, *a histogram is defined as a bar graph in block form produced by plotting frequency of occurrence vs. values obtained*. The information most readily available from such a bar graph is the range or spread of values obtained from a given set of measurements as well as, which numbers were repeated most often, which least often, and all the cases in between.

Figure 2-36 shows "before" and "after" histograms superimposed on one another for purpose of ready comparison. This graph was published by a leading manufacturer of transistors to show the characteristics of his product. In order to read the histogram, it is necessary first to determine what the axes represent. Notice that the *frequency* of avalanche breakdown (point of sharp increase in current) is represented on the *vertical axis* and the breakdown voltage applied to the units being tested is shown on the *horizontal* axis. Therefore the graph tells us that the histogram represents the results of a testing procedure in which a large number of transistors were tested by applying voltages to them in the range of from 0 to 180 volts. The voltage range is determined from the calibration range of

Table 2-2. Forty height readings used to yield the histogram of Fig. 2-35

Reading number	Height (inches)	Reading number	Height (inches)
1	68.50	21	68.53
2	68.50	22	68.53
3	68.47	23	68.53
4	68.47	24	68.52
5	68.51	25	68.52
6	68.51	26	68.52
7	68.52	27	68.50
8	68.52	28	68.50
9	68.48	29	68.50
10	68.48	30	68.50
11	68.49	31	68.51
12	68.49	32	68.51
13	68.49	33	68.51
14	68.49	34	68.51
15	68.50	35	68.49
16	68.50	36	68.49
17	68.50	37	68.49
18	68.50	38	68.49
19	68.48	39	68.50
20	68.48	40	68.50

Table 2-3. Data presented as table of values for histogram

X axis Height value	Y axis Frequency of occurrence
68.47	2
68.48	4
68.49	8
68.50	12
68.51	6
68.52	5
68.53	3

the horizontal axes. Notice now that the key shown in the upper right-hand corner of the graph sheet yields another important piece of information. It tells the reader that this test was applied to the transistors when new (initial readings) and that the results of this test are described graphically by the broken line histogram. Furthermore, the same test was applied to the same transistors after 1,000 hours of operation (1,000-hour readings), and the results of this test are shown in the solid histogram on the same graph sheet.

The next step in reading the histogram is an over-all view of the graph. It can readily be seen that no appreciable differences exist, in

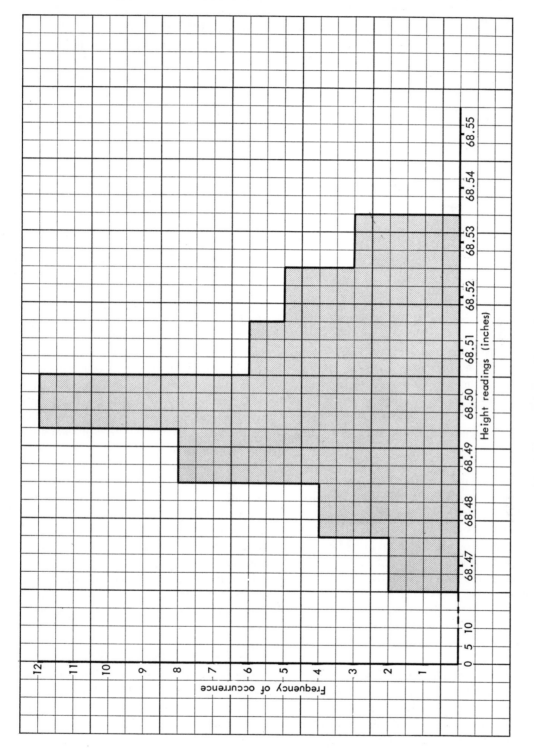

Fig. 2-35. Histogram of Table 2-2 readings

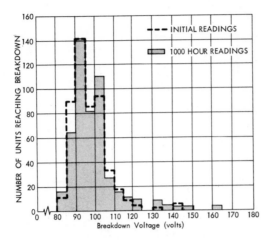

(Courtesy, Motorola Semiconductor Products, Inc.)
Fig. 2-36. Two superimposed histograms of power transistor stability

general, between the broken-line histogram and the solid-line one. It can be immediately stated, therefore, that the items being tested behaved generally the same after 1,000 hours of operation as when new. Furthermore, the breakdown rate increases with increasing voltage, reaches a peak, and then generally decreases. For additional information, a more detailed reading of the histogram yields the following:

1. The greatest frequency of avalanche breakdown occurred at a voltage of 90 volts, and this was exactly the same after 1,000 hours of operation as when new. At this voltage, 140 units of all those tested reached breakdown.

2. The second highest breakdown frequency occurred at 100 volts for both the new and the used units. The number of transistors reaching breakdown at this voltage is shown as 95 for the new units and 110 for the used. This difference represents an increase of 15.8 per cent.

3. In one case, an appreciable decrease in breakdown takes place after the transistors have been operated for 1,000 hours. This occurs at the breakdown voltage of 85 volts. Of the units tested at 85 volts, 87 of the new ones reached breakdown as compared to only 64 of the used transistors. This represents a decrease of 26.4 per cent.

4. A decrease in avalanche breakdown frequency also occurs when the testing voltage is at 95 volts, 105 volts, 110 volts, and 140 volts. These percentage changes are small, however, in comparison to that shown at 85 volts.

5. Several voltage regions exist at which no breakdown was reached at all for both the new as well as the used units. This is true above and below the shown plot, that is, below 80 volts and above 165 volts. In addition, no breakdown was experienced at 125 volts and 150 up to 160 volts.

6. Several voltages are shown at which breakdown did not occur for new units but did occur for used ones. These are 135 volts, 145 volts, and 160 volts.

7. The total number of units tested for avalanche breakdown can be determined by adding up the ordinates obtained from each of the new unit bars as well as the used-unit bars. The results show that approximately 488 new transistors and an equal number of used units were tested for breakdown. The same number of units should be expected, since the superimposed histograms imply that after testing a given number of new transistors, these units were operated for 1,000 hours and then tested again. The values obtained from the graph of Fig. 2-36 are given in Table 2-4.

8. Additional information can be obtained from these histograms by obtaining percentage differences between different bar lengths at various voltages and by obtaining the percentage differences between the frequency of breakdown before and after use at specific voltage values.

Thus, it can readily be seen that a histogram, like any other bar graph, contains a wealth of significant information for the practiced reader.

2.26. The bar chart recorder

The ease with which information can be obtained from a bar graph has led to the development of a machine that automatically records significant data in bar-graph form. This device, known as the "bar chart recorder," is depicted in Fig. 2-37. Basically, the device is made up of a rotating drum and a writing stylus (shown at the right side of the drum in

Table 2-4.

Breakdown voltage, volts	Number of units reaching avalanche breakdown	
	Initial readings (new units)	1,000-hour readings (used units)
0-75	0	0
80	12	16
85	87	64
90	140	140
95	85	81
100	95	110
105	34	26
110	19	18
115	8	10
120	4	9
125	0	0
130	1	8
135	0	2
140	2	1
145	0	1
150	0	0
155	0	0
160	0	1
165-180	0	0

(Courtesy, Electron Ohio, Inc.)

Fig. 2-37. Bar graph recorder—a device that automatically produces bar graph of operation of several machines and equipments

the figure) that rides vertically on a guide arranged parallel to the drum axis. The stylus moves from bottom to top and builds up each bar individually by recording a short horizontal stroke for the appropriate bar at every turn of the drum. Electrical signals taken from various operating machines and equipment are continuously fed into the stylus telling it when to record a horizontal stroke and when to leave a blank. This process continues until the stylus reaches the top of the drum at the end of the shift or the end of the day.

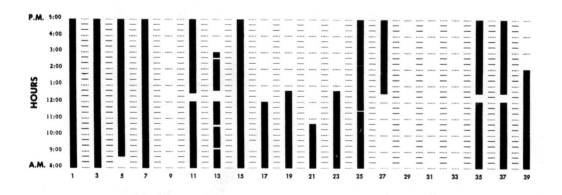

(Courtesy, Electron Ohio, Inc.)

Fig. 2-38. Bar graph produced by bar chart recorder (graph gives permanent record of when and for how long each machine was active or idle). Clock hours on left; channel numbers below bar areas; self-printed lines between. Channels are graphic recordings of almost any machine, process, operation, or series of events. Solid bars represent uninterrupted operations. Horizontal breaks in vertical bars show idle or down time.

Figure 2-38 shows a bar chart produced by a recorder that represents the operating and idle time of 16 different machines over a 9-hour working day. The descriptive material below the chart yields a concise explanation of the information obtained from it. Since the recorder produces a graph which is an easily read, continuous record of operation of several machines at different locations and also yields a permanent graphical record of the total operation at the end of the day, it has become a valuable tool in many industries.

2.27. The circle graph

A glance at Fig. 2-39 will show why the circle graph is often given the descriptive name of "pie chart." The graph is basically a complete circle, or "pie" if you will, that is "sliced up" into a number of wedges of different sizes. The circle represents the entire quantity of the item under consideration and each wedge, or sector, is drawn of appropriate size to show its percentage of the entire quantity. The sum of all the wedges shown must add up to the entire unit.

2.28. Advantages and disadvantages of the circle graph

It is common practice to express the circle sectors in terms of percentages of the entire unit, so that the sum totals 100 per cent, as is shown in Fig. 2-39. It is apparent, therefore, that the circle graph yields the same type of information as does the percentage bar graph (and is actually a modification of a percentage bar graph). The percentage bar graph has the advantage, however, that a comparison of several items can be made merely by showing a separate bar for each item, as is the case in Fig. 2-25. If the same information were to be shown with circle graphs, a separate circle would be required for each item and would thus take up far more space than the equivalent percentage bar graphs. This can clearly be seen by looking at Figs. 2-40 and 2-41 in turn. Note that although both graphs present the same information, that is, source and distribution of funds, the two bar graphs of Fig. 2-41 take up less space together than either one of the pie charts of Fig. 2-40. Any attempt to reduce the size of the circle graphs appreciably

LOCAL REVENUE SOURCES
Percentage Distribution

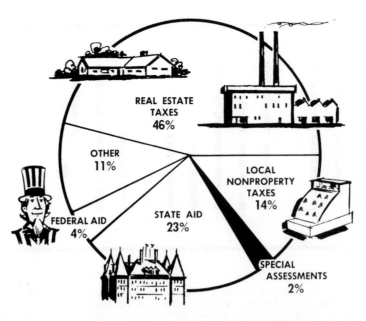

(Courtesy, New York State Department of Taxation and Finance)
Fig. 2-39. Typical circle graph or "pie chart"

WHERE THE MONEY COMES FROM

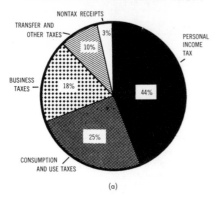

(a)

WHERE THE MONEY GOES

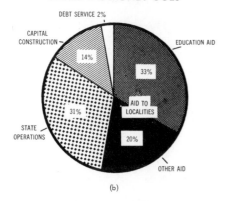

(b)

(Courtesy, THE SPEAKER)

Fig. 2-40. Two circle graphs showing source and distribution of funds in a state budget

would result in a corresponding decrease in readability. The bar graphs, on the other hand, could have their widths cut in half without affecting their clarity at all.

The advantage of the circle graph over the percentage bar graph is that more individual portions can clearly be shown with the pie chart. This can also be seen by comparing Figs. 2-40 and 2-41. Note that each of the circles of Fig. 2-40 is broken up into five sectors, and each wedge is clearly shown without any semblance of crowding. Twice that number of sectors could be shown, and the circle graphs would still not be duly overcrowded. However, an increase in the number of subdivisions of the bars of Fig. 2-41 would readily crowd the graph, so that comparison of one segment to any of the others, or to the

whole, would be difficult to accomplish at a glance. It would require close scrutiny.

In some applications, a percentage bar chart serves its purpose well and cannot adequately be replaced by a circle chart. Note the percentage bar graph of Fig. 2-42. Six pie charts would be required to replace this graph, and each would have only two sectors, one large and one small.

2.29. Reading the circle graph

As stated earlier, the sectors of a circle graph usually have the percentage or fraction of the total shown directly on the graph. This facilitates exact comparison between the wedges, since all that is required to compare one item with another is to set up a ratio between the numbers given. For example, reference to Fig. 2-39 shows that local revenue is obtained from six different sources, with real estate taxes being by far the greatest single source. To accent this latter point, real estate taxes can be compared to each of the other sources of revenue. Thus

$$\frac{\text{Real estate taxes}}{\text{Special assessments}} = \frac{46 \text{ per cent}}{2 \text{ per cent}}$$
$$\text{Ratio} = 23{:}1$$

$$\frac{\text{Real estate taxes}}{\text{Federal aid}} = \frac{46 \text{ per cent}}{4 \text{ per cent}}$$
$$\text{Ratio} = 11.5{:}1$$

$$\frac{\text{Real estate taxes}}{\text{Other sources}} = \frac{46 \text{ per cent}}{11 \text{ per cent}}$$
$$\text{Ratio} = 4.18{:}1$$

This process can be continued and five ratios obtained, each showing real estate as the greater source of income by a specific multiple.

Lack of accuracy in the circle graph is even more pronounced than in the bar graph. An attempt to read the values represented by each sector of the graph of Fig. 2-43 without reference to Table 2-5 readily attests to this fact. Without the table it can be determined that almost half of the total disbursements went to suppliers, but an attempt to estimate the other subdivisions would yield far poorer results. This deficiency of the circle graph can be cor-

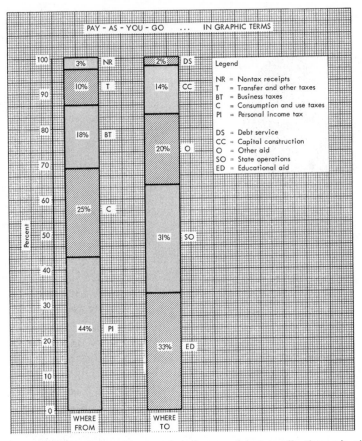

Fig. 2-41. Individual portions of percentage bar graph not as effective as in pie chart
(see Fig. 2-40 to compare both types of graphs from same data)

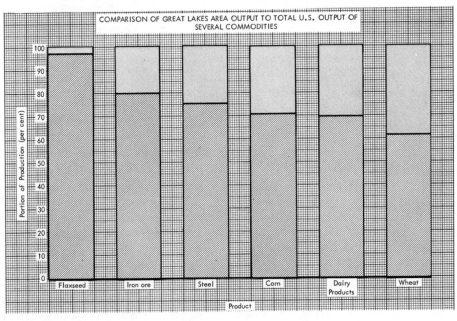

Fig. 2-42. In certain applications, percentage bar graphs are far more effective
than pie charts

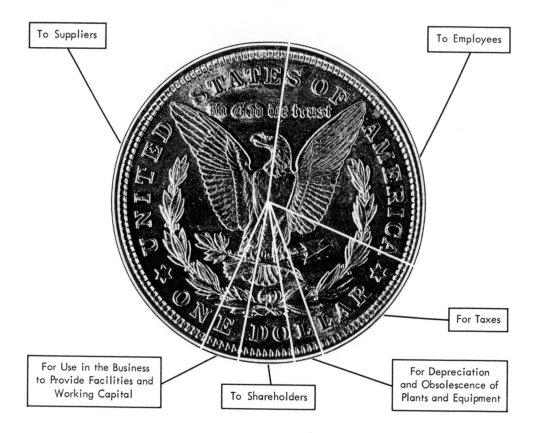

Fig. 2-43. Circle graphs are used to show readily the approximate distribution of a complete quantity rather than to provide highly accurate or detailed information

rected to a considerable extent by providing a scale, a circular scale, to which these "pie chart" wedges can be compared.

Table 2-5.

Disbursements	Per cent
To suppliers for materials, services, etc.	47½
To employes for payrolls, employe benefit plans, etc.	30½
For Federal, state, and local taxes	10¾
To provide for depreciation and obsolescence of plants and equipment	3½
To shareholders	6¼
For use in the business to provide facilities and working capital	1½

2.30. Producing the circle graph

Several types of graph paper are readily available that provide calibrations useful in making a pie chart. The type depicted in Fig.

2-44 is known as "circular percentage chart paper," and is designed specifically for the circle graph. Polar coordinate paper (Fig. 1-13) is designed for another application, but it is easily adapted to the needs of a circle chart. The same is true of *fluxolite paper* (Fig. 2-45), but it can be seen by looking at the three circular papers mentioned that fluxolite paper is the least useful for a circle graph. (Chapter 6 discusses the latter two papers in terms of the use for which they were originally designed.)

2.31. Circular chart paper

Use of the circular percentage chart sheets requires merely that the quantities to be shown be expressed as a percentage of the total. For example, in order to produce the circle graph of Fig. 2-40a the money received from various sources was expressed as a per cent of the total

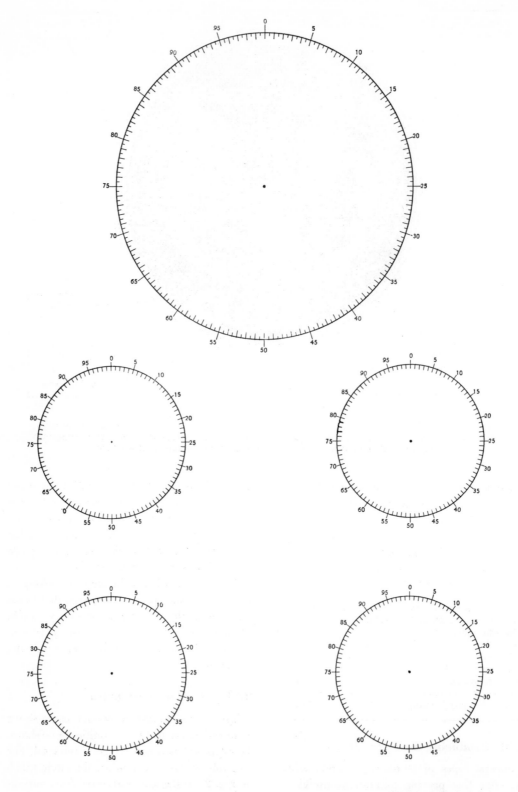

(Courtesy, Codex Book Co.)

Fig. 2-44. Circular percentage chart paper with five calibrated circles

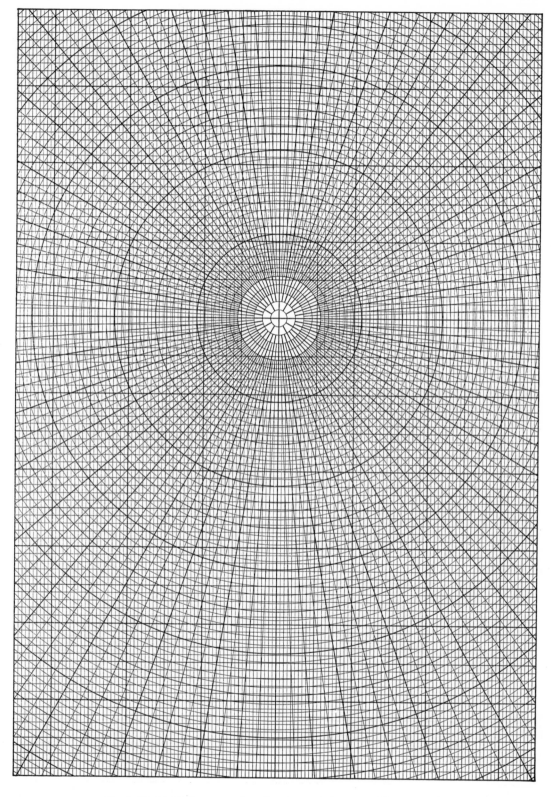

Fig. 2-45. Light flux paper (another type of circular graph paper)

money received. In this case, the various
sources were arranged in descending numerical order of their percentages and plotted in
that order. This is common practice. Note that
the zero position on the circular percentage
graph paper is at the top. Thus, the first item
plotted in Fig. 2-40a, "Personal Income tax,"
was started at the top (0 per cent) position and
continues around to the 44 per cent position.
"Consumption and use taxes," the second
largest item, was started at the 44 per cent
mark on the paper and carried around to the
69 per cent position, at which point the third
largest item was started. "Business taxes" was
extended to the 87 per cent position, which
also marks the start of the "Transfer and Other
Taxes" sector. This wedge has a 10 per cent
value and was thus extended to the 97 per cent
position. The 3 per cent "Nontax Receipts"
completed the circle.

The practice of arranging the sectors in ascending or descending numerical order is helpful in making comparisons. On occasion, however, two or more small sectors exist. These
are best separated from one another to permit
the graph reader to distinguish them readily.
Note, for instance, that in Fig. 2-43 the 3½
per cent wedge and the 1½ per cent wedge are
separated from one another by the 6¼ per
cent "Shareholder" sector. Had the two smaller ones been placed adjacent to one another,
it would have been difficult to determine their
relative sizes without referring to Table 2-5.

Since circle graphs are often shown in pairs
or larger groupings for purposes of comparison, circular percentage graph sheets are available with either one circle or with several
circles on the same sheet, all calibrated with
the percentage scale (Fig. 2-44).

2.32. Polar coordinate paper

Polar coordinate graph paper (Fig. 1-13) is
commonly used by the engineer, scientist, and
technician for other purposes and can readily
be adapted to the making of circle graphs.
Note that the polar coordinate paper is calibrated in degrees, both in the clockwise and
counterclockwise direction. Therefore, to use
this graph paper for "pie charts," it is necessary to convert the per cent calibration to
degrees by using a proportionality.

As an illustrative example let us use the data
that yielded the circle graph of Fig. 2-40b. It
is tabulated in Table 2-6 for convenience.

The proportionality referred to above is between the given percentage value and 100 per
cent set equal to the required number of degrees as compared to 360 degrees. Expressing
this in formula form, we have

$$\frac{\text{Given per cent}}{100 \text{ per cent}} = \frac{x}{360 \text{ degrees}}$$

Solving for x, we obtain

$$x = 360 \text{ degrees} \times \frac{\text{Given per cent}}{100 \text{ per cent}}$$

Applying this formula to the data of Table 2-6,
we have

for education aid

$$x = 360 \text{ degrees} \times \frac{33 \text{ per cent}}{100 \text{ per cent}}$$
$$= 119 \text{ degrees}$$

for other aid

$$x = 360 \text{ degrees} \times \frac{20 \text{ per cent}}{100 \text{ per cent}}$$
$$= 72 \text{ degrees}$$

for state operations

$$x = 360 \text{ degrees} \times \frac{31 \text{ per cent}}{100 \text{ per cent}}$$
$$= 112 \text{ degrees}$$

Table 2-6.

Expense	Education aid	Other aid	State operations	Capital construction	Debt service
Amount, per cent	33	20	31	14	2
Polar paper degree equivalent	119	72	112	50	7

The equivalents obtained by these calculations and expressed to the nearest degree are given in Table 2-6.

In order to produce the circle graph of Fig. 2-40b on polar coordinate paper, proceed as follows:

1. Hold the paper so that the 0° line is at the top of the sheet. Choose for your working circle the largest *complete* circle that appears on the graph sheet.

2. Using a straightedge, draw a line along the 0° line from the pole (center) to the circumference of your working circle.

3. Draw a second line from the pole to the circle circumference along the 119° line located at your right. The two radial lines thus drawn mark the boundaries of the first sector representing "Education Aid."

4. The "Other Aid" sector is 72° wide and will therefore extend to the 191° line. Draw a radial line at this position.

5. The "State Operations" sector, being 112° wide, will extend to the 303° position. Draw a radial line at the 303° position.

6. Complete the graph by drawing the next radial line at the 353° position. Crosshatch and label each wedge, making certain that all the lettering is *horizontally arranged*, not at an angle and not in the direction of the wedges. Put the name of the graph on the sheet with lettering in the same direction as the rest. Your result should compare very favorably with that shown in Fig. 2-40b.

2.33. Light flux paper

The light flux graph paper shown in Fig. 2-45 is also adaptable to circle graphs, although its primary application is entirely different. Note that this paper is also made up of concentric circles and radial lines. However, the center of these circles is not at the geometric center of the paper. Note also that no calibration markings or scale appears printed on the graph paper. The procedure for adapting this paper to circle graph use is similar to that used with polar paper:

1. Choose the largest complete circle on the paper as the working circle.

2. With the aid of the printed radial lines, calibrate the circumference into 100 equal parts. Put zero at the top and place a calibration mark and number every five divisions. The calibrated circle is now similar to that given on the circular percentage chart paper (Fig. 2-44) and is used in the same manner.

2.34. The band graph

At first glance, the circle graph certainly does not give the impression that we are dealing with a modification of the bar graph, although further investigation shows that this is the case. A similar situation exists with respect to the *band graph* otherwise referred to as a "strata chart," a "belt graph," or a "multiple-surface chart." A few minutes study of the band graph of Fig. 2-46 will show that we are dealing with a modification of the component bar graph. The modifications are these:

1. No separation exists between the bars, that is, they are all run together into block form.

2. The tops of the bars are not necessarily horizontal but show an increase or decrease in level from the left edge of the bar to the right. This change is shown by the use of a *straight line* connecting the left edge of the bar to the right edge.

For purposes of discussion let us refer specifically to the 1950–1960 bar. The information readily obtained from this bar alone can be listed as follows:

1. The total number of degrees granted in 1950 to both men and women was approximately 445,000.

2. The total number of degrees granted in 1960 was approximately 443,000, representing a decrease over the decade of 0.45 per cent. Since the values obtained from the graph are approximate, the decade decrease can be stated as being one-half of 1 per cent and was obtained by the following calculation:

Percentage difference

$$= \frac{445,000 \text{ degrees} - 443,000 \text{ degrees}}{445,000 \text{ degrees}} \times 100$$

$$= 0.0045 \times 100$$

$= -0.45$ per cent (the minus sign indicates a decrease)

3. The number of degrees granted to men in 1950 is shown as approximately 334,000. Subtracting this from the 1950 total of 445,000 yields the size of the component representing degrees granted to women and is evaluated to 111,000.

4. The number of degrees awarded to men in 1960 is shown as being approximately 328,000. Subtracting this from the 1960 total of 443,000 yields the height of the 1960 component representing degrees awarded to women and is evaluated to 115,000.

5. The percentage change over the decade for degrees awarded men is a decrease of 1.8 per cent.

Percentage difference

$$= \frac{334,000 \text{ degrees} - 328,000 \text{ degrees}}{334,000 \text{ degrees}} \times 100$$

$$= \frac{6,000}{334,000} \times 100$$

$$= -1.8 \text{ per cent}$$

6. The percentage change over the same period in degrees awarded women shows an increase of almost 3.6 per cent computed as in the above calculations in which the 1950 values are used as reference (denominator) value.

7. Comparing the percentage changes for the men and women shows more than a 5 per cent difference favoring the women, obtained as follows:

$$(3.6) - (-1.6) = 5.2 \text{ per cent}$$

8. Further information is obtainable from this single bar by comparing the degrees awarded to each group to the total number for that year, thus giving percentages of the annual totals.

9. Average values for the entire decade are also obtainable from the graph, by averaging the beginning and end values. By this procedure, the average number of degrees granted per year over the entire decade is

Average

$$= \frac{445,000 \text{ degrees} + 443,500 \text{ degrees}}{2}$$

$$= 444,000 \text{ degrees per year}$$

10. With the average per year known, the total number of degrees awarded for the en-

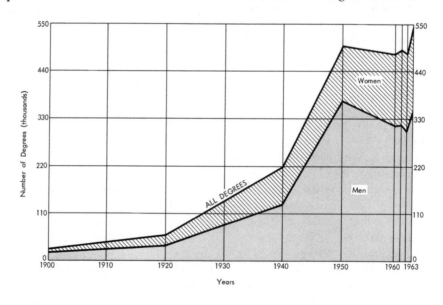

Fig. 2-46. Band graph or strata chart (modification of component bar graph)

tire decade can be obtained by multiplying the average per year by 10 years per decade. Thus

Total degrees

$$= \frac{444{,}000 \text{ degrees}}{\text{year}} \times \frac{10 \text{ years}}{\text{decade}}$$

$$= 4{,}440{,}000 \frac{\text{degrees}}{\text{decade}}$$

11. In addition, the average per year and the total for the decade can be calculated for degrees awarded to men and for degrees awarded women.

Since the calculations above described apply to only one of the bars of the band graph, they can be repeated for each of the bars and the results for each compared to one another. This will result in a numerical documentation of trends existing over the entire period covered by the graph.

It is apparent from the discussion of this modification of the bar graph that the primary purpose of the variation is to permit the inclusion of more information in the graph. The change in height values of the bar and of the components of the bar between the left and right edges of the bar is the means for including this additional information. The elimination of the spacing between the bars permits the changes in bar and component heights to be shown as what appears to be a continuous line. Actually the lines start and stop at the borders of each bar. This apparent continuity permits trends to be recognized more readily over the entire extent of the graph for the over-all quantities as well as for the components of the bars.

2.35. Coloring the graph

In the bar or circle graph as in all other graphs discussed later in this volume the use of different colors to designate various portions of the graph is not good practice. Colors do not blueprint or photostat uniformly, and yield lines of varying thickness. Consequently, much significant information can be lost. Since a graph is an extremely concise manner for presenting a wealth of information, it is often reproduced for distribution to personnel interested in that information. Graphing techniques that yield good copies are therefore an important consideration.

Coloring used as an embellishment, as well as underlinings or other form of adornments, should also be avoided on technical graphs. A graph is considered a significant piece of technical communication insofar as it presents its information effectively. Its decorative value is meaningless.

REVIEW

Define concisely each of the following terms:

2-1. Graph

2-2. Magnitude of a quantity

2-3. Coordinate axes

2-4. Bar graph

2-5. Rectangular coordinate gridwork

2-6. Linear calibration

2-7. Fine calibration; coarse calibration

2-8. Primary (major) calibration line

2-9. Origin

2-10. Dependent axis

2-11. Independent axis

2-12. The first quadrant

2-13. Broken scale

2-14. Legend (key)

2-15. List five useful properties of the bars of a bar graph.

2-16. What are at least two major advantages of the bar graph?

2-17. What are two major disadvantages of the bar graph?

2-18. List the eight steps for making an effective bar graph.

2-19. One fault with the bar graph of Fig. 2-6 is the need for, but lack of, a broken scale. (a) List at least three other faults in this graph. (b) Redraw this graph to present the information properly.

2-20. Distinguish between a Cartesian coordinate and rectangular coordinate graphical system.

2-21. Distinguish between a Cartesian coordinate and orthogonal coordinate reference system.

2-22. If "rectilinear" refers to straight lines, describe a graph paper that is rectilinear, Cartesian coordinate, but nonrectangular. Sketch the gridwork.

2-23. The variation of voltage with time is to be plotted. Which quantity, voltage or time, is to be calibrated along the vertical axis and which along the horizontal? Why?

2-24. If the quantities A vs. B are to be plotted, which quantity is to be calibrated along the horizontal axis? Why?

2-25. Of what importance is it to know that the horizontal axis always shows the independent variable and the vertical axis the dependent?

2-26. The number of homes in a particular town increased gradually from 8,000 to 13,000 over a five-year period. Compute the annual rate of home increase.

2-27. Refer to Fig. 2-21. (a) Determine the average annual rate at which Ph.D. degrees were earned in the 1930–1940 decade. (b) How does this compare to the 1940–1950 decade? (c) What is the percentage difference between them if the earlier decade is used for reference? (d) What is the percentage difference between them if the later decade is used for reference?

2-28. If the town growth rate of problem 2-26 continued unchanged for a score of years, what would be the total increase? Show clearly how the *units* are handled in your calculation.

2-29. (a) What is the significance of the last bar of Fig. 2-23? (b) Can the total income of this company be determined from this figure? Explain.

2-30. Make a positive-negative bar graph from the data obtainable from Fig. 2-22, using 1959 as reference.

2-31. From Fig. 2-24, determine: (a) The total revenue collected in the five-year period

shown; (b) the total mileage revenue for this period; (c) the percentage difference between the total revenue collected in 1957 and in 1961, using 1957 as reference; (d) the percentage difference between the permit tax revenues for 1957 and 1961, using 1957 as reference; (e) does this data tell whether or not a cost change occurred for truck permits between 1957 and 1961? Explain.

2-32. Figures 2-29 and 2-30 each compare four commodities for a period of four years, and each uses shading and an explanatory key. Explain the following: (a) What is the independent variable in Fig. 2-29? In Fig. 2-30? (b) What could be the reason for the difference in the independent variables used in the two graphs.

2-33. From Fig. 2-29, determine: (a) The average fuel revenue over the four-year period; (b) the percentage difference between the fuel revenue of each year and the average just computed; (c) the average cigarette revenue; (d) the average revenue from other commodities; (e) the average license revenue; (f) the percentage difference between the fuel revenue and each of the other three, using fuel revenue as reference; (h) the total revenue from the four sources over the four-year period?; (i) four additional comparisons possible from the data of the graph; (j) whether the amount of space occupied by the graph of Fig. 2-29 is appropriate for the information obtained from it.

2-34. By reading the ordinate maximum of each bar of Fig. 2-30, you can obtain sixteen pieces of numerical data. Describe at least six useful comparisons that can be made using this data.

2-35. In addition to the basic vertical (or horizontal) bar graph, seven special-purpose bar graphs find frequent application. Name and define each and the primary advantage of each type.

2-36. Make a circle graph of the time distribution of your average day on polar-coordinate graph paper. Determine the size, in degrees, of each sector, and tabulate the information below:

Sector title	Percentage of total day	Number of degrees in sector
1. Travel time		
2. Meal time		
3. Working time		
4. Leisure time		
5. Other		

2-37. Refer to the percentage bar graph of Fig. 2-42. (a) Read from it as much numerical information as you can. (b) Redraw this graph as a compound bar graph. (c) Name at least one advantage of each graph over the other.

2-38. (a) The band graph is known by three other names. What are they? (b) This graph is a modification of what other type of graph? (c) What are the advantages of a band graph over a bar graph?

2-39. In a given year, a survey of 240,880 manufacturing plants yielded the data given in the table below. Complete the table.

2-40. Draw a seven-bar graph of the number of plants per category vs. category designation with the data in the table completed in problem 2-39. Include a key to clarify the designations.

Plant category designation	Number of employees	Number of plants per category	Percentage of total number of plants
A	2,500 and over		0.2
B	1,000 to 2,499		0.6
D	250 to 499		1.1
C	500 to 999		2.2
E	100 to 249		6.0
F	20 to 99		24.4
G	1 to 19		65.5

3 - THE STRAIGHT LINE

We are at the point now where we appreciate more fully what is meant by "the language of graphs" and how much information is included in a properly made graph. We are also familiar with the basic graphs and through them with some of the standard graphics terminology, symbols, and ground rules. Let us progress now into a region beyond the basic graphs and deal with the basic "curve" in technology—the one most easily produced and read—the straight line.

3.1. Definition of the curve

It may sound odd to call a straight line a curve. However, in technology a curve is defined as a line smoothly drawn to connect, in order, a series of plotted points. Thus, the straight line as well as the curved line falls under this general heading of "curve."

3.2. Characteristics of the straight line

Our purpose in considering the straight line is to become familiar with its information-containing characteristics, to expand further our graphics vocabulary, and to learn how to produce, interpret, and more fully utilize this shorthand of technology. Let us base our dis-

cussions again on an illustrative graph. Refer, therefore, to Fig. 3-1 and note that it shows a smooth line connection between a series of plotted points representing a graph of distance vs. time. The plotted points are obtained from information known about the variables (in this case, distance and time), and this information can appear in several different forms. Let us start with descriptive information and present the problem as follows:

Draw a graph for an automobile traveling 30 miles per hour, showing how its distance covered changes with time for at least the first 7 hours of its travel.

1. As always, the starting point is the selection of the proper graph paper and the drawing and labeling of the axes. The axes are then calibrated so that the graph will occupy the major portion of the graph paper. Note in Fig. 3-1 that the time axis was carried out slightly beyond the minimum range requirements of from 0 to 7 hours and that the distance axis (vertical, dependent) was also continued beyond minimum needs.

2. The next step is the location (plotting) of the points on the graph, and for this a table

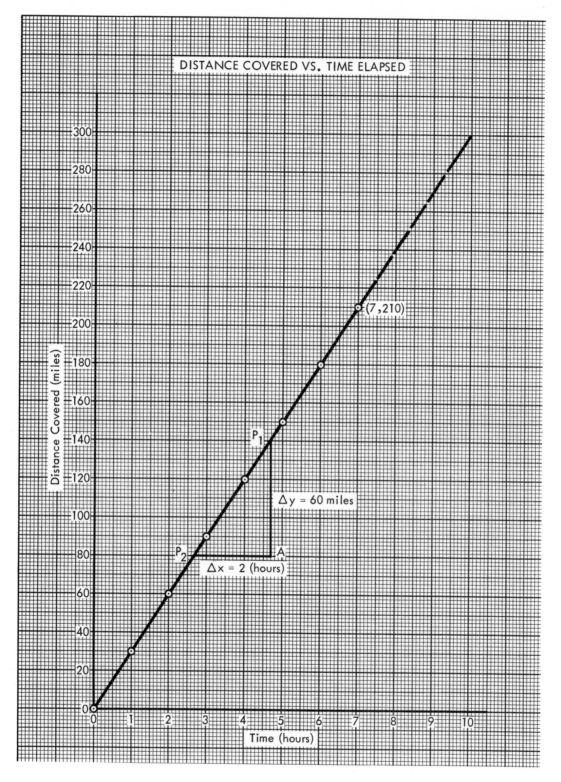

Fig. 3-1. Straight-line graph of distance covered vs. elapsed time

of values is necessary. The values referred to are the abscissa (time) and ordinate (distance) values of the points to be plotted, and although no such values were given, they should be readily available from the known information. Whenever possible, a graph should be started from a zero point. Thus, for this graph if time elapsed is considered 0 hours, the distance covered by the automobile is certainly 0 miles, regardless of its speed. This pair of values, therefore, represents our first set of *coordinates* (corresponding abscissa and ordinate values) to be included in the table of values (Table 3-1).

Table 3-1.

Time (hours)	Distance covered (miles)
0	0
1	30
2	60
3	90
4	120
5	150
6	180
7	210

3. The table is continued by choosing a series of values for the independent quantity and determining the corresponding dependent value. Integers are more easily plotted than are fractions, and therefore integral values are usually chosen for the abscissa values, as shown in Table 3-1. Since we know that the automobile is traveling at a speed of 30 miles per hour, we can find the distance covered corresponding to any of the chosen time values. Thus, for time = 1 hour,

$$d \text{ (distance covered)} = \text{speed} \times \text{time}$$
$$= 30 \frac{\text{miles}}{\text{hour}} \times \frac{1 \text{ hour}}{1}$$
$$= 30 \text{ miles}$$

This process is continued for each of the abscissa values chosen up to $t = 7$ hours. Therefore,

$$d = 30 \frac{\text{miles}}{\text{hour}} \times \frac{7 \text{ hours}}{1}$$
$$= 210 \text{ miles}$$

4. All the values, both chosen and computed, are tabulated as shown with the independent values listed in the left column of Table 3-1 and the dependent values to the right. If the table were arranged horizontally, as is sometimes done, the abscissa value would be placed in the top line and the ordinate values below, as shown in Table 3-2.

The reason for this convention is that when points are plotted on a graph sheet, it is customary to "measure off" or determine the x value of a point first and then the corresponding y value. Furthermore, if a point is to be designated on a sheet of graph paper, its abscissa value is shown first, followed by a comma, and then the ordinate value and the pair enclosed in parentheses. Thus, the general notation is (x, y). For example, the last plotted point on the graph of Fig. 3-1 is (7, 210) and is so designated on the graph.

5. The next step in making the plot is the location of the data of the table on the graph sheet. The first tabulated point is the origin. A dot is therefore placed at the origin, and the point clearly designated by drawing a geometric symbol around it, denoting a plotted point. In Fig. 3-1 circles are used to designate the plotted points. The second point is located by measuring along the horizontal axis a distance corresponding to 1 hour and moving up along the graph paper grid line to a height corresponding to 30 miles as determined by the vertical axis calibration. A dot is placed at this position and encircled to designate the plotted point clearly. The process is repeated for each of the next six points, and with a

Table 3-2.

Time (hours)	0	1	2	3	4	5	6	7
Distance covered (miles)	0	30	60	90	120	150	180	210

straightedge placed carefully along the plotted points, the straight-line graph is drawn.

Note from Fig. 3-1 that the line drawn was extended beyond the last plotted point. Normally a graph is not drawn into a region where no definite information about it is available. However, if the graph is obviously a straight line, then it may be extended in both directions if desired. This liberty of extending a graph beyond the plotted points can be taken only with a very few curve types. If, however, a directed guess or prediction is made in order to extend a curve beyond definitely known points, then the extended region must be clear-

ly designated by showing it as a broken line, as demonstrated in Fig. 3-2. Note in Fig. 3-2 that the last plotted point has an abscissa of 1958–60 but that the curve is extended *in broken line* up to the year 1964. This predicted region of the curve is clearly designated as such, even though the plotted points definitely indicate the smooth downward trend shown.

Now that the graph of Fig. 3-1 is drawn, just what information is available from it? What type of information is available here that could not readily be obtained from the basic graphs? If there are such features to this graph, do they apply only to the straight line or can they be

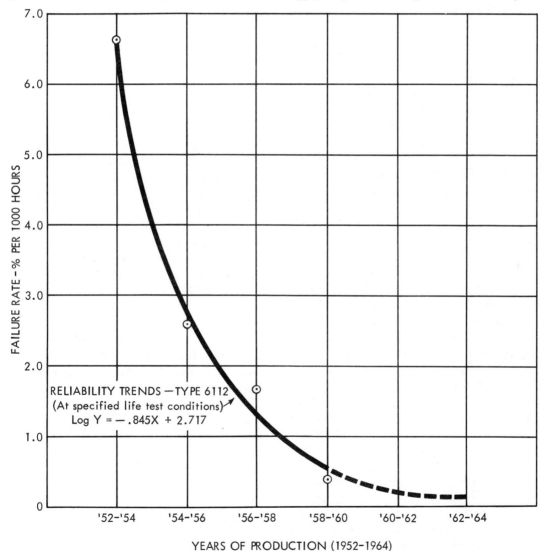

RELIABILITY TRENDS — TYPE 6112
(At specified life test conditions)
Log Y = − .845X + 2.717

FAILURE RATE — % PER 1000 HOURS

YEARS OF PRODUCTION (1952–1964)

(Courtesy, Sylvania Electronic Tube Division)

Fig. 3-2. Prediction region is clearly designated by broken-line portion of curve

extended to other types of curves? These and many other valid questions may occur to you regarding straight-line plots. Let's answer the last question first by saying that all properties of the straight-line graph discussed in this chapter will be extended to other graph types and that much of the terminology developed in this chapter will be generally applicable to other types of curves.

Now for specific points in answer to the first two questions above. Two direct pieces of information are obtainable from the plot of Fig. 3-1. One is the distance covered from the starting point in a given time interval. The second is the time in which a specific distance is covered. For example, how far (distance) has the car traveled in the first $5\frac{1}{2}$ hours? The answer, 165 miles is the y value corresponding to the x value of $5\frac{1}{2}$ hours. How long will it take for this car to travel 190 miles from the starting point? The answer is obtained by following the vertical axis to the 190-mile point and from there following the horizontal (abscissa) line to the graph. The length of this abscissa line can be determined to be about 6.4 hours by referring to the calibration of the horizontal axis. The exact answer is 6.33 hours obtained by calculation. However, we are interested in graphical accuracy, which in this case is better than 1.1 per cent.

If the automobile had continued traveling, what specific distance would it have gone in the 8 to $9\frac{1}{2}$-hour period? This information is not read from the graph as directly as the previous data. Two steps are required to obtain the answer. From the graph it can be seen that the ordinate for an 8-hour abscissa is 240 miles and for a $9\frac{1}{2}$-hour x value the y value is 295 miles. Therefore, in this particular $1\frac{1}{2}$-hour interval the automobile traveled the 45-mile distance between the 240- and 295-mile points.

3.3. Slope of a line

Let's look somewhat deeper now. The information given at the outset was that the car traveled with a constant speed of 30 miles per hour. Where is this speed information shown on the graph? How can we read out the speed of the automobile, and how does the graph tell us that the speed is constant throughout the entire run? The answer to both of these questions lies in what is known technically as the *slope* of the line, which is a means of describing the line tilt, slant, or inclination. In other words, the slope value tells us whether the line is horizontal or vertical or somewhere between. To see how such information can be useful in answering questions like those above, it is necessary to examine the technical definition of the term *slope*.

The slope of a line is defined as a change or (increment) of the y value divided by the corresponding change (increment) of the x value.[1] Expressing this in abbreviated form, we have

$$m = \frac{\Delta y}{\Delta x}$$

or

$$\text{Slope} = \frac{\text{change in } y}{\text{change in } x}$$

where m represents the slope of the line, and the Greek letter delta (Δ) represents change, or increment. This ratio is actually a measure of how much the line rises or falls vertically for a certain amount of horizontal travel. To apply the slope definition graphically, refer to Fig. 3-1 and proceed as follows:

1. Choose as a starting point any point whatsover on the line, such as P_1.

2. From this starting point, draw a vertical line of any length whatever and label it Δy, such as line P_1A shown.

3. From the end of this vertical line (point A) draw a horizontal line until it reaches the plotted line and label this horizontal line Δx, such as line AP_2 on the diagram.

4. The ratio of the Δy value to the Δx value yields the slope of the line. From the calibration of the vertical axis it can be seen that the Δy line represents 60 miles, since point A is at the 80-mile position and point P_1 is at the 140-mile position. The calibration of the horizontal axis shows that the Δx value is 2 hours since point A is at the 4.65-hour posi-

---

[1] Increment and "change in value" are synonomous terms.

tion and point P_2 is at the 2.65-hour position. The ratio therefore yields

$$\frac{\Delta y}{\Delta x} = \frac{60 \text{ miles}}{2 \text{ hours}}$$

$$m = 30\frac{\text{miles}}{\text{hour}}$$

which is read, "the slope equals 30 miles per hour." Thus, we realize that the slope of this line represents speed, since for such a plot a change in the vertical dimension over a change in the horizontal dimension is a ratio of distance covered over time elapsed. Such a ratio we know to be the definition of speed. Since an evaluation of the slope anywhere on the line will yield exactly the same value, regardless of the size of the increments used, we recognize that the given information of 30 miles per hour constant speed is contained in the slope of the line.

It is thus the *meaning* of the vertical increment (in this case, distance) and of the horizontal increment (in this example, time) that gives the slope its importance as a source of information.

Let us use the definition of slope with another plot to determine both slope value and its significance in a second application. Figure 3-3 is a straight-line plot of a rectangular area vs. length. Carefully examine all parts of this graph, and determine the meaning of the slope of the line. Try to answer the question, what information about this rectangle does the line slope supply? Once this has been decided, evaluate the slope numerically.

The correct meaning of the slope of the line of Fig. 3-3 is that it represents the width of the rectangles. This is so because slope is a ratio of the vertical increment over the horizontal increment. In the application of Fig. 3-3 the vertical increment represents an area and the horizontal increment a length. The ratio of area over length is width. Expressing this symbolically, we have

$$m = \frac{\Delta \text{ area}}{\Delta \text{ length}}$$

Therefore,

$$\text{Slope} = \text{width}$$

The exact numerical value of the width of

these rectangles can be determined by following the procedure outlined earlier. The arbitrary point chosen as the starting point could very well be the point P_1 shown in Fig. 3-3. Note that the vertical line P_1A representing Δy is drawn upward from the plotted line, whereas in Fig. 3-1 the Δy line is drawn downward from the starting point. Since this line represents a change in vertical value to be compared with a corresponding horizontal change, it is immaterial in which direction, upward or downward, the Δy line is drawn. Continuing with the construction to yield the slope, we then draw a horizontal line (Δx) from point A (the endpoint of the Δy line) to the plotted line. From the vertical calibration, the value of Δy is seen to be 15 square meters since point P_1 is at the 15 square-meter vertical level and point A is at the 30-square-meter level. From the horizontal axis calibration the value of Δx is seen to be 3 meters, since point P_1 is at the 3-meter calibration point, and P_2 is at the 6-meter point. The ratio therefore is

$$m = \frac{15 \text{ meters}^2}{3 \text{ meters}}$$

$$\text{Slope} = 5 \text{ meters}$$

Since the slope is the same throughout, the plot represents a series of rectangles of a constant width of 5 meters, the areas of which change as the length changes.

Is any further information obtainable from the slope of a line? To be specific, what is the slope of the Car 2 plot of Fig. 3-4? Notice that all three straight-line plots of Fig. 3-4 represent distance covered vs. time. The Car 1 plot shown is identical to that of Fig. 3-1, and we know that it has a slope of 30 miles per hour representing the constant speed of the car. In order to find the slope of the Car 2 line, a ratio of Δy over Δx is required as previously discussed. If the y and x increments shown on the graph are used, the slope value obtained is

$$m = \frac{\Delta y}{\Delta x}$$

$$= \frac{30 \text{ miles}}{1 \text{ hour}}$$

$$\text{Slope} = 30 \text{ miles per hour}$$

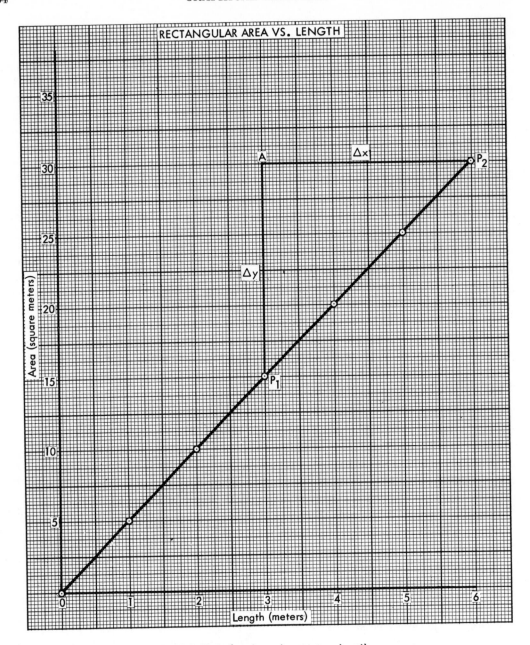

Fig. 3-3. Plot of rectangular area vs. length

This result is the same as that obtained for Car 1, and yet the two lines are quite different. Actually, the slopes of the two lines are not the same. Yes, they have the same numerical value, but the slope *directions* are different. The slopes are the negative of one another. We shall see in a moment how this comes about, but, first, what is the significance of the previous statement? How does the knowl-

edge that one slope is positive and the other negative add to our information about the quantities involved? In this particular case, what additional information does it tell us about the two automobiles? Since the slopes are the negative of one another, let us assume for the time being that Car 1 line has the positive slope and Car 2 line the negative. Since the slope of the Car 1 line represents a

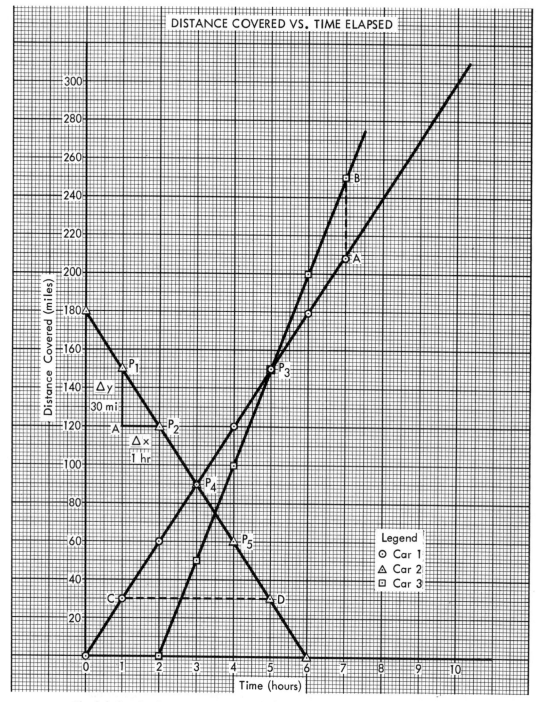

Fig. 3-4. Graphs drawn on common set of axes to permit relating one to another

speed of 30 miles per hour, what does the negative of this mean? In technology, sign, or polarity, means direction. Therefore, a negative slope of 30 miles per hour means that Car 2 is moving with a speed of 30 miles per hour in a direction *opposite*—or negative—to that of Car 1.

To determine how the plot shows whether the slope of a line is positive or negative, let us refer again to the line of Fig. 3-1, and trace out again the value for the slope. Starting at P_1, we measure *downward*. Since the downward direction is the direction of decreasing values, it is represented as the negative direction. Therefore, the Δy measured from P_1 to A is minus 60 miles (—60 miles). From point A we now measure horizontally to the *left* to point P_2 on the line. From A to P_2 we are traveling in a negative x direction, since this is in the direction of decreasing time value. The Δx is therefore minus 2 hours (—2 hours). To evaluate the slope completely, we have

$$m = \frac{-60 \text{ miles}}{-2 \text{ hours}}$$
$$= +30 \text{ miles per hour}$$

since a minus quantity divided by another minus quantity yields a plus quantity. Now let us refer to the P_1AP_2 triangle of Fig. 3-4 that we used to determine the slope of the Car 2 line. From P_1 to A we have an increment of —30 miles, but from A to P_2 we have an increment of +1 hour. Therefore, the slope evaluation becomes

$$m = \frac{-30 \text{ miles}}{+1 \text{ hour}}$$
$$= -30 \text{ miles per hour}$$

since a negative quantity divided by a positive quantity results in a negative quantity.

In general, therefore, we can say that if the increments Δy and Δx have opposite signs, then the slope is negative. If they have the same signs—either both positive or both negative—then the slope is positive. Another method for determining whether a line has a positive or negative slope is to note what is happening to the y values as the x values increase. A line of positive slope has its vertical values *increasing* as its horizontal values increase to the right. Note the lines for Car 1 and Car 3 in Fig. 3-4. A line of negative slope has its y values decreasing as its x values increase toward the right. Note the line for Car 2 in Fig. 3-4.

The significance of the sign (polarity) of the slope depends upon the meaning of the slope itself. In Fig. 3-4 the line slopes represent speed. The positive slope represents a given direction, and a negative one represents a direction opposite to it. In Fig. 3-3, on the other hand, the slope represents width, and here a negative slope would be meaningless. Certainly a negative dimension has no meaning at all.

3.4. Intercepts

In our example of the plotted lines of Fig. 3-4 we have determined so far that Cars 1 and 2 have the same speed but are traveling in opposite directions. The graph also tells us that the two cars started at different points. Notice that at the starting time (time = 0) Car 1 is at the zero distance position. Let us call this position the "true start" position. Notice then from the graph that Car 2 starts 180 miles ahead of this position. In other words, at starting time ($t = 0$) Car 2 is at the +180-mile point. This can be expressed in graphical terms by stating that the *vertical intercept* of the Car 2 line is +180 miles and the vertical intercept of the Car 1 line is 0.

From the example it is apparent that the vertical intercept of a line (or curve) is defined as the y value of the point at which the line (or curve) cuts the Y axis. Extending this idea to the X axis, we can define the X intercept as the x value of the point at which a line (or curve) cuts the X axis. In general, the term "intercept" refers to the point where a curve (straight line, etc.) meets an axis. It is the labeling, or calibration, of the axis that determines the significance of the intercept.

For example, refer to Fig. 3-4, and determine the meaning of the X intercept of the Car 2 line. This intercept represents the time (since the horizontal axis is labeled "Time") at which Car 2 passed the start point. Notice that the y value of the X intercept is 0 and similarly that the x value of the Y intercept is 0. It is this fact that makes the intercepts an important aspect of a graph to investigate. They yield information about one of the variables when the other is at a zero or starting value.

Refer now to the Car 3 line of Fig. 3-4. Note that the line as drawn shows an X intercept but no Y intercept. What is the significance of this X intercept? Since the X axis is calibrated in units of time, the X intercept must represent a specific time. Since the ordinate value of the X intercept is 0 miles, the X intercept represents the time at which Car 3 was at the starting point (distance). We know from this intercept that Car 3 started 2 hours later than the other two cars. Reading the graph further, would you say that Car 3 was traveling in the same direction as Car 1 or opposite to it? This question can be answered by noting that the line 3 slope is positive. Its ordinate values increase as the abscissa values increase. Since the speed of Car 3 is positive it is traveling in the same direction as Car 1. How fast is Car 3 traveling? This requires an evaluation of the value of the slope of line 3. If the previously discussed procedure is followed, the slope of line 3 can be determined to be 50 miles per hour. Therefore, by a careful reading of the distance-vs.-time plot for Car 3, we know that it started out with a 2-hour lag, that it is traveling in the positive direction (away from the starting point rather than towards it), and that it maintained a 50-miles per hour constant speed.

3.5. Information from comparison of graphs

We have so far considered the definition and significance of the slope and intercepts of straight-line graphs. As will be learned from later sections of this chapter, there are more information-yielding properties of graphs. However, let us use the graphic knowledge we have acquired so far to relate several graphs to one another to determine what type of information is obtainable in this manner. Obviously, if graphs are to be compared and related to one another, it is more convenient to do so if the several graphs are plotted on the same set of axes, as is shown in Fig. 3-4. The legend provides the code necessary for ready distinction between the several plots.

Since we are looking for information that relates one graph to another, the most obvious relationship is probably the points if intersection of the lines, that is, the points where the lines cross one another. Such a crossover point is a point that lies on both intersecting lines. Since every point in this figure represents a time and the corresponding distance from the starting point, the points of intersection represent a *time* (abscissa value) at which the two cars involved are at the same place or *distance* from the starting point (ordinate value). It can be said that the points of intersection tell us *where* and *when* the cars involved meet (or pass one another). For example, the point P_3 has the coordinates 5 hours and 150 miles, which represented symbolically appears as P_3 (5 hr, 150 mi). Since P_3 is the point of intersection of lines 1 and 3, we know that the two cars met 5 hours after the zero starting time at the 150-mile mark from the starting point. The graph shows the "starting time" is the time at which Car 1 started. Since Car 3 started 2 hours later, the intersection information can be stated as the distance traveled by the two cars in which Car 3 overtook Car 1. Similarly, by noting that the coordinates of the Car 1 and Car 2 intersection point are P_4 (3 hr, 90 mi), we know when and at what point these two cars pass one another. Recognizing that the slopes of these two lines are the negatives of one another and therefore that the cars are traveling in opposite directions, we can state the meaning of the intersection point as the time and position at which the two cars 1 and 2 pass one another.

Much more time and distance information is, however, readily available from the relationship between the graphs of Fig. 3-4. Note, for example, the broken line AB drawn between the lines of Cars 1 and 3. What does this line represent? Since it is a vertical line, it must represent distance because in this figure the vertical axis is calibrated in distance units. Since this vertical line goes from the Car 1 plot to the Car 3 line and since it is drawn along the 7-hour calibration line, the *line segment*[2] AB represents the distance separa-

---

[2] A *line segment* is a specific, limited portion of an infinitely long line. It has clearly designated end points. A directed line segment has a specific start and end point. Interchanging the two would produce a line directed opposite to the first.

tion between Cars 1 and 3 after 7 hours of travel of Car 1. Note that point A has an ordinate value of 210 mi and point B, 250 mi. Therefore, the line segment AB represents a distance of 40 miles.

Is there any other time at which the two cars are separated by the same distance? Again, since distance is represented by vertical lengths in this graph, the question can be put in graphical terms and stated, "Is there any other time at which the vertical separation between the Car 1 and 3 lines equals 40 miles? The answer can readily be found by the following procedure:

1. Place a strip of paper alongside the line segment AB. (Refer to Fig. 3-5.)

2. Place a pencil mark on the paper corresponding to the positions of points A and B. The distance between these two marks is thus equal to the length AB. Mark the upper point on the paper B' and the lower point A'.

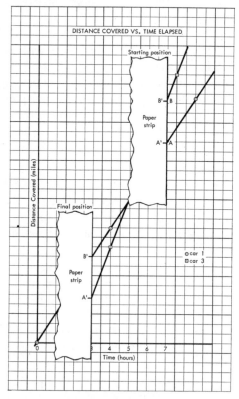

Fig. 3-5. How to determine graphically where two graphs show a desired separation

3. Place point A' on the paper strip in contact with point B on line 3.

4. Hold the paper vertically and slide the paper strip downward along the Car 3 line, keeping the point A' always in contact with the Car 3 line.

5. Continue sliding the paper strip downward with A' in contact with line 3 until point B' on the paper strip touches the Car 1 line.

6. Determine the time at which this occurs by noting where the paper strip intersects the X axis.

In this particular example the time determined by the procedure outlined above is 2.9 hours. Therefore, at 2.9 hours after the 0 starting time and again at the 7-hour time, the two cars 1 and 3 are separated by a distance of 40 miles. In this manner the times can be determined at which a specific distance (vertical) separation exists between two of the cars.

Why are there two times at which these cars are 40 miles apart? A look at the graphs of the two cars at the 2.9-hour and 7-hour times will give the answer. At the 2.9-hour time Car 1 is 40 miles ahead of Car 3, whereas at the 7-hour time Car 3 is 40 miles ahead of Car 2. The interval between these two times is how long it took Car 3 to turn a 40-mile lag into a 40-mile lead over Car 1. This time increment turns out to be

$$\Delta t = 7 \text{ hours} - 2.9 \text{ hours}$$
$$= 4.1 \text{ hours (within graphical accuracy)}$$

So we see that we can also easily find out from these graphs how long it takes one car to convert a lag distance of a certain amount into a lead of a desired distance. Again it is the labeling and calibration units of the axes that gives these vertical and horizontal increments their meaning. Had we been considering a pressure-volume plot, for example, then vertical increments would represent changes or differences in pressure and horizontal increments would represent changes in volume.

Note the horizontal line segment CD in Fig. 3-4. What does it represent? Since the line is horizontal, it must denote a time interval because the horizontal axis is calibrated in time units. Point C is on the Car 1 line, and point D

is on the Car 2 line. Also, the entire line segment is at the 30-mile ordinate position. Putting this information together, we find that the line segment CD represents the 4-hour time interval between the time that Car 1 reached the 30-mile mark and the time Car 2 reached the same mark. Is there another position (distance from the 0 starting point) that the two cars pass separated by the same time interval of 4 hours? By adapting the method described earlier, using a strip of paper this time held horizontally, we find that at the 150-mile position a 4-hour (horizontal) separation between lines 1 and 2 exists. This means that one of the cars reached this mark 4 hours before the other. The graph shows that Car 2 was at the 150-mile mark 4 hours earlier than Car 1, and that the reverse holds at the 30-mile mark.

In like manner any desired horizontal and vertical separations between the plotted lines can be evaluated and defined. It should be noted that only horizontal and vertical distances were considered since these are parallel to the named and calibrated axes. In general, it is such distances, measured parallel to the axes of the plot, that have useful meaning in connection with the graph.[3]

3.6. Area under a line or curve

It was mentioned earlier that other information yielding properties of graphs exist. One of these is the area under a specific portion of a plotted line or curve. The straight-line graph of Fig. 3-6 represents an object moving with a constant speed of 40 miles per hour. We see that this speed is constant because in this speed vs. time plot the speed (ordinate) value is the same for all time (abscissa) values. Constant speed can also be observed by a determination of slope. In doing so, we find the vertical increment to be 0 for any horizontal increment. Since the vertical increment here represents change in speed, we see that the

change in speed is 0, and therefore that the speed is constant. Let us consider the distance covered by this constant speed object in a period of 4 hours. To calculate distance covered, we need merely multiply the speed by the time of travel. Thus,

$$
\begin{aligned}
d &= \text{speed} \times \text{time} \\
&= 40 \ \frac{\text{miles}}{\cancel{\text{hour}}} \times 4 \ \cancel{\text{hours}} \\
&= 160 \ \text{miles}
\end{aligned}
$$

Now refer to the graph. What does this product of 40 miles per hour by 4 hours represent on the figure drawn? It represents the *area* of a rectangle the height of which is 40 miles per hour and the width of which is 4 hours. If for purpose of our discussion the graph of Fig. 3-6 is considered to end at the 4-hour position, and a vertical line imagined at this position, then we have the rectangle for which

$$
40 \ \frac{\text{miles}}{\cancel{\text{hour}}} \times \frac{4 \ \cancel{\text{hour}}}{1} = 160 \ \text{miles}
$$

is the area. Thus, the area under the line for a specific extent and bounded by the axes yields significant information. In this case the area under the line represents distance because area is a product of a vertical and horizontal dimension, and the vertical dimension here is in terms of speed and the horizontal is in terms of time. We know that speed multiplied by time yields distance. The units involved also show this. Notice in the computation shown above the hour in the denominator of the miles per hour fraction (miles/hour) cancels with the hour in the numerator of the 4-hour factor. The result is in terms of miles, which is certainly a distance unit.

In this discussion again it is the labeling and calibration units of the axes that give this graphical property—area—its meaning. Let us try another example. If in electrical discussions we were dealing with a plot of voltage vs. current, then the area under the curve would represent power. This is so because voltage times current equals power. The curve area involved can have any shape whatsoever. It could be rectangular as in Fig. 3-6, triangular

---

[3] It is possible by more elaborate means to determine the length of any plotted line or curve along the curve. However, the procedures involved are beyond the scope of our discussion, and the results obtained do not bear directly on the interpretation of graphs as described herein.

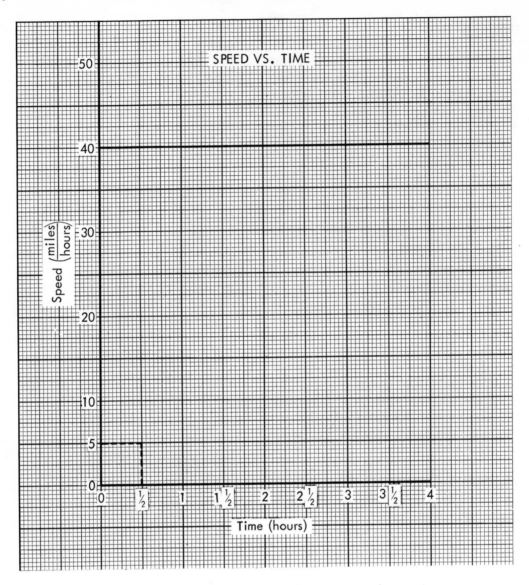

Fig. 3-6. Area under plotted line or curve has meaning

as in Fig. 3-4, or bounded by any odd-shaped curve. Regardless of the area shape, its value can be determined by the product of some vertical value and some horizontal value. This therefore relates the area to the name and calibration of the vertical axis and the horizontal axis. This is true even if the area is so irregular that the only way it can be determined is by counting the number of graph-paper squares bounded by the line or curve. If squares are counted, then the area of each little square is determined by a product of a vertical and a horizontal value.

This counting-of-squares procedure can easily be tested out with the rectangular area of Fig. 3-6. Suppose we use squares of the size marked off in broken line near the origin of Fig. 3-6. The vertical side of this square is 5 miles per hour and the horizontal side is ½ hour. The area of our unit square is thus 2½ miles, since

Area = vertical dimension $\times$ horizontal
       dimension

$$= 5 \, \frac{\text{miles}}{\text{hour}} \times \frac{1}{2} \, \text{hour}$$

$$= 2\frac{1}{2} \, \text{miles}$$

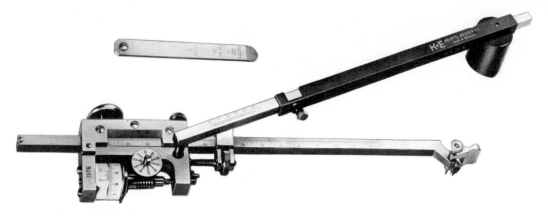

(Courtesy, Keuffel and Esser Co.)

Fig. 3-7. The planimeter—a precision instrument for accurately measuring plane areas of any form by simply moving tracing pin around periphery and reading from measuring dial

In the over-all rectangle of our discussion there are a total of 64 such squares. Thus, the total area of the large rectangle, by the counting-of-squares procedure, is $64 \times 2\frac{1}{2}$ mi, or a total of 160 miles.

3.7. The planimeter

With an area like a rectangle, triangle, or other regular pattern, this counting-of-squares procedure is not necessary. It is quite helpful, however, when dealing with areas under curves that vary considerably. This process of counting squares can be tedious and is often inaccurate when fractions of squares have to be considered. Under such conditions the graphical determination of the area under a curve can be accomplished with a high degree of accuracy with an instrument known as a *planimeter*, shown in Fig. 3-7.

3.8. Total characteristics of the line graph

The characteristics of the line graph that we have thus far discussed, when put together into a single composite, can yield a rather complete account of the subject of the graph. Figure 3-8 is a speed-vs.-time plot of a specific object. Let us investigate the characteristics of this line plot and see what we can learn about the object involved.

To begin with, we note that the line shows both a vertical and horizontal intercept. Since the abscissa value (time in this example), of the vertical intercept is 0 we know immedi-

ately that at time equal 0, that is, when we start measuring the motion of this object, its speed is $+96$ feet per second. The plus sign is indicated by the fact that the intercept is on the positive Y axis, that is, above the origin. Recalling that plus or minus refer to direction, we know that initially the object involved started with a 96-feet per second speed in the positive direction. The actual meaning of positive direction is not yet apparent, but later characteristics will give us more information on this point. Furthermore, since we know that the ordinate value (speed in this example) of the horizontal intercept is 0, we see from the graph that at a time of 3 seconds the speed of the object is 0. So far we have learned from the values of the intercepts that the speed of the object involved is initially 96 feet per second and that in 3 seconds it comes to a stop (speed equals 0).

The fact that the speed decreases continuously can also be seen from the graph, since the line shows a decreasing ordinate as the abscissa increases from 0 to 3 seconds. From our previous discussions we know that a decreasing ordinate with an increasing abscissa denotes a negatively sloped line. What does the slope of this line represent? The ratio of increments in this application is a change in speed per a specific time interval. Expressing this symbolically, we have

$$\text{Slope} = \frac{\text{speed increment}}{\text{time increment}}$$

A change in speed over an interval of time is an acceleration. Since in this case the slope and, therefore, the acceleration is negative, we can say it is opposite to the initial velocity direction, which we know to be positive. The value of the slope can readily be determined by using the large triangle formed by the plotted line and the X and Y axes. Δy measured from the vertical intercept to the origin is —96 feet per second. Δx measured from the origin to the X intercept is +3 seconds. Thus, the slope, which is acceleration in this case, is

$$m = \frac{\Delta y}{\Delta x}$$

$$= \frac{-96 \text{ feet/second}}{3 \text{ seconds}}$$

$$= -32 \text{ ft per second per second}$$

or as often written

$$m = -32 \text{ ft/sec}^2$$

This may be a familiar value to you. If it is, you know it to be the acceleration of gravity. Since the acceleration of gravity is toward the center of the earth and since the slope of this plot, representing acceleration, was found to be negative, we now say that the negative in this plot means toward the center of the earth, and therefore the positive direction in this plot means away from the center of the earth. The initial velocity of the object is now known to be away from the earth's center, or directly upward.

The straight-line plot being discussed produces a triangle with the vertical and horizontal axes, a figure whose area is readily evaluated. But what does the area under the plotted graph represent in this case? Since the area is a product of the vertical dimension, speed, and the horizontal dimension, time, we know it to be distance. Therefore, a calculation of the area under this line will tell how much distance this object covered from its starting point to the time it came to a stop at the end of 3 seconds. The area of any triangle equals one-half the product of its base and its altitude. Expressing this symbolically, we have

$$\text{Area} = \tfrac{1}{2}bh$$

Substituting the values from the graph, we obtain

$$\text{Area} = \tfrac{1}{2} \times 3 \, \cancel{\text{seconds}} \times \frac{96 \text{ feet}}{\cancel{\text{second}}}$$

$$= \tfrac{1}{2} (288 \text{ feet})$$

$$= 144 \text{ ft}$$

We now have all the significant characteristics of the motion of the object involved. Putting them together, the full account may be expressed as follows: An object was fired upward (away from the center of the earth) with a speed of 96 feet per second. Its speed decreased continuously at the rate of 32 feet per second every second. At the end of 3 seconds it came to a stop. In this time it had gone 144 feet from its starting point. We could continue this somewhat by saying that the 144 feet represents a height of that amount, since throughout the entire plot all the velocity values are positive. This means that the object was going straight upward (away from the earth's center). Thus, even without graphically determining the various positions and speeds of the object at different times, we are able to read this straight-line plot to obtain from it a complete picture of the motion of the object.

3.9. Characteristics of the straight line symbolically represented

Calculations for slope, areas, percentage differences, and others were described in many of the previous sections. In each case, it was convenient to use symbolic representations. Thus, a set of abbreviations or shorthand notations were introduced to permit expressing a great deal in limited space, permitting quicker and easier reading. Examples of these abbreviations are m for slope, Δy for a vertical increment, b for the base of a triangle, h for height, or altitude, and many others. A shorthand method also exists for expressing the characteristics of a straight line and stating their interrelationship at the same time. This abbreviated statement is the equation of the

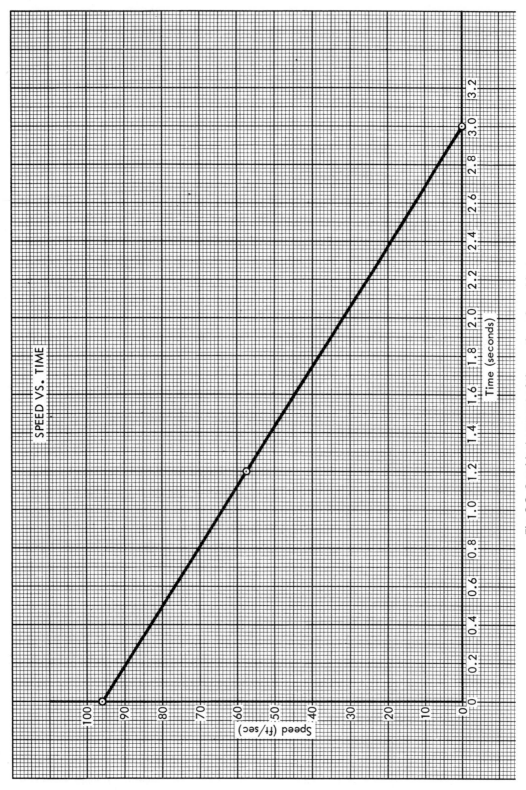

Fig. 3·8. Graphical account of the motion of an object

straight line. The most common form of the equation is

$$y = mx + b$$

where y = ordinate values
x = abscissa values
m = slope
b = vertical intercept

Other representations of the straight-line equation are often seen, but they are all based on the form shown above, and each one can be converted algebraically to the form shown above. It should be understood that y and x are general symbols and in any application are replaced by more appropriate designations. If a straight-line speed-vs.-time plot is being considered, the y would be replaced by s and the x by t, whereas in a distance-time plot, y gives way to d and x again to t. An equation of a pressure-volume straight-line plot would contain p and v instead of y and x. These are the variable quantities, that is, the quantities that are plotted along the axes and for which a range of values exists, usually both positive and negative. The values for m and b are fixed for any one line.

From what we know of the straight lines that we have discussed so far in this chapter, we should now be able to write the equation for each. Starting with the line of Fig. 3-8, we realize that instead of y and x, s and t would be more appropriate. We know that the slope is -32 and that the vertical intercept is 96. Therefore, the equation of this straight-line plot is

$$s = -32t + 96$$

where s = speed and t = time.

A test of the validity of this equation can readily be run by substituting values for t into the equation and computing the corresponding s values. These can then be checked against the plot of Fig. 3-8. To start with, let $t = 0$. Substituting in the equation, we obtain

$$s = 0 + 96$$

Thus, when $t = 0$, $s = 96$. This checks on the graph, since these values are seen to be the coordinates of the vertical intercept. Checking the equation with another point, let $t = 1.2$

seconds. The value for s thus becomes

$$s = -32t + 96$$
$$s = -32(1.2) + 96$$
$$= -38.4 + 96$$
$$= +57.6 \text{ feet per second}$$

By referring to the plot, we see that $(1.2, 57.6)$ are coordinates of a point on the line. To check the horizontal intercept coordinates, let $t = 3$ seconds. The value for speed computed from the equation becomes

$$s = -32\,t + 96$$
$$s = -32(3) + 96$$
$$= -96 + 96$$
$$= 0 \text{ feet per second}$$

This checks, since we know that the vertical coordinate of the horizontal intercept is 0.

What is the equation of the speed-time plot of Fig. 3-6? The slope of this line is 0, and its vertical intercept is 40. The ordinate values can be symbolized by s and the abscissas by t. Using the $y = mx + b$ general form of the straight-line equation and substituting the appropriate letters and values, we obtain for the Fig. 3-6 line the equation

$$s = 0t + 40$$
$$= 0 + 40$$

Since the 0 need not be written, because it would be understood as such if it does not appear, the equation finally becomes

$$s = 40$$

Note that no t term appears in the final equation. What significance does this have? It merely means that the value for speed, s, does not depend upon time, t. The speed is always the same, 40 miles per hour. What the equation, $s = 40$, tells us, is that s always equals 40, regardless of the value of t.

By following the same procedure, we find the equations of the distance-vs.-time line plots of Fig. 3-4 to be

Line 1: $d = 30t$

Line 2: $d = -30t + 180$

Line 3 is slightly different from the others, since the vertical intercept does not appear in the portion of the line shown. If the line is extended in the negative distance direction, that is, into the fourth quadrant, the vertical intercept can be obtained. This construction yields a point of intersection of the line and the vertical intercept is at -100 miles. With this information and a slope evaluated to be $+50$ miles per hour, the straight-line equation $y = mx + b$ for line 2 becomes

$$d = 50t - 100$$

Although we can see from the plots of the three lines of Fig. 3-4 that Car 3 starts out 2 hours later than Cars 1 and 2, the intercept of -100 miles indicates that if Car 3 started at the *same time* as the other two cars, but from a point 100 miles behind the true start position, the relationships between the three cars would be exactly the same as in our discussions of this set of graphs.

The ease with which a straight-line plot can be abbreviated into an equation helps make the equation a valuable tool. Much of the pertinent information about the line is available from the equation, just as it is from the plot itself. If values for the independent variable are substituted in the equation, the corresponding dependent values can be evaluated. This permits the line to be plotted from the equation. We see, therefore, that it is possible, in the case of the straight line at least, to translate readily from a graphical representation to an algebraic one and back again. Although we are not primarily concerned here with mathematical representations of lines and curves, the equation discussion does serve to show that translations back and forth between graphical and mathematical expressions are possible and are often very advantageous.

3.10. Families of lines. The parameter

A glance at the d-vs.-t graphs of Fig. 3-9 shows that the lines of part a have something in common with one another, and yet the three lines are quite different, and that the same is true of the lines of part b of the figure. Here again the three d-vs.-t lines have a characteristic in common, and yet the three lines

are separate and distinct from one another. In part a of Fig. 3-9 the three lines show a common Y-axis intercept of 100 feet. The slopes of the lines are, however, different. Since these are distance-vs.-time plots, the three objects started from the same point, that is, from the 100-foot mark. The velocities of the particles represented by the line slope are, however, different. A set of lines that have one characteristic in common is known as a *family* or *system of lines*. In the case of the lines of Fig. 3-9a, the common characteristic is the starting point of the particles, shown graphically as the vertical intercept. Furthermore, these graphs differ because the speeds of the three particles are different, this being represented graphically by the slopes of the lines.

Although the slope of each plot is constant throughout that entire plot, the slopes of the three lines are different from one another. A characteristic that remains fixed throughout one entire plot but differs from one plot to another is known as a *parameter*. Therefore, in Fig. 3-9a the parameter is the slope of the lines.

A comparison of the equations of the three lines also shows the similarities and differences among the lines. Thus,

Line 1: $\quad d = \ \ 50t + 100$
Line 2: $\quad d = 120t + 100$
Line 3: $\quad d = 250t + 100$

These equations were obtained from the plots by evaluating the slopes and reading the vertical intercept directly. The equations, therefore, also show that b is the common characteristic and m the parameter for these members of this line family.

What is the common characteristic and what is the parameter of the d-t plots of Fig. 3-9b? The graph shows the three lines to be parallel. Therefore, the common characteristic is the slope of the lines, which represents the speed of the particles involved. The differences among the three plots are the vertical intercepts, that is, the starting points of each of the three particles. The vertical intercept is, therefore, the parameter of this system of lines.

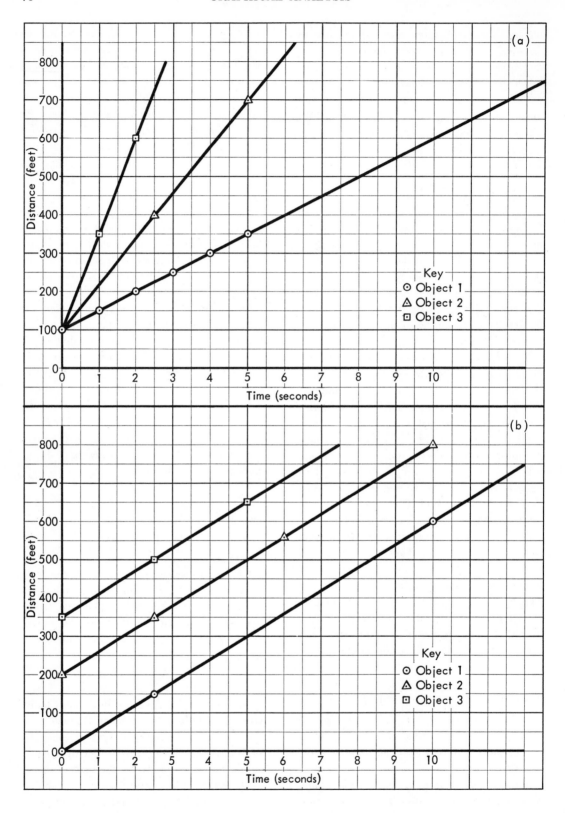

Fig. 3-9. Two families of lines: (a) m as parameter; (b) b as parameter

Here again the equations of the three lines also yield this information. Thus,

Line 1: $\qquad d = 60t$

Line 2: $\qquad d = 60t + 200$

Line 3: $\qquad d = 60t + 350$

Now that we see what is meant by a line "family" and how to recognize the similar characteristic and the parameter, of what value is such a set? The value lies primarily in the ready comparison among the several members of the family. Since (usually) only one quantity is varied from one plot to another, a comparison of the various family members with one another will readily show the effect of changing the parameter. Thus, in Fig. 3-9a a check of the distances covered for different times will show the effect of using a different speed for each of three objects starting at the same point. In part b of the figure, such a check will show the effect of different starting points for three particles having the same speed.

Line (or curve) families are also very useful in graphical solution of problems. Suppose it is desired to have four objects pass the same point at the same time. However, the particles are all to have different speeds and starting points. All that need be done to solve the problem is to draw any four d-t straight lines that go through the same point. The coordinates of the point will represent the desired time and position of the pass point. One possible solution is shown in Fig. 3-10. It can be seen from this diagram that any number of lines can be drawn at random through the point P, and each of the lines would satisfy the established conditions. The coordinates of point P are (5.5 sec, 500 ft). The lines drawn

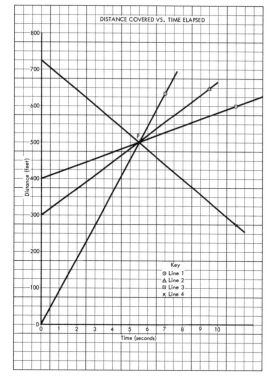

Fig. 3-10. Family of lines with two parameters, intercept and slope

through this point are all of one family that has as its common characteristic the point P, since point P necessarily lies on each of the lines drawn through it. Unlike the previous cases, this family has two parameters. Note that the lines have different slopes and different intercepts. Since this example again deals with a d-t plot, the intercept represents the starting point of the particular object, and the slope represents speed. It is left to the student to determine the equations of the four lines of Fig. 3-10 and also to obtain another set of four lines that satisfy the conditions of the problem.

REVIEW

Define concisely each of the following terms:

3-1. Curve

3-2. Straight line

3-3. Coordinate values

3-4. Slope of a line

3-5. Increment

3-6. Usual significance of sign (polarity)

3-7. Vertical intercept

3-8. Horizontal intercept

3-9. Line segment

3-10. Directed line segment

3-11. Family of lines

3-12. Parameter

3-13. System of lines

3-14. In many areas of technology, special graph papers are designed and other efforts made to cause a curve to plot as a straight line. Why?

3-15. Name and describe briefly the four basic steps in plotting a graph.

3-16. How is the "predicted-region" of a graph designated?

3-17. How are plotted points of a graph designated "called-out"?

3-18. List the four basic steps for determining the slope of a plotted line.

3-19. On a sheet of appropriate graph paper:

a. Draw a vertical axis and calibrate it from 0°C to 100°C.

b. Draw the horizontal axis and calibrate it from 0 to 10 minutes.

c. Draw a straight line through the points P_1 (0,20) and P_2 (6,100).

d. What is the slope value of the line P_1P_2?

e. What are the units of this slope?

f. What does the slope represent?

g. Draw a line P_2P_3 if the coordinates of point P_3 are (10,10).

h. Find the magnitude, direction, and units of the slope of line P_2P_3.

i. Discuss the comparison of the slopes of the two lines.

3-20. a. On the graph sheet of problem 3-19, construct a line of slope magnitude +2.

b. How many different lines of this same slope can be constructed?

c. How do they differ from one another?

d. The set of lines referred to in a, b, and c are known as a _____ of lines.

3-21. a. On the graph sheet of problem 3-19, construct a line of slope, $-\frac{1}{2}$ deg/min.

b. Determine from your plot the angle between this line and the line of problem 3-20a at their point of intersection.

c. The situation that occurs in b above is one example of a rule that always holds true. Can you state that rule from your observations?

3-22. What is the ordinate value of the horizontal intercept of a curve?

3-23. The _____ value of the vertical intercept of a line is zero.

3-24. Obtain the graphical solutions to the following by referring to Fig. 3-4.

a. Which car, 1 or 3, passes the 50 mile point earlier? By how much time?

b. At what time is car 3 exactly 50 miles behind car 1?

c. At what time is car 3 exactly 50 miles ahead of car 1?

d. How long has car 3 been traveling when cars 1 and 2 pass one another?

e. How far is car 3 from the others when cars 1 and 2 pass one another?

f. How long after cars 1 and 2 pass one another does car 3 reach that point?

g. If the finish line were at the 120 mile position, would car 1 or car 3 get there first?

h. Where should the finish line be so that car 3 would win the race?

3-25. Obtain graphical solutions to the following by referring to Fig. 3-4.

a. If the finish line were at the 120-mile point, at what time (or times) could car 3 start in order to win the race, assuming that all speeds remain the same? Explain your graphical solution.

b. Using the same 120 mile finish line and the same starting time for car 3 as shown in the figure, at what (minimum) constant speed should the car travel to win the race? Explain your graphical solution.

3-26. If the straight line of Fig. 3-8 is extended to the point where time equals 3.4 seconds,

a. What would be the magnitude and direction of the speed of the object at this time?

b. How much distance does the object cover in the time interval from 3.0 to 3.4 seconds?

c. How far is the object above its starting level at the 3.4 second point.

3-27. A trapezoid is a four-sided figure with two of its sides parallel to one another. The area of a trapezoid is found by adding the length of the two parallel sides and multiplying that sum by half the perpendicular distance between the sides. Expressing this as a formula, we have

$$A = \tfrac{1}{2}h(y_1 + y_2)$$

where y_1 = length of one of the parallel sides
y_2 = length of the other parallel side
h = perpendicular distance between the sides

Using this information, determine from figure 3-8:

a. The distance covered by the moving object in the first second of its flight.

b. The distance covered in its second second of flight.

3-28. Refer to Fig. 3-10:

a. Write the equation for each of the four lines.

b. What does the slope of each line represent?

c. Draw a line of this family that has a zero slope and write its equation.

d. Draw a vertical line through point P and write its equation.

e. What is the slope of the line drawn for part d above?

3-29. A negatively sloped line is easily recognized at a glance because _____

_____

3-30. If $d_1 = 30t + 15$, representing the distance, d, covered by a car moving 30 mph, is plotted on linear paper, then d is plotted along the _____ axis, because _____
    (a)   (b)
and t is plotted along the _____ axis,
                    (c)
because _____
    (d)
The plot of this equation will produce a _____. If
    (e)

$d_2 = -30t + 20$, representing the distance covered by a second car, is plotted on the same set of axes, the two plots will intersect. The point of intersection tells _____.
    (f)

3-31. Plot the two lines of problem 3-30 and determine the coordinates of their point of intersection.

3-32. The area of a triangle of constant base changes if its altitude is varied. A plot of the area, A, versus the altitude, h, if a triangle, will yield a straight line.

a. What does the slope of the line represent?

b. What is the vertical intercept of the line?

3-33. A certain plot of velocity vs. time turns out to be a straight line.

a. The slope of this line represents _____

_____

b. The area under the curve represents

_____

3-34. If the equation, $E = IR$ (Ohm's Law), were plotted with I as the independent variable and E as the dependent variable, the slope of the resulting line would represent

_____

3-35. Sketch the line of problem 3-34 above and label the axes.

b. The coordinates of the horizontal intercept are _____.

3-36. The "derating curve" of a semi-conductor device known as a Zener diode is usually a straight line and is a plot of power (watts) vs. temperature (°C). Two points on one such line are (25°C, 1 watt) and (100°C, 0.2 watts).

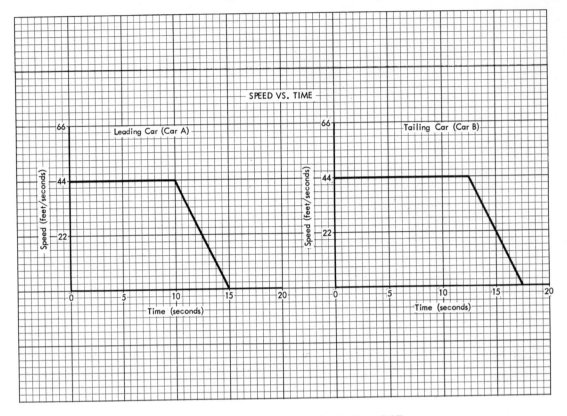

Fig. 3-11. Speed vs. time plot for Problem 3-37

a. Draw the derating curve on a properly labeled set of axes.

b. Find the "derating factor," which is the slope of the line. Give its magnitude, polarity, and units.

3-37. Car A of Fig. 3-11 was traveling at 30 miles per hour (44 feet per second) and was being "tailgated" by car B traveling at the same speed. At the 10-second point, the driver of car A had to jam on his brakes because of trouble ahead of him and came to rest in 5 sec. It took the driver of car B 2½ sec to recognize the trouble and to react by jamming on his brakes. Car B also took 5 seconds to come to a full stop. Fig. 3-11 depicts graphically the conditions described, assuming that the cars decrease speed at a uniform rate. Determine

from the graphs the answer to each of the following questions:

a. What is the deceleration rate of each car?

b. What is the distance required for car A to come to rest after the brakes have been applied?

c. What is the distance required for car B to come to rest after the brakes have been applied?

d. What is the total distance covered by car A from time zero to the time it stops?

e. What is the total distance covered by car B from time zero to the time it stops?

f. Do the cars collide? Why? How far behind should car B have been to avoid a collision?

g. Can this distance be depicted graphically, putting both the car A and car B plot on the same set of axes? If so, show how; if not, explain why not.

4 - A SAMPLING OF SIGNIFICANT CURVES —Trigonometric, Hyperbolic, and the Conics

Is there any similarity between a stone swinging at the end of a string, the vibration of a musical tuning fork, and the output from a huge electrical generator? Yes, there is. Their characteristics can all be expressed graphically with the same type of curve, the sinusoidal waveshape. How are a flashlight reflector, a stone falling in a vacuum, the area of a circle, and a uniformly loaded bridge cable related? Here again characteristics of these quantities, expressed graphically, yield the same type of curve, in this case a parabolic shape. A complete list of such comparisons of seemingly completely unrelated phenomena is long indeed. The reason for this is that there are sets of curves that find frequent application in many different technical areas.

In this chapter we shall consider several of these curve sets. We shall discuss their development, plot them, consider their important characteristics, call them by the proper names, mention their equations, and cite a few applications.[1] In other words, our purpose here is to become familiar with some of the graphical shapes met in technology, time and again.

4.1. Trigonometric curves

Trigonometry dates back to the Greek astronomers of the first and second century B.C. This study centers around measurements of angles and triangles and joins together the mathematics branches of geometry and algebra. The most fundamental and most important relationships growing out of these measurements of angles are a set of curves called the *trigonometric functions*[2] that can be obtained from length measurements of a 90° triangle (see Appendix C). However, this set of six curves can also be developed from a circle, and as such the curves are often referred to as *circular functions*. It is this latter approach that will be used in the discussion below.

Consider a ball whirled vertically around at the end of a string at a constant number of

---

[1] Where the discussions of the curves involve units, commonly-used abbreviations will be shown in this and later chapters.

[2] The term *function*, as used in technology, refers to a quantity the value of which depends upon one or more other quantities. For example, the weight of a sample of material is a *function* of the density and volume of the sample. The area of a circle is a *function* of its radius.

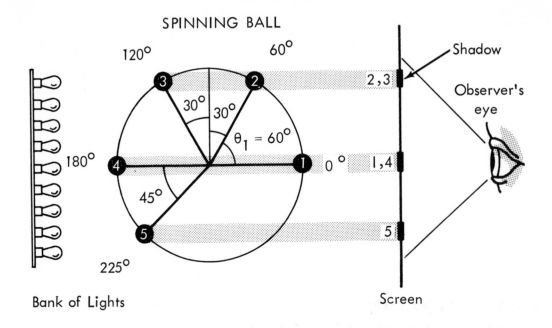

Fig. 4-1. Development of circular function—the sine wave

revolutions per minute. Looking at the whirling ball head-on, we would certainly see the ball describing a circle. However, instead of watching the ball itself in circular motion, suppose we observe the path described by its shadow on a screen set up perpendicular to the plane of the circle. The arrangement is shown pictorially in Fig. 4-1. Notice that the lights throw the ball's shadow onto the screen and that the observer is on the opposite side of the screen viewing the moving shadow, but not able to see the circling ball itself. Under these conditions what would the observer see? He would see the up-and-down straight-line path described by the ball's shadow on the screen. Remembering that the ball is going around the circle at a constant number of revolutions per minute, would the observer see the shadow moving with constant speed up and down along its straight-line path? The answer to that question is, No. The shadow would not move up and down with the same speed throughout. At the middle of its travel the shadow would be moving at its greatest speed and would slow down as it reached the top of its path and the bottom of its path. To help visualize this, note the several positions of the ball shown in Fig.

4-1. If the number 1 position is taken as the starting or 0° position, then at that instant the ball's shadow would be in the position marked 1 on the screen. After 60° of counterclockwise travel, the ball would be in position 2 on the circle, and its shadow will have traveled almost 9/10 of the distance to the top of its path. For the next 30° of travel the shadow would move upward only 1/10 of the total path to the top of its travel. If the ball were circling at the rate of one revolution every 6 sec, it would take the ball 1 sec to cover the first 60°. In that 1 sec the shadow would go up almost 9/10 of its distance to the top. In the next ½ sec the ball would travel an additional 30°, and its shadow would reach the top of its path. Thus, in this ½ sec the shadow would travel approximately 1/10 of the distance to the top, whereas in the previous second it went 9/10 of the way up. Obviously, therefore, the shadow is moving at a much slower rate from point 2 to the top than it was up to point 2. As a matter of fact, its speed on the upward portion of its travel was continuously decreasing, and at the instant it reaches the top, its momentary speed at that point is 0. For the next 30° of travel, the ball goes to position 3 on the circle and the shadow to position 3 on the screen. In this ½-sec interval the shadow has traveled almost 1/10 of the way down. In the next second, the ball reaches the 180° position, and the shadow is back at the midpoint of its travel. Again it has traveled some 9/10 of the way down to midpoint position in 1 sec and the previous 1/10 of the path in ½ sec. This downward travel of the shadow occurs with an ever-increasing speed to a maximum value at the 4 position. The process is repeated for the bottom half of the path of the ball's shadow on the screen.

Since the ball is revolving at constant angular speed, it is reasonable to assume that the change in position of the shadow along its straight-line path also follows some type of regular pattern. In order to see this pattern, imagine the screen replaced by a roll of photosensitive film. Assume also that the film is being unrolled by being pulled out of the paper, towards you, at a constant rate. It is, therefore, being exposed by the light except where the shadow protects it. The shadow path would thus appear on the film. If this film were then placed in the plane of the paper, the result would be the curve shown in Fig. 4-2b. This waveshape is known as the *sine wave* and is the basic trigonometric, or circular, function.

The sine wave is called the vertical *projection* of uniform circular motion. If in the above discussion of the production of the sine wave pattern we considered not only the position of the shadow but its distance from the midpoint at each of these positions, we would then be considering the vertical projection of the entire rotating ball and string holding it. To clarify this point, refer to Fig. 4-2a, in which is depicted several positions of the rotating radius $0R$. The vertical projection of this radius is the vertical distance from the tip of its arrowhead to the horizontal, 0°-180° line. For each position of the rotating radius, its vertical projection will be plotted as an ordinate and the angle representing the radius position as the corresponding abscissa. In the 0° position the vertical projection of the radius $0R$ is 0, since the arrowhead is on the horizontal line. Note, therefore, that in Fig. 4-2b an ordinate

of 0 is plotted for an abscissa of 0°. The next shown position of the counterclockwise rotating radius is the 30° position. Its vertical projection is represented by the line EA. This line length is then plotted at the 30° abscissa position of Fig. 4-2b. At the 60° position of the radius, the line FB represents its vertical projection. This ordinate length is shown plotted at the 60° abscissa position. Note that this is also the 1-sec position of the previous sine wave discussion, since in 1 sec the rotating ball travelled through 60° of circle. If all the vertical projections of the rotating radius of Fig. 4-2a are carefully plotted as described, the result will be the expected sine wave shown.

The equation of the sine wave is merely

$$y = R \sin \theta$$

where y represents the vertical distance from the horizontal axis and R represents the maximum ordinate value that the sine wave achieves throughout the entire 360° of revolution. This is to be expected, since R represents the length of the rotating radius, and the sine wave is produced by plotting the vertical projections of that radius. Certainly, therefore, the vertical projection of the radius can never be greater than the radius itself. Reference to Fig. 4-2a will show that at the 90° position of the radius, the vertical projection is equal to the radius itself. This occurs again, within the first revolution, at the 270° position. However, the radius at the 270° position is pointed downwards, or in the negative y direction. The vertical projection is thus considered to be $-R$. Note that the sine curve of Fig. 4-2b shows this maximum value as the ordinate when the abscissa is 90° and the negative maximum at the 270° abscissa. Any ordinate of the sine curve is known as the *displacement*, since it represents the distance from the horizontal axis to the arrowpoint of the rotating radius. The maximum displacement is referred to as the *amplitude* of the wave. To use correct terminology, therefore, we say that the R term of the given equation is the *wave amplitude*.

In addition to amplitude and maximum ordinate, the term *peak value* is often used. In order to distinguish between the positive and

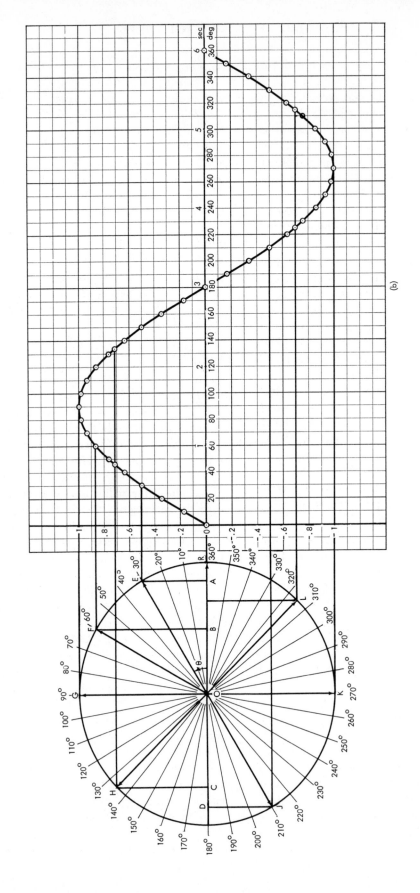

Fig. 4-2. A sine wave is a plot of the vertical projections of a rotating vector versus the angle swept through

(b)

negative amplitudes, these adjectives are used with peak. Thus, a sine curve has its positive peak at 90° and its negative peak at the 270° position. The region of the wave on either side of the positive peak is referred to as the *crest,* whereas the curve region on either side of the negative peak is the *trough.* The negative amplitude of a sine wave shape is also referred to as the *minimum.*

The Greek letter θ (theta) shown in the equation is commonly used to represent the angle position of the rotating radius. Since these values are plotted along the horizontal axis, θ is the abscissa designation. This symbol is commonly used for the abscissa, rather than the previously used designation x merely to accent the fact that the abscissa values are angles rather than any other type of quantity. It can be seen from the sine plot that only the positive portion of the horizontal axis is shown, although both positive and negative ordinate values appear in the plot. Recall from our two previous methods of generating the sine wave that in both cases the rotation was designated as counterclockwise. Counterclockwise is established by convention as the positive direction of rotation in technical applications. Angles that are swept out in the clockwise direction are therefore considered as negative angles. It is apparent from Fig. 4-2 that if the rotating radius $0R$ had been turned in the clockwise (negative) direction, then the negative (downward) vertical projections would have been obtained for the first 180° of the revolution and the positive vertical projections for the second half-revolution. The waveshape thus obtained is known as a *negative* sine wave and should be sketched by the student using the plot of Fig. 4-2b as reference.

4.2. A sine table obtained from the sine curve

In our previous discussion of graphs it was often necessary to establish a table of abscissa and ordinate values before the graph could be plotted. In this paragraph we will reverse the procedure and use the graph to obtain a table of values. The abscissa values will be angle values in degrees, and the ordinate values will be fractions of R. In order to simplify matters we will let R equal 1. Thus the ordinate values obtained will vary over a range of from a maximum of $+1$ to a minimum of -1. By reading the curve of Fig. 4-2b, we obtain the values shown in Table 4-1.

You should carefully check each of the values listed in Table 4-1 against the plotted curve and should fill in the blank spaces. Note the repetition of values. This characteristic of repeating values with both positive and negative polarities is a significant property of the sine wave and will be seen again in connection with other waves of the same general shape.

A sine table is included in Appendix B. Note that the sine values are only listed up to 90 deg and that the accuracy is far beyond that obtainable from the plot of Fig. 4-2. From Table 4-1 it is apparent that the values that occur for the angles from 0 to 90 deg occur again in "reverse order" for the angle values from 90 to 180 deg. Furthermore, this entire set of values is repeated, in the negative direction, for the second half of the revolution of the rotating radius. Once this symmetry is recognized and the pattern and its origin understood, all the sine values from 0 to 360 deg can be written with only a 0 to 90 deg table of sine values. The four-place accuracy shown in the table of Appendix B is produced by a method known as a *series expansion,* rather than reading of curves. A consideration of that technique would be of no advantage in our discussion and is not included in this volume.

4.3. Other sinusoids

The sine wave described in the previous paragraphs was obtained by plotting the vertical projections of the rotating radius $0R$. What

Table 4-1.

θ Degrees	0	30	45	60	90	120	135	150	180	210	225	240	270	315	330	360
$\sin\theta$ Numeric	0	0.5	0.71	0.86	1	0.86			0	—0.5			—1	—0.71		0

waveshape would result if the horizontal projections were plotted as the radius changed position? The horizontal projection is the horizontal distance of the radius arrowpoint from the vertical 90-270 deg line. Figure 4-3 shows the resulting curve as it is produced by the rotating radius. Note that the projection values are plotted along the horizontal axis and the angles along the vertical. However, if the graph is turned so that the angle axis is held horizontally with the 0 deg position at the left, it can be seen that the waveshape obtained has the same general *shape* as the sine wave. It is, in fact, known as the *cosine* wave.

Figure 4-4 shows both the sine wave and the cosine wave drawn on the same set of axes. It is quite apparent here that the two wave shapes are the same and the curves are different only in "starting point." In other words, at 0 deg the cosine wave is at its maximum value of 1, whereas the sine wave is at its 0 ordinate value. Expressing this in graphical language, we can say that the vertical intercept coordinates for the cosine curve are $(0°, 1)$. For the sine curve, the vertical intercept has the coordinates $(0°, 0)$. This means that the cosine wave can also be produced by the use of vertical projections. The rotating radius would then have to be started in the upward vertical position and this would be called the 0 deg position. The counterclockwise rotation would then be continued for 360 deg and the vertical projections plotted. The result would be the cosine curve shown in Fig. 4-4. The equation for the curve would then be $y = R \cos \theta$, where R and θ have the same significance as in the sine equation. Since this curve is produced from a circular motion in the same way as the sine wave but is different from the sine wave in "starting point," the wave is one of the general group of curves known as *sinusoids*.

From the above we can say that a sinusoid is any curve that is produced by plotting the vertical projections of a rotating radius regardless of where on the circle the radius started. The starting position is always taken as the 0-deg position both on the circle and on the plot of the curve.

4.4. Characteristics of sinusoids and related graphical terms

Several terms used to express different properties of sinusoids[3] have been defined in previous paragraphs. They include *displacement* defined as the ordinate distance of any point, *amplitude* defined as maximum displacement, *peak*, which is a synonym for amplitude, *crest* defined as the wave in the region of the positive peak, and *trough* defined as the wave region in the vicinity of the negative peak. There are, in addition, other properties of these (and other types of) waveshapes that are significant in different applications. Several of these are depicted in Fig. 4-4. For example, the two sinusoids shown in Fig. 4-4 could have been produced by the vibrations of a tuning fork. If one leg of the U-shaped fork were fitted with a small stylus and this stylus held lightly against a sheet of waxed paper, the vibrating stylus would scribe a line on the paper. Now if the paper were moved at constant rate in the direction of the horizontal axis of Fig. 4-4, with the stylus moving back and forth in the vertical-axis direction, then a sinusoidal waveshape would be produced. If the paper were started moving when the stylus was on the horizontal axis, a sine curve would result. If the paper were started moving when the scribing stylus was at the top of its travel, then a cosine wave would result. Both of these possibilities are shown in Fig. 4-4.

It is apparent from the two complete *cycles*, or *variations*, of the waves shown in Fig. 4-4 that the sinusoids are repeating waveshapes, that is, the ordinate values shown for the first 360 deg are exactly duplicated in corresponding position for the second 360 deg. If a third, fourth, fifth, etc., cycle were shown, the same set of ordinate values would appear in each cycle. Any one ordinate value would appear in the same relative position in each cycle. For example, the ordinate 0.5 appears at the 30 deg position of the first variation of the sine curve and also at the 390 deg position, which is the 30-deg abscissa of the second variation.

---

[3] These terms are also applicable to other waveshapes.

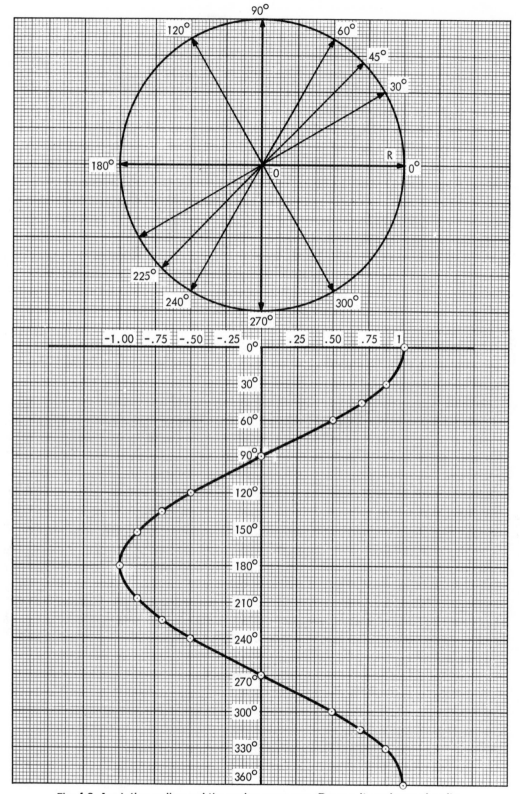

Fig. 4-3. A rotating radius and the cosine curve, **y** = **R** cos θ, it produces when its horizontal projections are plotted

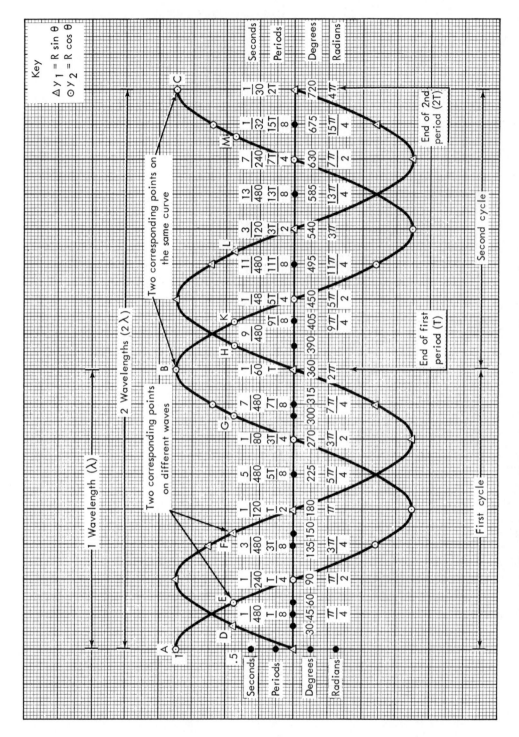

Fig. 4-4. The sinusoids, $y_1 = R \sin \theta$ and $y_2 = R \cos \theta$. Four different calibration methods are shown for the independent axis, that is, fractions of a second, fractions of a full period (T), degrees, and radians

If additional cycles were shown, this $+0.5$ ordinate would appear at the 30-deg position of each successive variation. Any waveshape that shows this property is known as a *periodic wave*. To express this more succinctly, *a periodic waveshape is one that identically repeats its set of values at regular, fixed intervals.* These intervals can be expressed in time units. If so, *the time for one complete variation of a periodic wave is known as the period.* A period is symbolized by the upper case letter *T*, and the units for period are seconds per cycle.[4]

The reciprocal of the period is also a significant property of a wave in technologies dealing with sound, electronics, light, reciprocating engines, and oscillatory motions of all kinds. Since the period is expressed as $\frac{\text{time}}{\text{cycle}}$ 1 divided by this expression becomes $\frac{\text{cycles}}{\text{time}}$ and the units usually used are cycles per second (cps). The reciprocal of the period of a wave is known as its *frequency*. Therefore, the definition of *frequency is the number of variations of the wave that occur in one unit of time.* The symbol most often used to represent frequency is lower case *f*, and the most frequently used time unit is the second.

For example, the lowest limit of human hearing is considered to be a sound having a frequency (*f*) of 15 cps. To find the period (*T*) of the sound, that is, the time for one cycle of the sound, we take the reciprocal of the frequency, thus,

$$T = \frac{1}{f}$$

$$T = \frac{1}{15 \text{ cycles/second}}$$

$$T = \frac{1 \text{ sec}}{15 \text{ cycles}}$$

$$T = 0.0667 \frac{\text{sec}}{\text{cycle}}$$

giving us the information that the time per cycle for this lower limit of hearing is 0.0667 sec.

---

[4] Other time units are also used.

From the above discussions, it is apparent that several designations for the horizontal coordinates are useful. Figure 4-4 shows four different methods of calibrating the horizontal axis. The calibration immediately below the axis is in degrees, with which we are already quite familiar. The calibration shown directly above the horizontal axis is in terms of the period *T*. Note that at the end of one complete cycle of the sine wave, corresponding to the 360-deg position of the degrees calibration, the period calibration is marked *T*. This represents one full period. The 180-deg degree mark, being the halfway position for the sine wave, is thus marked $T/2$. The 45-deg position is marked $T/8$, since this position represents $1/8$ of a complete variation. It can be seen from the diagram that the period calibration is shown in terms of eighths of a full period for the entire two cycles. Wherever possible, the fraction is reduced so that the 90-deg position is shown as $T/4$ rather than $2T/8$, and the 540-deg position in the second cycle appears as $3T/2$ rather than $12T/8$.

If the time in seconds corresponding to a full period is known, the period calibration can be replaced by fractions of a second. For example, the sinusoids shown could well represent the voltage variations with time of the a-c electricity available at a wall outlet. Throughout the United States, the standard frequency for a-c electricity is 60 cps. This means that the period, the time for one cycle, is $1/60$ sec. Note in Fig. 4-4 that the horizontal calibration line marked "seconds" shows $1/60$ corresponding to the one period (*T*) position. Thus, the half-period position is marked $1/120$ sec and the quarter-period point is shown to be $1/240$ sec. In this calibration scheme, as in the case of fractions of *T*, the lowest subdivision was taken as $1/8$ of a full variation. Since the complete cycle takes $1/60$ sec, the time for $1/8$ of a cycle is

$$\frac{T}{8} = \frac{1}{8} \times \frac{1 \text{ sec}}{60}$$

$$= \frac{1}{480} \text{ sec}$$

Thus, the calibration in seconds corresponding

to the $T/8$ position is seen in the figure to be 1/240 sec, and the other calibration points are seen to be multiples of this time value, with the fractions reduced wherever possible.

A little practice in calibrating the independent axis in terms of fractions of a period and in time units, based on the problems at the end of this chapter, will help make you proficient in these calibrating methods. The fourth method of subdividing the period of a wave, shown in Fig. 4-4 below the degrees calibration, will be discussed in a later paragraph.

4.5. Corresponding points

As described earlier, the periodic character of the sinusoids means that the ordinate values are repeated in corresponding position in each successive cycle of the wave. However, within any one cycle each ordinate value also appears twice. For example, the sine wave ordinate +0.5 appears both at the 30-deg position and at the 150-deg position of the first cycle as well as at the 390-deg position in the second cycle. There is a meaningful difference between these ordinates, however, and this distinction makes necessary the definition of the term *corresponding points. Corresponding points are points that have the same displacement and are moving in the same sense or direction.* Note that in Fig. 4-4 eight points are shown that have the same displacement, +0.5. However, these points are not all corresponding points, since when we read from left to right, the curves at all these points are not moving (changing) in the same direction or with the same sense. Consider, for example, the points D and F of the sine curve. Both of these points are at the same elevation or displacement, but at point D the curve can be said to be moving generally upward, whereas at point F the curve is moving downward. These points are, therefore, not corresponding points. Consider now point D in the first cycle of the sine wave and point H in the second cycle. These two points are again at the same distance from the horizontal axis, and the curve at both these points is seen to be moving in the same sense, that is, generally upward. Thus, the two points D and H are corre-

sponding points. Both of these points happen to lie on the same curve but in successive cycles of that curve.

Corresponding points need not necessarily refer to points on the same wave. Note the points E and F in Fig. 4-4. Both of these points have the same displacement, and the two curves at these points are moving in the same direction. The two points E and F are, therefore, corresponding points. They lie on different waves, but the two curves are similar, since the curve containing point E is the cosine curve and the other is the sine curve. Are points G and H corresponding points? What about points G and L? The first pair are corresponding points, since their ordinates are both +0.5 and they are both moving in the same direction. The same is not true for points G and L. Corresponding points, both on the same and on different but similar curves, are used as the basis for defining and explaining further characteristics of these waveshapes.

4.6. Wavelength

In connection with the example described at the opening of this section, in which a sinusoidal waveshape is produced by the vibrating stylus of a tuning fork, we know that the vibrating tuning fork would also produce an audible sound in air. The fork gives rise to a sound "wave" by alternately compressing and separating clusters of air molecules. A plot of the density of these clusters vs. distance yields the same sinusoidal waveshapes as those shown in Fig. 4-4. The distance between successive peaks of this wave is known as one *wavelength* of the wave and is so shown in Fig. 4-4. However, the length of one wave can be measured by referring to points on the wave other than the peaks. If the horizontal axis of Fig. 4-4 were calibrated in distance units, the distance between the peak points A and B would be one wavelength of the cosine wave. Note that this same span of one wavelength covers a complete cycle of the sine curve as measured between two of the horizontal intercepts of this curve. It is thus apparent that wavelength can be determined by using different sets of points. Actually, *one wavelength is the distance between any two successive corresponding points on the same waveshape.* Note that the wavelength can be read directly from the plotted curve only if the horizontal axis is calibrated in distance units. However, wavelength can be calculated with the use of a curve characteristic we have already defined, *frequency.* The wavelength of a sinusoid (symbolized by the Greek letter lambda, λ) is related to the frequency (f) of the wave and the velocity (v) with which the wave travels by the formula

$$\lambda = \frac{v}{f}$$

This expression is useful in converting a wave plotted against time on the horizontal axis to one plotted against distance on the independent axis. For example, if we desired to convert the horizontal axis calibration of a sound wave plot from time units to distance units, it would be necessary to know the speed with which the sound travels. Sound in air travels with a speed of 1,100 feet per second (fps). Therefore, the length of one wave is

$$\lambda = \frac{v}{f}$$

$$\lambda = \frac{1,100 \text{ ft/sec}}{1,000 \text{ cycles/sec}}$$

$$\lambda = 1.1 \text{ ft/cycle}$$

The unit, cycle, is often dropped, since the wavelength is now known to be 1.1 feet. The horizontal axis is so marked at the end of one cycle and the subdivision of the cycle marked with proportional fractions of one wavelength. The solution to this problem is shown in Fig. 4-5.

4.7. Phase

In the above discussion, corresponding points on the same wave were used to define wavelength. Corresponding points on similar but separate curves are important in the discussion of the *phase* relationship between two similar waveshapes. In electronics, for example, it is possible to determine the type of circuit one is dealing with by examining the phase relationship between the current and voltage waveshapes of that circuit. If in Fig.

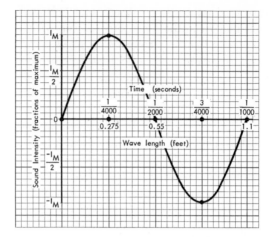

Fig. 4-5. Sound intensity plotted vs. time and length of wave (frequency: 1,000 cycles per sec; speed in air: 1,100 fps)

4-4 the cosine curve were the current waveshape of a given circuit and the sine curve the voltage waveshape of that electrical network, then we could say that we are dealing with a purely capacitive circuit. The phase relationship between the two curves is sufficient to give this information without further investigation. Similar situations exist in other technologies. The phase displacement, or phase difference, most often referred to as *phase angle,* is defined as the separation between two corresponding points on two similar waveshapes. In Fig. 4-4 the phase angle between the cosine and the sine curve can be determined from the corresponding points E and F. Note that the abscissa for point E is 60 deg and for point F is 150 deg. The difference between these abscissas is 90 deg. Thus, the phase angle between the cosine and the sine curve is 90 deg. Points G and H represent another pair of corresponding points on the two curves, and here again their separation is 90 deg. Point H is at the 390 deg abscissa, and point G is at the 300-deg point. The separation is thus 90 deg.

4.8. Lead and lag

When we refer to phase angle between two curves, it is not sufficient merely to state the amount of phase difference. It is also necessary to tell which curve is "ahead" and which curve is "behind." The terms *lead* and *lag* are used rather than "ahead" and "behind," but they mean the same thing. *A curve leads another when its corresponding point occurs first as the waves are read from left to right. A curve lags another when its corresponding point occurs second as the waves are read from left to right.* Referring again to the corresponding points *E* and *F* of Fig. 4-4, we note that, reading from left to right, point *E* occurs first. Since point *E* is on the cosine curve, we say that the cosine curve *leads* the sine curve. We know from the previous discussion that the phase separation between the two curves is 90 deg. The complete statement of the phase relationship between the two curves is therefore that *the cosine curve leads the sine curve by 90 deg.* Since point *F* on the sine curve occurs later than *E*, the same information can be presented by saying that *the sine curve lags the cosine curve by 90 deg.* Since both statements mean exactly the same thing, neither is considered to be preferable. When we deal with sinusoids, if one of the curves involved is the true sine, then it is usually considered as the reference curve, and the phase angles of the other curves are given with respect to the sine. Thus, in the case shown in Fig. 4-4, it would be preferable to state that the cosine leads the sine curve by 90 deg, thereby using the sine curve as the reference.

In all of our discussions of corresponding points and phase displacement, reference has been made to *similar waveshapes*. The definitions given above in these areas are valid only if similar waveshapes are involved. In this discussion *similar waveshapes are waves of the same type or form that have the same frequency (or period).* Sinusoids are all of the same type or form, but phase displacement between different sinusoids can be measured only if their periods are equal. For example, it is not possible to discuss phase angle between the two sinusoids of Fig. 4-6, since the period of curve 1 is half of that of curve 2. The two curves are of the same type, since both are sinusoids; but they are not *similar*, since they are of different frequency, the frequency of curve 1 being twice that of curve 2.

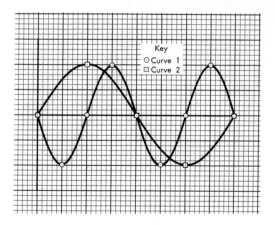

Fig. 4-6. No phase displacement between two sinusoids shown can be measured since they are of different frequency

4.9. Effect of amplitude on phase measurement

Phase measurement becomes somewhat of a special problem when we deal with two waveshapes of different amplitudes that are otherwise the same. The two sine waves of Fig. 4-7 are in phase, yet if we use the "corresponding point" definition of phase, we would say that the two waves are out of phase on the basis of the separation between points *A* and *B* shown. By the same token we could consider the two points *C* and *D* shown, since this pair are at the same elevation and are roughly moving in the same sense. The separation between these two points is less than that between *A* and *B* and if used as phase-indicating points would yield a different phase reading. Actually, neither of these pairs can be used for phase measurements, since they are not truly moving in the same sense. The general direction of the two curves at the points *A* and *B* is the same, but the *A* curve is much steeper at point *A* than the other curve is at point *B*.

Phase measurement between curves of different amplitudes can therefore be determined in one of two ways. If possible, the scale for one of the curves should be changed and the curve redrawn so that its peak value has the same physical height as the other. This is possible only if the two curves represent different quantities, such as current and voltage. However, this is time-consuming even when it is

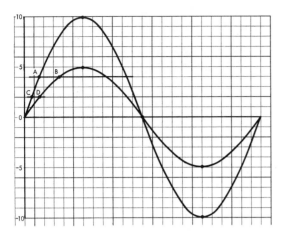

Fig. 4-7. Two sine waves shown are in phase with one another

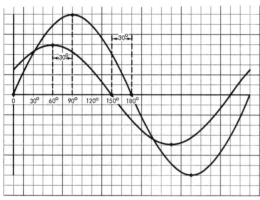

Fig. 4-8. Sinusoid with smaller amplitude leads that with larger by 30 deg

possible. If the two curves represent the same quantity, such as sound level, then rescaling of one curve will also affect the other and nothing will have been accomplished. Thus, *when we deal with two similar waveshapes of different amplitudes, phase relationship between them is determined by measuring the separation between their peaks or their inter-*cepts. One such case is depicted in Fig. 4-8, in which the 30-deg phase separation between the two waves is measured between their inter-cepts. Figure 4-8 also shows that exactly the same separation is found by measuring the horizontal separation between the peaks of the two curves. Since the shorter peak is reached first when we read from left to right, we know that the shorter amplitude curve leads the sine curve by 30 deg.

4.10. Can a curve be both lead and lag?

Refer again to Fig. 4-4 and note the points *D* and *G*. Do they satisfy the conditions necessary to make them corresponding points? They both have the same displacement ($+0.5$) and are both moving in the same direction. They are, therefore, corresponding points. Reading from left to right, point *D*, the first of the two, is on the sine curve and point *G*, the second of the two, is on the cosine curve. Their separation is seen to be 270 deg, since point *D* is at 30 deg and point *G* at 300 deg. This means that the cosine curve *lags* the sine curve by *270* deg. Is this in contradiction of the above discussion, in which we found that the cosine curve *leads* the sine curve *by 90 deg?* Figure 4-9 will help show that the two statements are not contradictory and that a lead of 90 deg and a lag of 270 deg are two ways of stating the same thing.

In all discussions relating to circular motion or the results of such motion, the 0 deg position is taken as the reference, with counterclockwise considered the positive direction of rotation and clockwise the negative. Note, therefore, that in order to go from the R_0 position of the rotating radius of Fig. 4-9 to the R_1 position, a counterclockwise rotation of 90 deg is required. We can therefore say that the R_1 position is ahead of, or leads the R_0 position by 90 deg. It is also possible to arrive at the R_1 position from R_0 by traveling clockwise 270 deg. From this second point of view, it can be said that the R_1 position is behind, or lags, the R_0 position by 270 deg. Since in both rotations we started at the R_0 position and arrived at the R_1 position, the two rotations yield the same result. Thus, a lead of 90 deg or a lag of 270 deg are considered to be synonomous. A similar situation exists for any pair of rotations, one counterclockwise and the other clockwise, as long as the two add up to 360 deg. Note, for example, the R_2 position of the rotating radius of Fig. 4-9. This position leads the reference R_0 by 200 deg but also lags it by 160 deg. As stated earlier, when we discuss phase displacement between sinusoids, the reference curve is conventionally the true

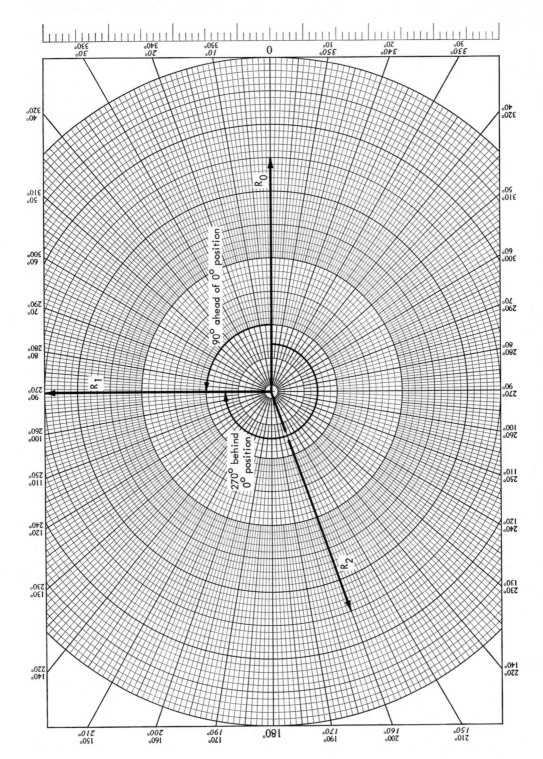

Fig. 4-9. Lead of 90 deg and lag of 270 deg are two statements of same information

sine curve. However, in many cases the true sine does not happen to be one of the curves involved. In that case, it is conventional to express the phase relationship between the two curves in the manner that will yield the smallest phase angle. By way of illustration, refer to the curves of Fig. 4-10. The displacement at which we will investigate for corresponding points is arbitrary. In Fig. 4-10 it was taken at the —0.5 level. Reading from left to right at this displacement level, note that point A leads its corresponding point B by 90 deg. This means that curve 3 leads curve 2 by 90 deg. These same two curves can be compared for phase angle by using the corresponding positive peak points G and H. These show a separation of 270 deg and therefore the first pair of points used for these two curves is preferred. Points A and D are corresponding points and show curve 3 to lead curve 1 by 150 deg. Here again the phase relationship between curves 3 and 1 can be expressed as curve 3 lagging curve 1 by 210 deg (see points J and K) ; but the first method, using the smaller angle, is preferred. Corresponding points B and D (or E and F) show that curve 2 leads curve 1 by 60 deg. Find two labeled points on the diagram that show the phase displacement between these two curves to be 300 deg.

4.11. Radian measure

Figure 4-4 shows four different methods of calibrating the horizontal axis, and up to this point only three of these have been discussed. The fourth, known as *radian measure calibration,* is widely used throughout all engineering and technology, primarily because it often simplifies calculations. This simplification results from the way the radian is defined. This definition will become clear if an angle of one-radian magnitude is drawn as follows:

1. Draw a circle of any radius.

2. Draw one radius of that circle, for example, radius OA of Fig. 4-11.

3. On a separate thin slip of paper[5] mark

---

[5] More accurate results can be obtained if a flexible curve guide is used instead of a strip of paper. However, when carefully done on a circle of large radius, the method described yields reasonably accurate results.

off the length of this radius. Label one end of this line A on the paper strip and the other end B.

4. Curve the paper strip and put point A on the paper strip in contact with point A at the end of the circle radius OA.

5. With the paper strip held curved so that it is in contact with the arc of the circle, mark a point B on the arc of circle corresponding to the point B on the paper strip.

6. Draw the circle radius OB.

The angle between the two radii OA and OB is one *radian*, because the arc of the circle, AB, cut off by these two radii is equal in length to the radius of the circle. Thus, the definition of *an angle of one radian is an angle that cuts off an arc equal in length to the radius producing the arc.* One of the advantages of radian measure thus becomes clear. All one need do in order to find the size of an angle in radians is to measure two lengths. One, the length of one of the two radii bounding the angle, and second, the length of the arc cut off by the radii. The ratio of the arc length divided by the radial length is the value of the angle in *radians*. This is very often expressed symbolically by the formula

$$\theta \text{ (in radians)} = \frac{\text{arc length}}{\text{radial length}}$$
$$\theta = \frac{s}{r}$$

As described in the six-step procedure above, the arc length is measured along the arc, so that its "stretched out" length is obtained. As an example of the ease with which the radian measure of an angle can be determined, compute the angle produced by two 10-cm radii of a circle that cut off (subtend) an arc of that circle 25 cm long. Using the above formula, we obtain

$$\theta = \frac{s}{r}$$
$$= \frac{25 \text{ cm}}{10 \text{ cm}}$$
$$= 2.5 \text{ radians}$$

Note that the units (centimeters) of the numerator and denominator are the same and

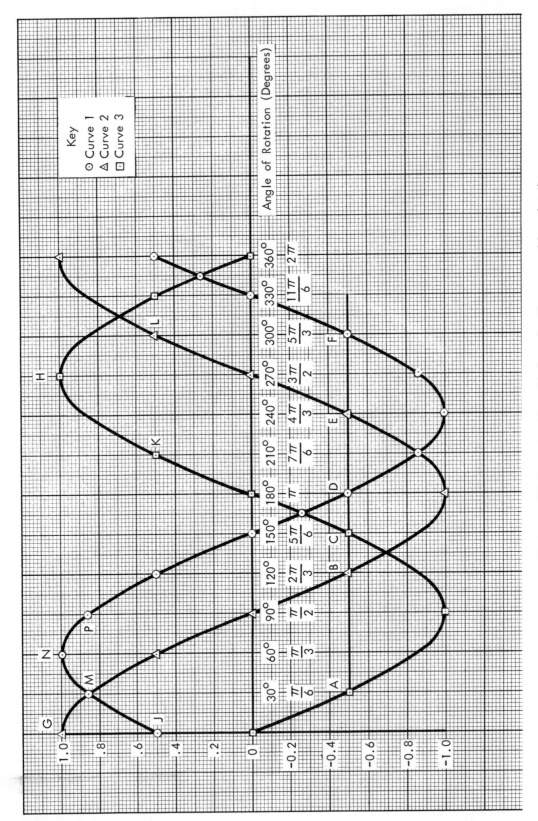

Fig. 4-10. Phase displacement between two sinusoids is preferably expressed by using the smaller of two possible phase angles between curves

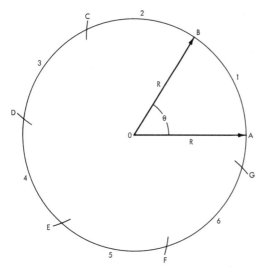

Fig. 4-11. Angle θ is one radian since arc **AB** is equal in length to radius **R** (complete circumference is 2π radians)

therefore cancel out. The resultant measure of the angle is therefore without units, and as such the term radian is known as a *pure numeric.*

If the construction yielding Fig. 4-11 were very carefully and accurately carried out, and the resulting 1-radian angle θ accurately measured in degrees, a value of 57°17′44.8″ (read 57 degrees, 17 minutes, 44.8 seconds) would be obtained. In technology, however, the "deci-trig" system is commonly used. In this system, degrees of angle are subdivided into tenths and hundredths of a degree. In the deci-trig system, to a reasonable degree of accuracy, an angle that measures *1 radian equals 57.3 deg.*[6] If the arc *AB* of Fig. 4-11 were stepped off consecutively around the circle, a total of 6, and something less than 1/3 such arcs would fit around the circumference. The number of such arcs around the complete circle is designated as 2π. Since each arc is equal to one radius in length, the total length is 2π times x, or the familiar $C = 2\pi r$, where C is the length of the total arc, or circumference, of the circle and r is the length of the radius. The term π is far from being an exact value and is normally considered as 3.14. (The accuracy of the numerical expression for π can

be carried out beyond 10,000 places by a modern computer. Expressed to a mere 57 decimal places, the value of π is 3.14159265358979323-84626433832795028841971693993751058209-74).[7] Using the expression $\theta = s/r$ and substituting for S the total circumference of the circle, we obtain

$$\theta = \frac{s}{r}$$
$$= \frac{2\pi r}{r}$$
$$= 2\pi \text{ radians}$$

Since the entire arc of circle was used in the numerator, the resulting angle represents the radian measure of a complete revolution. In degrees a complete revolution equals 360 deg. Since both values represent one full revolution, they can be equated, and we obtain the relationship

$$2\pi \text{ radians} = 360 \text{ deg}$$

Dividing both sides of the equation by 2, we obtain

$$\pi \text{ radians} = 180 \text{ deg}$$

This equation is used to convert from degrees to radians or radians to degrees. If both sides of the above equation are divided through by 180 deg, we obtain

$$\frac{\pi \text{ radians}}{180 \text{ deg}} = \frac{180 \text{ deg}}{180 \text{ deg}}$$
$$\frac{\pi \text{ radians}}{180 \text{ deg}} = 1$$

The reciprocal of this statement is also true; that is,

$$\frac{180 \text{ deg}}{\pi \text{ radians}} = 1$$

These expressions can be used to obtain the radian calibration of the horizontal axis shown in Fig. 4-4. For example, to convert the 45 deg designation by the equivalent radian measure, multiply as shown:

$$\frac{45 \text{ deg}}{1} \times \frac{\pi \text{ radians}}{180 \text{ deg}} = \frac{45\pi \text{ radians}}{180}$$
$$45 \text{ deg} = \frac{\pi}{4} \text{ radians}$$

---

[6] More accurately, 1 radian = 57.295780°.

[7] Courtesy, Precision Instrument Co.

To convert back from radians to degrees, use the reciprocal of the above conversion ratio. For example, in order to convert $7\pi/4$ radians to degrees, multiply as shown:

$$\frac{7\pi}{4} \text{ rad} \times \frac{180 \text{ deg}}{\pi \text{ rad}} = \frac{7}{4} \times 180 \text{ deg}$$

$$= 315 \text{ deg}$$

Note that in each case the angle to be converted was multiplied by a conversion ratio, which was either π radians/180 deg or its reciprocal, 180 deg/π radians. In each case, the ratio was used so that the unwanted term would cancel out and the desired term would remain. Therefore, when converting from degrees to radians, we used the ratio with degrees in the denominator to cancel out the term degrees and permit radians to remain in the final solution. When we converted from radians to degrees, the conversion ratio with radians in the denominator was used in order to cancel out radians and permit degrees to remain in the solution. Check back over the above examples to verify this. Check the corresponding degree and radian calibration points of Fig. 4-4.

4.12. Slope of a curve

In our discussion of the straight line in Chapter 3, the significance of the slope and intercepts of the lines was accented. These characteristics are of similar importance when you read information from curves and when you compare curves with one another.

The term *intercept* has exactly the same definition when applied to curves as to lines. However, some slight modification of the term *slope* is required to make it applicable to curves. Recall that the slope of a line shows how rapidly the line ordinates change with respect to changes of the abscissa values. Remember also that we defined slope as the ratio of a vertical increment to the corresponding horizontal increment, that is,

$$m = \frac{\Delta y}{\Delta x}$$

This ratio value was shown to be exactly the

same for a line regardless of where along the line the slope was measured. It is apparent from even a cursory glance at the curves discussed in this chapter that the same is not true for curves, that is, the slope is not the same throughout the length of a curve. Note for instance curve 1 of Fig. 4-10. If we consider the slope of the curve between points J and M, we obtain

$$m = \frac{0.87 - 0.5}{\pi/6}$$

$$m_1 = 0.706$$

If now we investigate the slope of the same curve, using the same procedure and the same horizontal increment between the points M and N, we obtain,

$$m = \frac{1.00 - 0.87}{\pi/6}$$

$$m_2 = 0.248$$

The slope m_2 is almost 1/3 of m_1—and both apply to the same curve. Note from the curve that the slope between points N and P is the same in magnitude as the M to N slope but is negative in direction. It is obvious from these examples, that the slope of a curve is not constant throughout its length. As a matter of fact, we can see now that the straight line is a special case of a curve. *A straight line is a curve with constant slope throughout its length.*

Since the slope of a curve can vary, it is not possible to refer to *the* slope of a curve. It is possible to consider the slope of a curve at only one point at a time. *The slope of a curve at a point is the slope of the line drawn tangent to the curve at that point.* To clarify what is meant by a line drawn tangent to a curve at a point, refer to Fig. 4-12, and note the line drawn through the points A and B on the curve. This line is a *secant line*, since it *cuts the curve at two points.* In order to find the tangent line to the curve at point A, consider that point B is free to move along the curve. Now imagine that it moves slowly toward point A with the secant line always passing through the two points A and B. As the point B moves toward A, the secant line pivots about A. When B reaches A, its limit, the two points

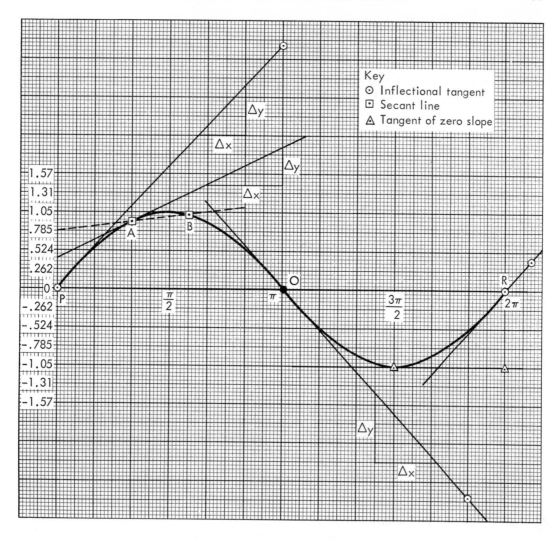

Fig. 4-12. Tangent line is limiting condition of secant line

A and *B* superimpose. The secant line has then become a tangent line. *Thus, a tangent line is the limiting condition of a secant line. The point where the tangent line touches the curve is known as the point of tangency.* In this example, point *A* is the point of tangency. The slope of the curve at point *A* is the slope of the tangent line at point *A*. Using a vertical-to-horizontal increment ratio (see Fig. 4-12), we find the slope of the line to be

$$m = \frac{0.524}{1.05}$$
$$= 0.50$$

Therefore, the slope of the curve at point *A* is 0.50.

4.13. The inflectional tangent

Note the tangent line to the curve of Fig. 4-12 at the π-radian abscissa. This tangent line "cuts through" the curve at the point of tangency instead of just touching it. If additional cycles of the curve were drawn to the right and left, it would be apparent that the same would be true of tangent lines drawn at the 0-radian and at the 2π-radian abscissas. *A tangent line that cuts a curve at a point rather than just touches it is known as an inflectional tangent, and its point of tangency is known as a point of inflection.* Three points of inflection appear in Fig. 4-12. They are point $P(0,0)$, point $Q(\pi, 0)$, and point $R(2\pi, 0)$. This type of tangent is given a specific name because of its importance in reading and sketching curves. A careful examination of Fig. 4-12 will make evident the two primary areas of its importance. Note first that in the case of each of the three inflectional tangents shown, the curve seems to run along the tangent line for a distance on either side of the point of tangency. This shows that the slope of a curve varies very little in the immediate vicinity of the point of inflection, and the curve is almost a straight line for a distance on either side of this point. The curve slope over this range can be taken as the slope of the inflectional tangent, without much error. That this is not true for other tangent lines can be seen from the tangent to the curve at point A.

4.14. Concavity

The second area of importance of the inflectional tangent and the point of inflection can be found by again examining the curve on either side of the inflectional point but, this time, over a wider range. Note that the curve to the right of the inflection point Q $(\pi, 0)$ is shaped in the form of a cup that opens upward. To the left of this point Q the wave is curved so that it opens downward. The point of inflection is the point where the curve changes the direction in which it opens. The technical term used to state that a curve opens upward is that the curve is *concave upward*. To state that the curve opens downward, we say that the curve is *concave downward*. Therefore, we can more correctly redefine *the point of inflection as the point where a curve changes concavity.*

4.15. Simple harmonic motion

The waveshape shown in Fig. 4-12 is, of course, a sine wave, and a discussion of various tangent lines drawn to different points on the sine wave will yield some interesting and applicable properties of this ubiquitous waveshape. Many mechanical and electrical vibrations and oscillations yield a sinusoidal waveshape. As representative of these conditions, let us consider the motion of a weight hanging from a helical coil spring. In order to start

the weight oscillating up and down, consider that the weight has been raised 1 ft above its rest position and released. The weight will therefore start at the height of 1 ft, fall to the position from which it was originally raised (rest position) and continue to descend until it travels 1 ft below its rest position. The spring will then pull it upward past the rest position to the 1-ft height. Let us assume that this complete variation, or cycle, or oscillation takes 1 sec. If the distance of the weight from its original rest position were plotted against time, the resultant waveshape would be that shown in Fig. 4-13a—a cosine wave. Thus, Fig. 4-13a is a distance-vs.-time plot for a weight oscillating up and down at the end of a coil (helical) spring. When the distance-vs.-time plot of a vibrating body is a sinusoid, as is the case here, the oscillation is known as *simple harmonic motion.* Simple harmonic motion is a most important type of periodic motion, since it appears in reciprocating engines, in the vibration of a tuning fork, the swinging of a pendulum, the workings of a watch, and applications throughout all technologies. Let us use our knowledge of slopes of lines and curves to investigate this significant motion. In Chapter 3 we discussed distance-vs.-time plots and also the slopes of these graphs. Note, for example, the distance-time plot of Fig. 3-1. True, the plot is a straight line, but the definitions and ideas developed in Chapter 3 are equally applicable to any type of curve. As can be seen from Fig. 3-1, the slope of the curve represents the velocity of the moving object. Since in Fig. 3-1 the slope is everywhere the same, then the velocity of the moving object is constant. The slope of the distance-time plot of Fig. 4-13a also represents the velocity of the moving object, but here the slopes are not the same throughout the entire curve. Therefore, the velocity of the vibrating weight is not constant. By determining the slope of Fig. 4-13a at different points, we can learn just how the velocity of the weight changes. As a matter of fact, if we evaluate the slope of Fig. 4-13a at different points and plot these slope values against time, we will be able to see clearly exactly how the

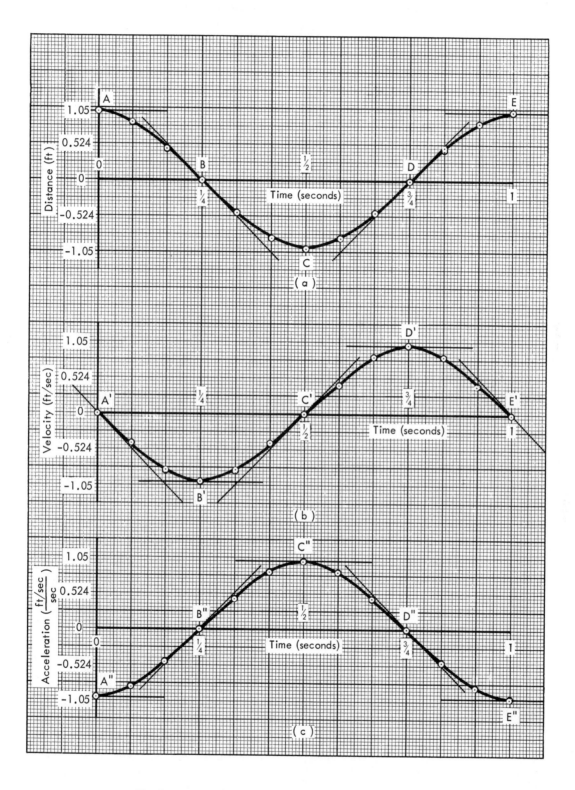

Fig. 4-13. Graphical description of simple harmonic motion

velocity of the vibrating weight changes with time.

4.16. Evaluating the slopes of the curves of harmonic motion

Note the tangent line drawn to curve a in Fig. 4-13a at time $= 0$ (point A). The line is horizontal. What, therefore, is its slope? For a horizontal line there is no vertical increment possible. Thus, the slope is $0/\Delta x$, which, of course, equals 0. Thus, at time equals 0 (starting time), the velocity of the vibrating weight is 0. This means that the coordinates of the first point of a velocity time-plot are (0,0). This is point A' of Fig. 4-13b. Note now the tangent line drawn to curve a at time $= \frac{1}{4}$ sec (point B). What is the slope value of this tangent and what is its direction? Is there anything special about this tangent line? From Fig. 4-13a the slope of this tangent can be seen to be

$$\frac{\Delta y}{\Delta x} = \frac{1.57 \text{ ft}}{\frac{1}{4} \text{ sec}}$$

Thus, the slope value is

$$|m| = 6.28 \text{ fps}[8]$$

Looking at this tangent line, we can see that its slope is negative, since the ordinate values decrease as the abscissa values increase. Therefore, at the $\frac{1}{4}$-sec point (point B) the velocity of the vibrating weight is -6.28 fps. Since the minus sign refers to direction and we have chosen upward as the positive direction (see curve a) we know that at the $\frac{1}{4}$-sec point the object is moving downward with the speed of 6.28 fps. These time velocity coordinates ($\frac{1}{4}$ sec, -6.28 fps) are plotted to yield point B' of curve b. The special property of this tangent (as questioned above) is that it is an inflectional tangent. Its significance will be seen very shortly. Next, note the tangent line drawn to curve a at time $= \frac{1}{2}$ sec (point C). Here again we have a horizontal tangent, meaning

that the slope of the curve at this point (point C) is also 0. The coordinates, time $= \frac{1}{2}$ sec, velocity $= 0$ fps, yield point C' of figure b when plotted. The next tangent is another inflectional tangent shown drawn at the $\frac{3}{4}$-sec abscissa point (point D) of curve a. Measurement of the Δy-to-Δx ratio shows the same slope magnitude of 6.28 fps as does the previous inflectional tangent. This slope, however, is seen to be positive. Thus the coordinates of another point that will yield curve b are ($\frac{3}{4}$ sec, $+6.28$ fps). This point is shown plotted in Fig. 4-13b and is labeled D'. The last tangent line shown in figure a is at the point of abscissa, 1 sec (point E). The slope of this tangent is 0, meaning that the vibrating weight is again at a 0 velocity position after 1 sec and has thus completed a full cycle of its oscillation. The value of the slope at point E is shown plotted in figure d as point E'. In the preceding discussion the slope of curve a was investigated at only five points, yielding the velocity of the oscillating weight at five different time instants. These velocity values are shown plotted at the appropriate time position in figure b. If the slopes of curve a were investigated at 10 or 15 points and all the values plotted, the curve obtained by connecting these points would yield the negative sine curve of Fig. 4-13b. Check this last statement for at least four additional points.

It is apparent from the above development that curve b shows how the *velocity* of the swinging weight varies with time. Note that the velocity of the swinging weight varies from 0 (point A') to a maximum value in the negative (downward) direction of 6.28 fps (point B') and then back to 0 velocity again (point C'). During the entire first half-second, the velocity of the weight is negative, meaning that during this entire time the weight is moving downward. The second half of curve b is entirely above the horizontal axis, meaning that all these velocity values are positive. Thus, from the $\frac{1}{2}$-sec (point C') to the 1-sec time (point E'), the weight is moving upward. During this time interval the speed of the weight varies from 0 (point C') to a maximum value of 6.28 fps (point D'). It then

---

[8] The vertical bars on either side of the letter m mean that only the numerical value of m is being given, with no reference to direction. These vertical lines are often referred to as "magnitude bars."

decreases in speed during the last ¼ sec to an instantaneous standstill at the 1-sec point (0 velocity at point E').

4.17. Meaning of the inflectional tangent

Let us return for an instant to the velocity of the oscillating weight at the ¼-sec and ¾-sec times (points B' and D'). Note that at each of these two instants the speed of the weight is at its highest value of 6.28 fps. How are these values determined? A glance at the tangents drawn to curve a shows that the slopes of the two inflectional tangents to curve a yielded these speeds. There is, nevertheless, a difference in the velocity of the weight at the two points B' and D'. One is in the negative direction and is therefore called the *minimum*, the other is in the positive direction and is therefore called the *maximum* value. Thus, the significance of an inflectional tangent to a curve is that *it yields a maximum or minimum point in a plot of the slope values of that curve.* The positively sloped inflectional tangent yields a maximum point, and the negatively sloped inflectional tangent yields a minimum point.

When, earlier in this chapter, the inflectional tangent was first discussed, it was related to the concavity (direction of opening) of the curve to which it was drawn. Does this concavity of curve a have any significance in a plot of its slope values (curve b)? The full answer to this question is left to you, but first notice these relationships:

During the first ¼-sec the distance-time plot is concave downward, and during this same time interval, curve b shows the speed values to be increasing in the negative direction. During the second ¼-sec curve a is concave upward. The velocity-time curve during this time becomes continuously less negative—or, we can say, more positive. During the third ¼-sec interval, curve a is still concave upward and the slopes of curve b remain positive in this interval. What are the relationships during the last ¼-sec? Can you now express the significance of the concavity of a curve as related to its slope values?

4.18. Examining the sinusoidal velocity-time curve

By investigating the slopes of the distance-time plot, we were able to learn a good deal about the velocity of the moving object. Can anything be learned from a similar examination of the velocity-time curve of this simple harmonic motion? Glance back for a moment at the simpler speed-time plot of Fig. 3-8. What does the slope of this line represent? A vertical increment is in this case a change in speed, and the horizontal increment represents a time interval. The slope ratio, therefore, represents acceleration. Let us return now to our sinusoidal velocity-time curve (Fig. 4-13b). The slope of this curve at any point on the curve represents the acceleration of the bobbing weight. Note the three tangent lines drawn to curve b of the figure. What is the slope of each of these? At what time will the weight change its speed most rapidly? Is there any time when the speed of the object does not change at all? How can we learn from the curve when the speed is increasing and when it is decreasing? The answers to these and other questions appear in the curve. All we have to know is where to look. Let's find them.

We know now that the slope of the curve b at any point tells us how rapidly the velocity of the weight is changing at that time. The first tangent line shown for this curve is drawn tangent to point B'. Since the line is horizontal, its slope is zero, meaning that the slope of curve b at this point is 0. The same is true at the ¾-sec mark, as can be seen from the slope of the curve at point D'. If we plot the slope values obtained from curve b against time, the resultant curve is an acceleration-vs.-time plot. This permits us to see how the acceleration of the oscillating weight varies with time. Two points on such a plot would be the 0 acceleration of points B' and D'. These acceleration values are plotted in Fig. 4-13c as points B'' and D''. The tangent line drawn at point C' of the velocity-time curve passes through the curve, and is thus an inflectional tangent that yields the maximum or minimum acceleration value. To measure this slope, it is convenient to use a horizontal increment of

1/6 sec. The corresponding vertical increment measures $+6.67$ fps. The slope of the curve at point C' is therefore

$$m = \frac{+6.67 \text{ ft/sec}}{1/6 \text{ sec}}$$

$$m = \frac{40 \text{ ft/sec}}{\text{sec}}$$

$$m = 40 \frac{\text{ft}}{\text{sec}^2}$$

This means that if the curve continued at the same slope, instead of changing sinusoidally, it would show the weight to be increasing its velocity by 40 ft/sec^2 (that is, 40 feet per second every second). Actually this is the maximum acceleration and exists for an instant of time when the object is at the bottom of its swing (see point C on curve a). We know that the velocity of the object *increases* at this rate because the slope at C' is positive. This value of $+40$ ft/sec^2 at an abscissa of $\frac{1}{4}$ sec is plotted in Fig. 4-13c as point C''. We know C'' to be a maximum value because it represents the slope at a point of inflection. Therefore at this time—the $\frac{1}{4}$ sec point—the speed of the weight changes most rapidly.

If tangent lines are drawn to points on curve b between B' and D', they will all show positive slopes. During this time the velocity value can be seen to vary from its minimum to its maximum value. Hence, the velocity values increase when the velocity-time plot shows a positive slope. Using this idea, we can readily determine that the velocity of the swinging weight decreases in the negative slope regions, which can be seen to be the first and last quarters of the cycle. If various slopes from A' to E' are evaluated and these accelerations plotted, the curve resulting from this plot would be curve c of Fig. 4-13. This curve can readily be recognized as a sinusoid. Specifically, it is a negative cosine curve.

4.19. The slope of a sinusoid

We have just discussed the characteristics of simple harmonic motion, but what is even more important, we have seen how the sinusoidal curves behave. We have carefully in-

vestigated the slopes of several sinusoids and have seen that in each case the slope of a sinusoidal waveshape varies sinusoidally. Only the sinusoids show this particular characteristic. It is this property of the sinusoids that has made the sine wave the basis for electrical a-c theory, in addition to its numerous other applications. The many other points relating to slopes of curves that were brought out in this discussion are equally valid for other curves and waveshapes.

4.20. The other trigonometric functions

We have so far discussed the circular (trigonometric) functions that are obtainable directly from the circle—the sinusoids. The other four trigonometric (circular) curves are readily obtained from the sine or the cosine curve, or the two in combination. The curve known as the *tangent* (abbreviated tan) is obtained from the sine and cosine in combination, the relationship being

$$\tan \theta = \frac{\sin \theta}{\cos \theta}$$

Let us investigate a few ordinate values of the tangent curve, using this expression, to determine their range and to compare them with those of the sine and cosine functions. From Fig. 4-4 we note that at 30 deg the sine curve ordinate is 0.5 and the cosine ordinate is approximately 0.87. Thus, the tangent ordinate at 30 deg is

$$\tan 30° = \frac{0.5}{0.87}$$

$$= 0.58$$

At 45 deg the sine and cosine ordinates are both 0.71. The tangent ordinate at 45 deg is therefore 1. At 60 deg the sine is seen to be 0.87 and the cosine is 0.5. Thus, the tangent ordinate is

$$\tan 60° = \frac{0.87}{0.5}$$

$$= 1.73$$

Note that the tangent ordinate computed above is greater than 1, even though the two circular functions, sine and cosine, that yield the tangent have a maximum magnitude of 1. Now, let's investigate the tangent curve ordinate at 90 deg. Note from Fig. 4-4 that at 90 deg the sine ordinate is $+1$, and the cosine curve is at 0 ordinate value. Therefore,

$$\tan 90° = \frac{1}{0}$$

$$= \infty$$

The symbol shown represents *infinity, that is, a quantity greater than any possible number regardless of the value of the number.* Obviously, therefore, the values through which the tangent curve varies are drastically different from those of either the sine or the cosine curves. As such, additional terms will be required to describe them. Table 4-2 contains the ordinate values of the tangent and other trigonometric functions that will be useful in sketching and discussing the curves. The abscissa values are given in both degree and radian measure. A more accurate table of values is given in Appendix B.

4.21. The tangent curve

The result obtained when the tangent ordinates are plotted against θ, as θ varies from $0°$ to $360°$ appears as curve y_1 in Fig. 4-14. That this curve is drastically different from the sinusoids discussed so far is evident at a glance. There is one property that the two have in common and that is periodicity. All six trigonometric functions are periodic; that is, every cycle duplicates exactly the values of the previous cycle in exactly the same position. There are, however, significant differences. Let's consider these one at a time.

4.22. The asymptote

We have already noted that the ordinates of the tangent curve extend far beyond the unity limit of the sine and cosine curves. Indeed, we've shown that at 90 deg the tangent curve has an ordinate of infinity. How does one plot such a curve? What kind of a scale is used? How is the infinity quantity indicated? The

Table 4-2. The trigonometric ordinates as functions of the angle θ

θ, Rad.	θ, Deg.	Primary Functions			Secondary Functions		
		Sin θ	Cos θ	Tan θ	csc θ	sec θ	ctn θ
0	0	0.00	1.00	0.00	$+\infty$	1	$+\infty$
$\frac{1}{12}\pi$	15	0.26	0.97	0.27	3.84	1.04	
$\frac{1}{6}\pi$	30	0.50	0.87	0.58	2.00	1.15	
$\frac{1}{4}\pi$	45	0.71	0.71	1.00	1.41	1.41	
$\frac{1}{3}\pi$	60	0.87	0.50	1.73	1.15	2.00	
$\frac{5}{12}\pi$	75	0.97	0.26	3.73	1.04	3.86	
$\frac{1}{2}\pi$	90	1.00	0.00	$\pm\infty$	1.00	$\pm\infty$	0
$\frac{7}{12}\pi$	105	0.97	-0.26	-3.73			
$\frac{2}{3}\pi$	120	0.87	-0.50	-1.73			
$\frac{3}{4}\pi$	135	0.71	-0.71	-1.00			
$\frac{5}{6}\pi$	150	0.50	-0.87	-0.58			
$\frac{11}{12}\pi$	165	0.26	-0.97	-0.27			
π	180	0.00	-1.00	0.00	$\pm\infty$	-1.00	$\pm\infty$
$\frac{13}{12}\pi$	195	-0.26	-0.97	0.27			
$\frac{7}{6}\pi$	210	-0.50	-0.87	0.58			
$\frac{5}{4}\pi$	225	-0.71	-0.71	1.00			
$\frac{4}{3}\pi$	240	-0.87	-0.50	1.73			
$\frac{17}{12}\pi$	255	-0.97	-0.26	3.73			
$\frac{3}{2}\pi$	270	-1.00	0.00	$\pm\infty$	-1.00	$\pm\infty$	0
$\frac{19}{12}\pi$	285	-0.97	0.26	-3.73			
$\frac{5}{3}\pi$	300	-0.87	0.50	-1.73			
$\frac{7}{4}\pi$	315	-0.71	0.71	-1.00			
$\frac{11}{6}\pi$	330	-0.50	0.87	-0.58			
$\frac{23}{12}\pi$	345	-0.26	0.97	-0.27			
2π	360	0.00	1.00	0.00	$-\infty$	$+1.00$	$-\infty$

answers to these and other questions are obtainable from Fig. 4-14. Note particularly the first quarter-cycle of the tangent curve, that is, the plot from 0 to 90 deg. At 0 deg the tangent ordinate is 0, and at 45 deg it is 1. Even as far as 75 deg the ordinate is only 3.73. These values are not exceptionally large and therefore are not at all difficult to scale and plot. But note what happens to the ordinate values in the next 13°. At 85 deg the tangent curve is at 11.5, and at 88 deg it has more than doubled in value to reach 28.5. The plot of Fig. 4-14 doesn't show it, but in the next degree the tangent more than doubles its value again and becomes 57.3 at 89 deg! The slope of this curve obviously increases drastically as it speeds its way upward in the last few degrees before 90 deg. And at 90 deg the ordinate is infinite. Infinity is not a true number. It is a quantity greater than any conceivable number, in other words, an unattainable quantity. If we say that the tangent is infinite at 90 deg and also that infinity is an unattainable quantity, then we are saying that the tangent curve never reaches the abscissa value of 90 deg. The tangent curve gets closer and closer to a line drawn vertically through the 90 deg calibration point, but it never touches this line. Such a line is known as an *asymptote*. Thus, an asymptote is defined as *a straight line that is approached by a curve but is never reached by that curve.* We say that the tangent curve is *asymptotic* to the 90 deg line. In the case being discussed here, the asymptote is a vertical line, but not all asymptotes are vertical. Asymptotes can be lines of any slope whatever, and later we shall discuss curves that have asymptotes that are far from being vertical.

4.23. Significance of the asymptote

The significance of the asymptote is multiple. When a curve is asymptotic to a line, it runs very close to that line for much of its length and at the extremes is indistinguishable from it. This means that the curve is almost a straight line over much of its length and that the slope of the curve in this region is very much the slope of its asymptote. For example, what is the slope of the 90-deg line

to which the tangent curve is asymptotic? Since this line is vertical, no horizontal increment exists. Thus, an attempt to find a ratio of increments will result in

$$m = \frac{\Delta y}{0}$$
$$= \infty$$

The slope of a vertical line is infinitely large, since the vertical increment is some finite value and the horizontal increment is 0, smaller than any finite quantity. Whenever a finite quantity of any size is divided by one infinitely small, the result is a value infinitely large—just called "infinity." Since the tangent curve approaches a vertical line as we come closer to 90 deg, we realize that the slope of the tangent line approaches infinity as we come closer to 90 deg. We can also say that at 90 deg the slope of the tangent curve is infinite, or what is the same thing, that at 90 deg the tangent curve is a vertical straight line. This is of course, true only at 90 deg and 270 deg. Going back to the 45-deg point, we find that a measurement of the slope of the tangent curve yields 2 (using the radian calibration for the horizontal increment), a value far below infinity.

4.24. Discontinuity

If you were asked, "What is the value of the tangent at 90 deg?" you would probably answer "infinity." However, another way of correctly answering the same question is to say that at 90 deg the tangent is *undefined*. This means that no exact numerical value can be stated as the ordinate value of the tangent curve at 90 deg. Infinity is a quantity greater than any number, but infinity itself is not a fixed number. *A curve is said to be discontinuous if for any abscissa its ordinate is undefined (infinite in value). A curve is also discontinuous if for any ordinate its abscissa is undefined (infinite in value).* The tangent curve is discontinuous at 90 deg and again at 270 deg. The curve shown in Fig. 4-27e and f (equilateral hyperbola) has both a horizontal and vertical asymptote and shows a discontinuity in the horizontal direction and also in the vertical direction.

Although the tangent curve is discontinuous at 90 deg, a cursory glance at Fig. 4-14 shows that the tangent curve does not end at 90 deg. The curve is asymptotic to the 90-deg line in both the positive and the negative directions. As the abscissas increase from 90 to 180 deg, the tangent ordinate values recede rapidly from negative infinity. At 135 deg the ordinate has risen to −1. The slope of the tangent curve also drops sharply as the ordinates decrease. At the 135-deg point the slope of the tangent line can be measured to be +2, and at 180 deg it is +1. It is interesting to note that although the slopes of the tangent curve vary from 1 to infinity, the slope of the curve is never negative. It is left to you to verify by construction and measurement that the slope of the tangent curve is never less than +1.

4.25. Further examination of the tangent curve

In each of the sinusoids discussed earlier, it was noticed that the curve is very much the same from 0 to 180 deg as it is from 180 to 360 deg. In the case of the tangent curve, the two half-cycles are not only similar but identical. The positive values of the first quarter-cycle are exactly duplicated in corresponding position during the third quarter-cycle, and the negative ordinates of the tangent curve from 90 to 180 deg appear again in corresponding positions in the region from 270 to 360 deg. Furthermore, if by looking at Table 4-2 or Fig. 4-14, we compare the values of the tangent in the first quarter-cycle to those of the second quarter, an additional pattern of the tangent curve becomes evident. The ordinates in the first quarter appear again in the second quarter-cycle but negative and in the reverse order. Thus, at 15 deg the tangent ordinate is +0.27, and at 15 deg back from the half-cycle point, that is, at 165 deg, the tangent ordinate is −0.27. Once these patterns are recognized, it is necessary to be given only the tangent values for the first quarter-cycle to be able to complete a table of values for the entire 360 deg or to sketch the curve for the entire cycle.

Since all the circular functions show a readily recognizable pattern or symmetry, it is possible to build an entire table of values or sketch an entire curve from information given for the first quarter-cycle only. It is for this reason that most tables for the trigonometric functions extend only from 0° to 90°.

Refer again to Fig. 4-14, and note that in this diagram two different uses are made of the broken line. First of all, the asymptotes are shown dotted. It is common practice to include asymptotes in this form when an asymptotic curve is drawn simply as an aid to the reader of the curve. The asymptote is, however, not part of the curve itself, and its appearance with an asymptotic curve is optional, not mandatory.

Note also that the vertical axis of Fig. 4-14 contains a broken-line section. From earlier discussions we know that this symbolizes a change in calibration scale. Since the tangent ordinates change so rapidly toward the end of each quarter-cycle, no exact scale was used above the +5 and below the −5 calibration points. The values that are shown in the broken-line region of the axis are the correct ordinates for the corresponding abscissas.

4.26. The primary and secondary circular functions

The three curves, the sine, the cosine, and the tangent, are known as the *primary trigonometric* (circular) functions. There are three secondary trigonometric functions, and each is derived from a primary function. Each of the three secondary functions is a reciprocal of a primary function.

4.27. The cosecant curve

The cosecant curve is the reciprocal of the sine function. Thus, to determine the ordinate values of the cosecant curve, we must divide each of the sine values into 1. From Table 4-2 we see that the value of the sine θ at 0 deg is 0. Therefore, at 0 deg the value of the cosecant θ is

$$\csc 0° = \frac{1}{0}$$

$$= \infty$$

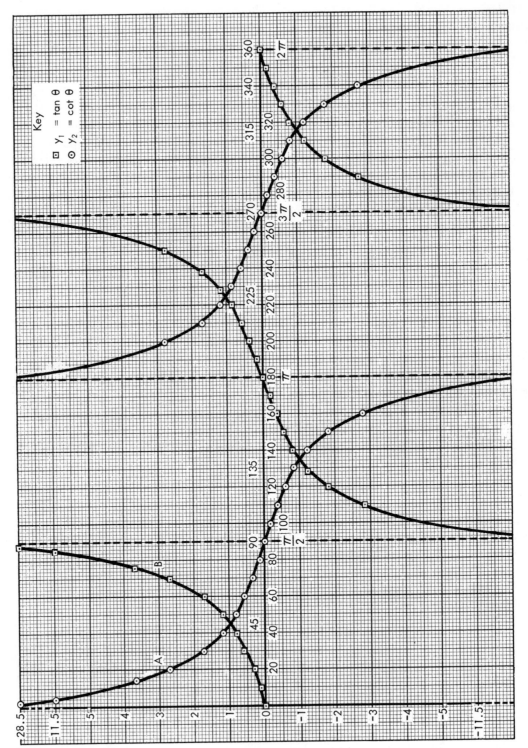

Fig. 4-14. Tangent and cotangent curves

We see immediately that at 0 deg the cosecant is undefined and that it is therefore a discontinuous curve. Verify this by referring to Fig. 4-15. At 15 deg the sine is $+0.26$. Hence, at 15 deg the cosecant value is

$$\csc 15° = \frac{1}{+0.26}$$
$$= +3.84$$

Here again, as was the case with the tangent, the ordinates recede from (and approach) infinity very rapidly. The two curves are not the same, but they do have that characteristic in common. The ordinate $+3.84$ is plotted at the abscissa 15 deg (Fig. 4-15). Each of the following values shown in the cosecant column of Table 4-2 is evaluated by finding the reciprocal of the corresponding sine value. It is left as an exercise for you to complete this column by writing in the proper values, complete with the plus or minus sign.

4.28. Extent

Is the cosecant an asymptotic curve? An examination of Fig. 4-15 will show that it is. The curve is asymptotic to the 0- and the 180-deg lines. To avoid crowding the diagram, the asymptotes are not shown. However, if the cosecant is to be shown alone, it is good practice to include the asymptotes in broken-line form. The cosecant curve shows an additional significant characteristic that none of the curves discussed thus far have exhibited. Note from Fig. 4-15 that there is a range of ordinates for which the cosecant curve does not exist. Although the cosecant curve has ordinates ranging from plus to minus infinity, it has no values in the region between $+1$ and -1. It is said that *the curve is nonexistent in this interval of values. A discussion of the range or interval of values for which a curve does and does not exist is a discussion of its extent.* The range of values for which a curve does not exist at all should not be confused with the discontinuity of a graph. A curve is discontinuous only if its ordinate goes off to infinity for one or more abscissa values, or if its abscissa goes to infinity for one or more ordinate values. In the region between $+1$ and

-1 (Fig. 4-15), in which the cosecant doesn't exist, there is certainly no question of any quantity being infinite in value. On the other hand, the tangent curve is discontinuous, but there is no range of ordinate or abscissa values where the tangent does not exist.

4.29. The secant curve

If the reciprocal of each of the cosine ordinates were computed and then plotted against the corresponding angle, the curve obtained would be the secant curve (Fig. 4-15). This is the second of the three secondary trigonometric functions and as expected is very similar to the cosecant function. The similarity was expected because the secant is derived from the cosine curve in the same manner in which the cosecant is obtained from the sine. This curve is therefore asymptotic, but to different lines, has the same range of slopes as the cosecant, and is non-existent in the same region. Actually, the two curves are the same except that they are displaced from one another. The same displacement exists between the sine and cosine curves from which they come.

4.30. The cotangent curve

Figure 4-14, discussed earlier in connection with the tangent curve, shows a second curve quite similar to the tangent function. These two are not similar in the same sense that the sine and cosine are similar to one another or the cosecant and secant curves are similar to one another. In other words, it is not possible to shift the tangent curve to the right or left in order to obtain the second curve of Fig. 4-14—the cotangent. The tangent and cotangent have the same general shape, are both asymptotic and show no nonexistent range. There is, however, a marked difference between them.

Note from Fig. 4-14 that the cotangent curve is asymptotic to the 0 deg line and that its ordinate values drop rapidly from infinity to 0 in the first quarter-cycle. What significant property do the slopes of the cotangent curve show in these first 90 deg? Any line drawn tangent to this curve at any point in the first quarter-cycle will be sloped negatively. At 0 deg the

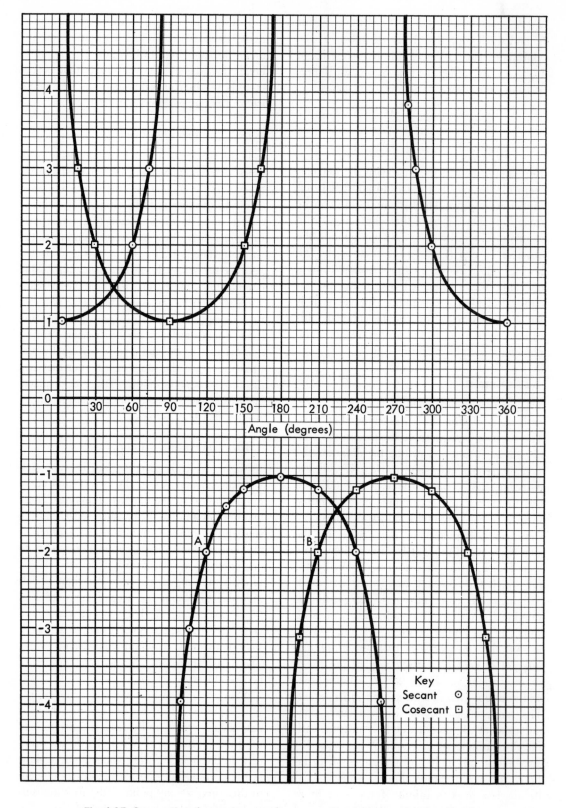

Fig. 4-15. Cosecant and secant curves (two secondary trigonometric functions)

slope of the cotangent curve is infinite but negative, and at 90 deg the slope value is -1. What happens to the slopes of the cotangent curve in the second quarter-cycle? Here, it can be seen, the slopes increase in magnitude; that is, the curve becomes steeper. However, all the slopes are still negative. From 180 to 360 deg the curve is an exact repetition of itself in the first half-cycle. Thus, throughout the entire cycle the cotangent shows negative slopes. How does this property of negative slopes throughout compare with the tangent curve characteristics? Recall that the tangent curve also shows the same direction of slope throughout its length. However, the tangent slopes are all positive, and this is one of the prime differences in the shapes of these two curves.

In keeping with the criterion for the secondary functions, the ordinate values of the cotangent are obtained by finding the reciprocals of the tangent values. Expressing this in equation form, we have

$$\cot \theta = \frac{1}{\tan \theta}$$

Using this relationship, fill in the missing values in the cotangent column of Table 4-2. Since we know that the tangent function can be expressed in terms of the sine and cosine as

$$\tan \theta = \frac{\sin \theta}{\cos \theta}$$

then the cotangent function values can also be obtained by using the relationship

$$\cot \theta = \frac{\cos \theta}{\sin \theta}$$

Check several of the values you computed for the cotangent column of Table 4-2 with this relationship.

4.31. Phase angles between the trigonometric functions

In the discussion of phase earlier in this chapter, we learned that the cosine curve leads the sine curve by 90 deg. If a phase separation between one pair of the trigonometric functions exists, what will happen when we consider phase relationships between other pairs of trigonometric curves? Since phase measurement can be accomplished only between similar curves, let us consider the cosecant-secant pair shown in Fig. 4-15. Note the corresponding points A and B shown on the negative portions of the curves. These are separated by 90 deg, with point A being ahead of B. We see, therefore, that the secant curve leads the cosecant by 90 deg. This is to be expected, since the secant curve is derived from the cosine and the cosecant from the sine.

Fig. 4-14 shows the tangent and cotangent curves. What is the phase displacement between these two? This question can be answered only after a pair of corresponding points is determined. Are the points A and B corresponding points? They have the same displacement, but are they "moving in the same sense" on their respective curves? The answer to this last question is, No, since the cotangent curve is decreasing in value at point A and the tangent curve is increasing in value at point B. We can also say that A and B are not corresponding points, since at point A the cotangent curve is negatively sloped and at point B the tangent curve is positively sloped. However, the cotangent curve has a negative slope throughout, and the tangent curve has a positive slope throughout. Does this mean that no pair of corresponding points can be found? Yes, it does; and, therefore, *it is not possible to express a phase relationship between these two trigonometric functions.*

4.32. Conic sections

Anyone whose vocation or avocation is related to present-day science or technology is familiar with such terms as "elliptical orbit," "parabolic reflector," "hyperbolic navigation," "circular function." These are only a tiny sampling of a long list of terms from all phases of engineering and the sciences that are related to one another. They are all based on a particular set of curves—the conic sections. The terms *ellipse, parabola,* and *hyperbola* are credited to the Greek mathematician, Appolonius of Perga, who lived about 300 B.C. and wrote eight books on the subject. He showed that when a plane is passed through a right circular cone at several different angles, a set of curves of intersection is produced that have many interesting geometrical properties. Today we know that these properties have application in areas as diverse as airplane design and nuclear physics. In addition, two curves of this set, the circle and the hyperbola, are each the basis of an essential system of graphs.

4.33. The right circular cone

The right circular cone, the solid figure that yields the curves named above, is a solid of revolution. This means that the figure is produced by revolving a plane figure around a specified axis. In this case, the plane figure is a right triangle, and the axis is either one of the two legs of the triangle, exclusive of the hypotenuse. The resultant solid figures are shown in Fig. 4-16b and 4-16c. Note that in each case shown we can clearly see the distinguishing characteristic of the right circular cone. That is, the altitude (the line going from the peak, or vertex, of the cone to the circular base) makes a right angle with the base. This 90-deg angle accounts for the "right" in the name of the cone. The word "circular" refers, of course, to the revolving process involved. A cone-shaped figure would also be produced if the right triangle were revolved about its hypotenuse. However, this figure would be a double cone, with a common base, which is useless for our application here.

4.34. One nappe and two

The right circular cones of Figs. 4-16b and 4-16c are cones of *one nappe*, so called to distinguish them from the cone of Fig. 4-16e. The double-nappe cone of Fig. 4-16e can be considered to be two identical single right circular cones with their vertices placed together so that their axes coincide. However, the figure is truly a volume of revolution which can be produced by starting with two intersecting straight lines, as shown in Fig. 4-16d. The generating line is then revolved around the other, the axis, at their point of intersection. The resultant figure is the double-nappe right

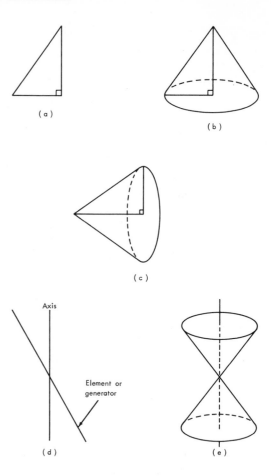

Fig. 4-16. Right circular cone is a solid of revolution

circular cone shown, the altitude of which is clearly the original axis line.

4.35. Conic sections produced

The sections referred to earlier are the plane figures, or curves, produced when a plane is passed through the cone. In three of the four cases that we will consider, use of the single-nappe cone will suffice. In the fourth case, the hyperbola, such a cone would yield only a partial result, and it thus requires the use of the double-nappe form. In order to discuss the properties of these curves of intersection, it is necessary to position them on a set of cartesian coordinate axes. Many different orientations are possible, and in three of the four cases we will discuss more than one, since these are very commonly encountered and have become standard. The various arrangements of the

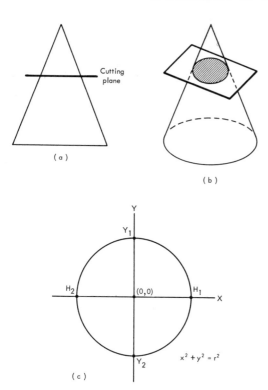

Fig. 4-17. Conic section produced by
cutting plane parallel to base of a cone
is a circle

The letters x and y represent the independent and dependent variables, and r represents the radius of the circle. For example, the equation $x^2 + y^2 = 5^2$ represents a circle of radius 5 units, with its center at the origin. Furthermore, it can be seen from Fig. 4-17c that the circle has two horizontal and two vertical intercepts, each a radial distance (5 units in this example) away from the center. The (x, y) coordinates of the two vertical intercepts are therefore $Y_1(0, 5)$ and $Y_2(0, -5)$. The coordinates of the horizontal intercepts are $X_1(5, 0)$ and $X_2(-5, 0)$. Thus, not only does the symmetrically located circle provide considerable information about the curve, but it yields the simplest possible equation for a circle. Any other position of the circle center with respect to the origin would result in an equation of more terms and one more cumbersome to handle analytically.

The circle, as well as the other conic sections, has a *locus* (path) definition, that yields the applicable properties of the curve. As we know, the circle is the path described by a point moving so that it maintains a fixed distance from a given point. This simple definition permits us to design an instrument with which to draw a circle and machines with which to produce circular gears, shafts, and wheels for a host of applications.

4.37. The ellipse

As shown in Fig. 4-18 the plane position that yields an ellipse differs only slightly from its circle-producing position. If the cutting plane makes an angle with the plane of the base but does not intersect the base of the cone, then the curve of intersection on the surface of the cone is an ellipse. As is the case with the circle, it is most convenient to arrange the ellipse symmetrically on the $X - Y$ axes. However, the ellipse can be symmetrically arranged in many different positions, and each position will result in a different form of the equation of this section. The two standard arrangements and their associated equations are shown in Fig. 4-18c and 4-18d. Note that the ellipse appears to be a distorted circle, or if need be, the circle can be considered a special

curves on the axis are not named but are distinguished by their equations. Those orientations have become classic that yield the simplest equations for the curves of the conic sections. In each of our discussions the equation will be given and clarified.

4.36. The circle

From the time of the invention of the wheel during the Bronze Age to the present time of the Atomic Age, no mechanical form or device has been developed that even approaches the circle in range of application. Yet the circle is the simplest of the conic sections. The plane of Fig. 4-17a passes through the cone parallel to the plane of the base. It can readily be seen from the three-dimensional view of Fig. 4-17b that the curve of intersection of the cone surface and this plane is a circle. When the circle is placed on the X-Y axes so that its center is at the origin as shown in Fig. 4-17c, then its equation is

$$x^2 + y^2 = r^2$$

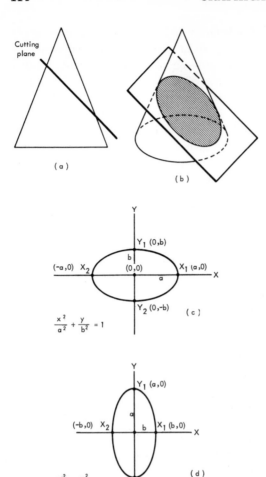

Fig. 4-18. Ellipse is produced by cutting plane that makes an angle with, but does not intersect, base of a cone

case of the ellipse.

The intercepts of the ellipse are not the same in both the vertical and horizontal directions, making it necessary to distinguish between the shorter and longer directions. The two "endpoints" of the ellipse are known as its *vertices*, and in Fig. 4-18c they appear as the horizontal intercepts of the curve. The line joining the two vertices is known as the *major axis* of the ellipse, and its length is designated as 2a. The distance a is referred to as the *semimajor axis* and it is the distance from the center of the ellipse to a vertex. Thus, when the major axis of the ellipse is along the X-axis and its center at the origin, the coordinates of the vertices are $X_1(a, 0)$ and $X_2(-a, 0)$. As

pointed out above, the vertices are here the X intercepts, so that these coordinates are also the intercept coordinates. The *minor axis* of the ellipse intersects the major axis at the ellipse center and is perpendicular to the major axis. Its length is commonly designated as 2b and the distance b referred to as the *semiminor axis*. In the orientation of Fig. 4-18c the minor axis falls along the Y axis, and the coordinates of the Y intercepts are thus $(0, b)$ for Y_1 and $(0, -b)$ for Y_2. For the Fig. 4-18c position of the ellipse discussed in this paragraph, the equation of the ellipse is

$$\frac{x^2}{a^2} + \frac{y^2}{b^2} = 1$$

where a and b represent the length of the semimajor and semiminor axes, respectively. If, for example, we have the equation

$$\frac{x^2}{9} + \frac{y^2}{4} = 1$$

It can be rewritten as

$$\frac{x^2}{3^2} + \frac{y^2}{2^2} = 1$$

From this we know that the semimajor axis is 3 units long and that the semiminor axis is 2 units long. Since the major axis is along the X axis and the center of the ellipse is at the origin, the horizontal intercepts can immediately be marked off and these noted as the vertices of the ellipse. The vertical intercepts can also be marked off, since the length of the semiminor axis is known. With these points designated and with a knowledge of the general shape of the ellipse, the balance of the curve can readily be sketched in. Thus, a critical examination of the equation of the conic section for one or two key values avoids a tedious and lengthy process of tabulating and plotting values to obtain the desired curve.

It was mentioned in the above paragraph that the circle could be considered a special case of the ellipse. This can be accented by comparing the equations of the two curves. If we start with the equation of the circle, $x^2 + y^2 = r^2$, and divide both sides of this equation by the radius squared, we obtain

$$\frac{x^2}{r^2} + \frac{y^2}{r^2} = \frac{r^2}{r^2}$$

Then since

$$\frac{r^2}{r^2} = 1$$

the equation of the circle becomes

$$\frac{x^2}{r^2} + \frac{y^2}{r^2} = 1$$

By comparing this equation with that of the ellipse, we can easily come to the conclusion that we are dealing with an ellipse of equal semimajor and semiminor axes.

One application in which the circle, ellipse and straight line are considered as being different cases of one another, occurs in electronics, when an oscilloscope *Lissajous pattern* is used to determine the phase relationship between two circuit waveshapes, such as current and voltage. Phase angles of 0° and 180° yield straight lines, and 90° and 270° phase separations produce a circle on the screen. All other phase angles between the two quantities being measured produce ellipses enclosing areas of different size. Several of the Lissajous configurations showing this application appear in Fig. 4-19.

4.38. A second orientation of the ellipse

In some applications it is convenient to have the ellipse oriented with its major axis on the Y axis and its minor axis on the X axis, as shown in Fig. 4-18d. This positioning yields the equation

$$\frac{x^2}{b^2} + \frac{y^2}{a^2} = 1$$

Note that this equation differs from the previous equation of the ellipse in the position of the a^2 and b^2 terms. When the vertices of the ellipse are on the Y axis, the a^2 appears below the y^2 term. Also, the b^2 term appears below x^2, showing that the minor axis of the ellipse is along the X axis. For example, if it were desired to sketch the curve whose equation is

$$\frac{x^2}{4} + \frac{y^2}{9} = 1$$

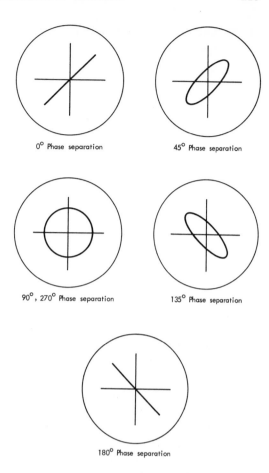

Fig. 4-19. Oscilloscope Lissajous patterns (the straight line, circle, and ellipse indicate different conditions of phase separation of input sine waveshapes)

we could first rewrite the equation as

$$\frac{x^2}{2^2} + \frac{y^2}{3^2} = 1$$

From the equation format we recognize an ellipse, of semimajor axis 3 units in length and semiminor axis of 2 units in length. Furthermore, since the smaller quantity appears below the x^2 term, we know that the minor axis of the ellipse is along the horizontal axis and that the major axis and the vertices are on the vertical axis. The vertical intercepts can now be marked off 3 units above and below the origin and the horizontal intercepts 2 units to the right and left of the origin. The balance of the ellipse can now readily be sketched in.

4.39. The ellipse redefined for application

The shape of the ellipse is readily determined by defining it as a section of a cone, but this definition does not accent its applicable properties. The ellipse can also be defined as the path described by a point moving in such a manner that the sum of its distances from two fixed points is always equal to a fixed length. The two points are known as the *foci*, or *focal points* (F_1 and F_2 of Fig. 4-20), and the fixed length is the length of the major axis ($2a$). An ellipse can very readily be produced by applying this definition, and the few minutes spent in carrying out the construction are very well rewarded. Proceed as follows:

1. Tap two small nails into a piece of wood or fiberboard, some inches apart, permitting the nails to protrude above the board. The nails will be the foci (F_1 and F_2) of the ellipse to be constructed.

2. Obtain a piece of string somewhat longer than the distance between the nails. Tie one end of the string to the protruding head of one of the nails and the other end to the second nail. The free length of the string between the two nails is the fixed distance referred to above and is equal to the major axis length of the ellipse to be drawn.

3. Place the point of a pencil against the string and pull it taut so that the string forms two straight lines that join at the pencil point. These straight lines could well be the lines F_2P_1 and P_1F_1 of Fig. 4-20. Point P_1 of the figure is the position of the pencil point; F_1 and F_2 are the focal-point positions of the two nails; and the lines joining these three points represents the string.

4. Travel the pencil in a generally clockwise manner, always keeping the string taut by holding the pencil against it. In this manner move the pencil around to points P_2, V_1, P_3, V_2 of Fig. 4-20 and back to the starting point P_1.

5. By the use of a compass or a pair of dividers, lay out on a straight line the distance F_1P_1 added to P_1F_2. Compare this total length with the length of the major axis V_1V_2 of the

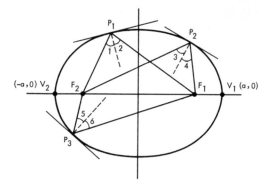

Fig. 4-20. Ellipse is locus of a point that moves so that the sum of its distances from two fixed points is always the same

ellipse just produced. Note that they are exactly equal.

6. Repeat this comparison of lengths for the sum of distances from the foci to any point on surface of the ellipse just drawn. Note that these distance sums are all equal to one another and to the length of the major axis.

As shown in Fig. 4-20, the two portions of the string make equal angles with a line drawn normal (perpendicular) to the ellipse at the pencil point. A line perpendicular to a curve is actually drawn perpendicular to the tangent to the curve at that point. Note, for example, point P_1 of Fig. 4-20. A tangent line is shown drawn to the ellipse at that point. The dotted line shown at P_1 is the *normal*, since it was drawn perpendicular to the tangent at the point P_1. The two portions of the string F_1P_1 and P_1F_2 make equal angles, angles 1 and 2, with this normal line. The same is true at points P_2, P_3, and all points on the surface of the ellipse. If these equal angles are considered an angle of incidence and an angle of reflection, we realize that any energy or object following one of these straight-line paths from a focal point to the surface of the ellipse will be reflected from the ellipse along the other straight line to the second focal point. For example, if a sound emanating from focal point F_1 is directed toward point P_3 on the ellipse, it will be reflected from the ellipse along the line P_3F_2 and will be heard by a listener at F_2. The room utilizing this property of the ellipse that is on display at the Chicago

Museum of Science and Industry is shown in Fig. 4-21. Applications of this characteristic of the ellipse are also based on reflected light and reflected moving objects such as billiard balls or steel spheres.

4.40. The parabola

Figure 4-22a shows a plane cutting through the right circular cone in such a manner that it runs parallel to a "line" of the cone surface and cuts through the circular base of that cone. A "line" of the cone surface is referred to above. Since the cone surface can be considered as being made up of an infinite number of lines, each line can be said to originate at the apex (peak) of the cone and terminate at a point on the circumference of the circular base. These lines are technically known as *elements* of the cone. *When a plane cuts through a right circular cone parallel to an element of that cone, it describes a parabola on the surface of the cone,* as shown in Fig. 4-22b. This curve can be shown on a set of cartesian coordinate axes in any one of an infinite number of locations and positions. However, as is the case with the other conic sections, when the curve is arranged symmetrically with respect to the axis, its equation is simplest and its properties are more readily observed and discussed.

Fig. 4-21. (a) "Whispering gallery" at Julius Rosenwald Museum of Science and Industry (major axis of this elliptical room is 47′4″ long, the minor axis 18′6″ long, and the foci—where the two men are standing—40′7″ apart). (b) The plan of the gallery (below)

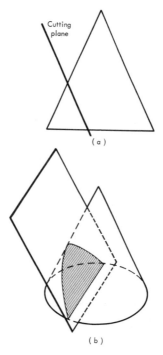

Fig. 4-22. Parabola is produced when cutting plane is parallel to an element of the cone

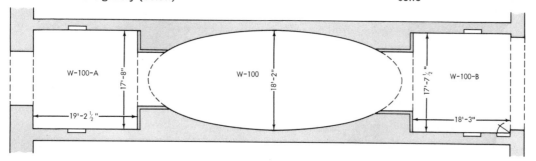

4.41. The simplest form of the equation of the parabola

Note the parabola shown in Fig. 4-23a. Here the parabola is shown with its vertex at the origin and opening to the right. Note also that the horizontal axis runs through the "center" of the curve so that equal portions of the curve appear above and below the axis. Regardless of the position and direction of opening of the parabola, a line can be drawn through the vertex of the parabola so that it separates the curve into two portions that are the mirror image of one another. This "line of symmetry" falls on the X axis in the orientation of Fig. 4-23a. *When the vertex of the parabola is at the origin, and its line of symmetry is on the X axis, and the parabola opens to the right, then its equation is* $y^2 = kx$. This is one of the simplest forms of the parabola's equation and is therefore the one most often used. The k term of the equation is a number that refers to the width or the opening of the parabola. The larger the value of k, the wider is the parabola. This constant is of considerable importance in applications of this curve and is referred to again in a later paragraph.

The only difference between the parabolas of Fig. 2-23a and 4-23b is the direction of opening of the curve. Note that the effect on the equation of this turning around of the parabola is the introduction of a minus sign. Thus, *when the parabola's line (or axis) of symmetry is on the X axis, and its vertex is at the origin, and the parabola opens to the left, then its equation is* $y^2 = -kx$. The minus sign, therefore, indicates the direction of opening of the parabola.

The parabola of Fig. 4-23c has no minus sign in its equation, since it opens in the positive direction, but its opening is in the positive Y direction, and as can be seen from the figure, the axis of symmetry of the parabola coincides with the Y direction in this position. The result is a slight change in the equation. *When the vertex or the parabola is at the origin, and its axis of symmetry is along the Y axis and opens upward, then its equation is* $x^2 = ky$. By comparing the three equations of

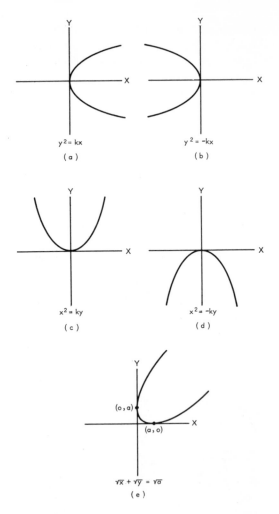

$y^2 = kx$
(a)

$y^2 = -kx$
(b)

$x^2 = ky$
(c)

$x^2 = -ky$
(d)

(o, a)

(a, o)

$\sqrt{x} + \sqrt{y} = \sqrt{a}$
(e)

Fig. 4-23. Parabola is often seen in any number of positions on cartesian coordinate axis

the parabola discussed so far, we can see that the position of the square exponent indicates which axis is the axis of symmetry. In Fig. 4-23b the curve is symmetrical to the X axis, but the y is the term that is squared. In Fig. 4-23c, the curve's axis of symmetry is along the Y axis and the x is the term that is squared. In Fig. 4-23b the X axis is again the curve's axis of symmetry, and again the exponent 2 appears over the y term. Here the curve opens in the negative direction, as signified by the minus sign of the equation. From these observations the equation of Fig. 4-23d can be written. Here we have a parabola opening in the negative direction; thus, a minus sign must appear in its equation. The vertex of the curve is at the origin, and its axis of symmetry is along the Y axis. This means that the square term will be the x. The equation therefore becomes $x^2 = -ky$.

4.42. Changing the equation

The simplified form of the equation discussed thus far is valid only if the parabola is positioned with its vertex at the origin and its line of symmetry on one of the axes. If the vertex is shifted to any other position, or if the parabola's axis of symmetry is in any position other than truly vertical or horizontal, then a considerable change occurs in the equation of the parabola. Note, for example, the position of the parabola in Fig. 4-23e. Here the curve is entirely in the first quadrant, the vertex is not at the origin, and the parabola's line of symmetry is not along the X or Y axis. Note the considerable difference in the form

of the equation shown for this position of the parabola as compared to the other four equations of Fig. 4-23. It is apparent that the "rules of recognition" that we discussed for the first four equations hold only for the specified conditions.

4.43. The parabola redefined for application

Probably the most common occurrence of the parabola is the curve described in the air by an object that is thrown or fired. If the effect of air friction is negligible, then the path of a projectile in air is a true parabola. A vivid demonstration accenting the parabolic path of projected objects was developed by H. M. Waage of Princeton University. A photograph of the result is shown in Fig. 4-24. A comparison of the curve of this figure with that of Fig. 4-23d shows readily that a plot of

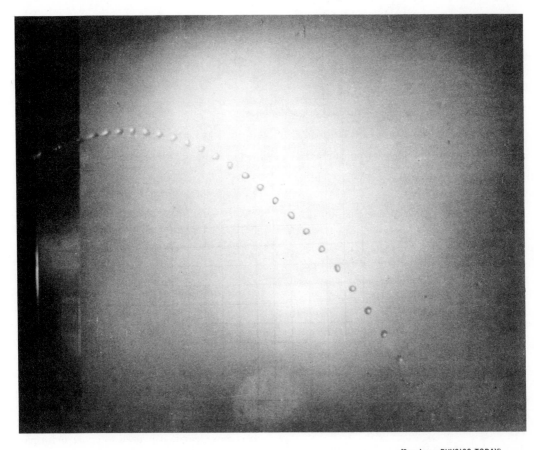

(Courtesy, PHYSICS TODAY)

Fig. 4-24. Pulsed water-drop parabola (water stream, displayed with strobe light, is broken into seemingly stationary drops)

(Courtesy, General Bronze Corp.)

Fig. 4-25a. Parabolic radio telescope antenna system

(Courtesy, Technical Appliance Corp., Sherburne, N. Y.)

Fig. 4-25b. A peep-sight is provided at the vertex of some large reflectors. Using the cross-hairs in the peepsight, the feed is accurately positioned at the focal point of the reflector and the antenna is oriented by sighting on distant objects.

the equation form $x^2 = -ky$ will yield the curve of an object in free flight.

As another example of common application, let us consider the "beaming" property of a parabola that is utilized in a headlight or spotlight, as well as the reverse "collecting" property of a parabola applied to radio telescopes and solar ovens. Some devices, like the 16-ft parabolic antenna shown in Fig. 4-25, can both "beam out" (transmit) radio energy and collect (receive) it.

Discussion of these properties centers around the *focal point* of the parabola. This point is not on the parabola itself but is critical to the development of a parabola as the locus of a moving point, much as the center is to a circle or the foci are to an ellipse.

Point F of Fig. 4-26 is a point chosen arbitrarily, and line AB is a line drawn at an arbi-

trary distance from that point. This combination of the point and line when used according to the "locus" definition of a parabola yields the parabolic curve of Fig. 4-26. The point F is known as the *focus* and the line AB as the *directrix*. The locus definition of a parabola states that *if all points on a curve are equidistant from a fixed point (focus) and a fixed line (directrix) then that curve is a parabola*. In other words, every one of the plotted points shown on the curve of Fig. 4-26 is the same distance from the focus, F, as it is from the directrix, line AB. As discussed in Chapter 2, the distance from a point to a line is measured along a perpendicular to that line. The locus definition of the parabola readily becomes clear if it is used to construct a parabola. A slight addition to such a construction points out the often-used beaming property of the parabola.

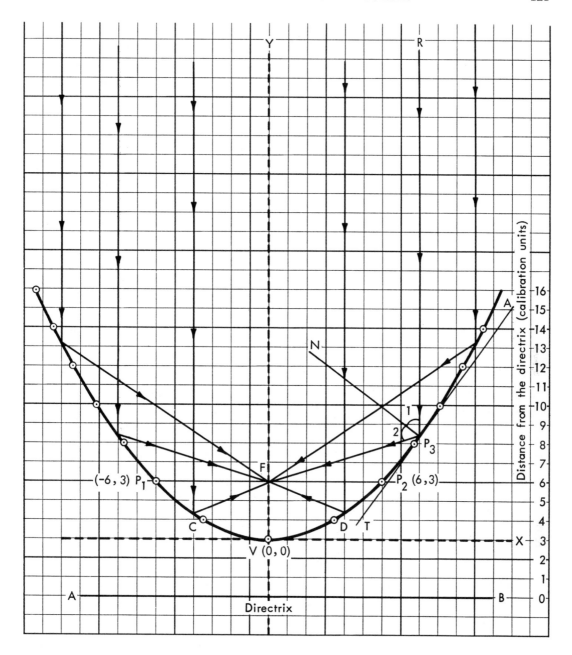

Fig. 4-26. If all points on a curve are equidistant from a fixed point and a straight line, then that curve is a parabola

4.44. The parabola constructed as the locus of a point

To follow the construction of Fig. 4-26 or to produce a parabola of your own, proceed as follows:

1. Start with a sheet of linear cartesian coordinate graph paper. The use of graph paper

is not essential. However, it will be necessary to measure perpendicular distances to a line, and because of the cartesian coordinate nature of the graph paper suggested, this operation will be much simplified.

2. Locate a point F to be used as the focal point. This point can be chosen absolutely arbitrarily. However, the construction will be

simplified if the point is chosen on an intersection of a pair of coordinate lines of the graph paper. Be certain to allow sufficient distance above, and on either side of, the focal point for the parabola itself.

3. At some distance from the focal point, F, draw a line AB to be used as the directrix of the parabola.

4. Draw a line through the focus, F, perpendicular to the directrix line AB. Extend this line in both directions. The line just drawn is the *principal axis* of the parabola (shown broken line in Fig. 4-26), and is the *line of symmetry* of the curve. This means that the curve produced on one side of the axis will have its "mirror image" on the other side of the axis.

5. Locate a point halfway between the focus, F, and the directrix, AB, along the axis of the parabola. Since each point on the parabola is an equal distance from the focus and from the directrix, the point just located is on the parabola. Since it is also on the axis of symmetry, this point is the vertex of the parabola and should be labeled V. From our earlier discussion we know that the simplest form of the equation of the parabola is produced when the vertex of this curve is at the origin of the X-Y axes. For this reason the coordinates of the vertex V are shown in Fig. 4-26 as $(0, 0)$. The coordinate axes are also shown. The axes and the coordinates of the vertex are not, however, an integral part of the parabola construction.

6. The next few steps of the construction involve measurement of distances from the focus and from the directrix. This procedure will be considerably simplified if the unit of distance is taken as the distance between a successive pair of calibration lines of the graph paper. Therefore, number on the graph paper at least 16 unit distances from the directrix. These distance units are shown numbered at the right in the diagram of Fig. 4-26. Note that the directrix is taken as the 0 distance position for these measurements.

7. Open a compass to 4 distance units as measured along the distance scale.

8. Place the point of the compass at the focus, F, and strike an arc on both sides of F on the number 4 line. The two points, C and D, produced by the intersection of the arcs and the number 4 line, are on the parabola. The points are 4 units distant from the directrix, since they are on the 4 line, and they are 4 units distant from F, since they were so set with the compass. The points C and D thus satisfy the requirement that they be equidistant from the directrix and the focus and are necessarily points on the parabola.

9. Repeat this procedure for distances of 6, 8, 10, 12, 14, and 16 units. The result will be the location of the 15 points on the parabola as shown in Fig. 4-26. Draw a small "locating circle" around each of these points.

10. Connect these points, using a curve guide, to obtain the parabolic curve. If no guide is at hand, locate 14 additional distance points by using 3, 5, 7, 9, 11, and 13 units and carefully connect the located points freehand. The positions of the points that yielded the parabola are still apparent after the curve is drawn because of the small "locating circles" drawn around each point.

4.45. The latus rectum

From the position of the constructed parabola on the axes (Fig. 4-26), we know its equation to be of the general form $x^2 = ky$, but here we have a specific parabola constructed on the basis of a definite focus and directrix. The general equation should therefore be made into a specific one that defines this particular parabola and no other. This means that the numerical value of k that applies to the parabola constructed is required. As described earlier, the k term of the equation determines the "width" of the parabola. Since the curve continues to widen as we go further from the vertex, the "width" must be measured at the same predetermined position for all parabolas. This measurement is made at the focus and is shown in Fig. 4-26 as line P_1FP_2. This line length, drawn through the focus, F, parallel to the directrix and terminated at each end by the parabola, is the "width" of the parabola. It is known as the *latus rectum* (straight line). The length of the latus rectum is the k term of the parabola. Since the line P_1FP_2 is 12 units long, the equation of the parabola shown is $x^2 = 12y$. Let's test this equation with the coordinates of the end points of the latus rectum, P_1 and P_2, that can be read from the graph sheet. As noted, the coordinates of P_2 are $x = 6$ and $y = 3$. If these values are substituted in the equation written for this parabola we obtain

$$x^2 = 12y$$
$$6^2 = 12(3)$$
$$36 = 36$$

A similar check can be carried out with the coordinates of point P_1 that are read from the graph sheet as $(-6, 3)$. Thus, we obtain

$$x^2 = 12y$$
$$(-6)^2 = 12(3)$$
$$36 = 36$$

Since the equation checks, we know that any point on the parabola can now be found by substituting a value for x into the equation and solving for the corresponding y value. Therefore, without additional construction the curve can be extended out as far as desired.

4.46. "Beaming" and "collecting"

As mentioned earlier, a single additional construction will clarify a significant characteristic of the parabola. Consider that a ray of light, or any other form of energy, is directed at the inner surface of the parabola parallel to the axis of the parabola. Such a ray is represented by the line marked R in Fig. 4-26. This line strikes the parabola at point P_3 and makes an angle of incidence, angle 1, with the normal, N, to the parabola. The normal, N, is the line drawn perpendicular to the tangent line, TA. Light, or any form of energy, will reflect from a surface so that its angle of reflection, angle 2, from the normal is exactly the same as its angle of incidence, angle 1, with the normal. In the case of the parabola, this will cause the reflected ray to go directly to the focus of the parabola.

To verify this by construction,

1. Draw a tangent line to any point on the constructed parabola, such as point P_3 of Fig. 4-26.

2. Draw a normal (perpendicular) to the tangent line (TA) at this point (P_3).

3. Draw a "ray line" (R), parallel to the axis of the parabola, to the point P_3. This line makes the incident angle (angle 1) with the normal.

4. With a compass mark off this angle and reproduce an equal angle on the other side of the normal. This is the reflection angle (angle 2).

5. Extend the leg of the angle (angle 2) just constructed and note that it goes directly to the focus (F).

6. Repeat this construction for any other point on the parabola and note that it produces the same result.

Thus, light energy, radio-wave energy, or any other form will be concentrated at the focal point of the parabola, where a receiving device can be located. But under what conditions does energy enter the parabola parallel to its principal axis? This occurs whenever the energy is being received from a far distant point, such as the sun in the case of a solar oven or a distant transmitter as in the case of a receiving antenna. Refer again to the antenna of Fig. 4-25. Can you recognize a parabolic curve and the position of its focal point? We now know what is meant by the "collecting" property of a parabola, but how does a parabola produce a beam?

The parabola is used to produce an energy beam merely by reversing the direction of energy flow. Suppose light or radio wave energy is emitted or radiated from the focus (F), what happens to it then? To answer this question, merely consider the direction arrows of Fig. 4-26 to be in the reverse direction. Now, angle 2 becomes the angle of incidence and its equal angle, 1, the angle of reflection. The reflected rays travel out of the parabola parallel to the axis of the parabola. Since such a ray will reflect from every point on the inner surface of the parabola, an energy beam will be formed. Flashlight and auto headlight reflectors are probably the most commonly seen application of this property of the parabola. Can the same parabola be used for both its beam-forming and energy-collecting properties? The answer is, Yes, as long as only one direction of energy transfer is used at a time. Thus, the parabolic antenna shown in Fig. 4-25 is used for both transmission and reception of radiofrequency energy, but at different periods of time.

4.47. The hyperbola

The three conic sections discussed thus far are produced by a plane cutting through a right circular cone of one nappe. However, to produce a complete hyperbola, a two-nappe cone (Fig. 4-16e) is required. As depicted in Fig. 4-27, a hyperbola is produced when the cutting plane passes through the two nappes of the cone so that it is perpendicular to the bases of the two nappes. The plane orientation can also be expressed as being parallel to the axis of the cone. Note, however, that the plane should not pass through the axis of the cone. In such a case, the resulting curve will be a pair of intersecting straight lines, where the point of intersection is the apex of the cone. By comparing the position of the cutting plane shown in Fig. 4-27a with those yielding the other conic sections, we see that only in the case of the hyperbola is the plane in such a position that it can cut both nappes of the cone. Since in the first three cases only is one nappe involved in producing the conic section, the second nappe of the right circular cone is not shown or considered.

Each of the two nappes of the right circular cone of Fig. 4-27b is cut by the plane in the same manner. Therefore, the resulting curve of intersection, the hyperbola, is made up of two similar sections that are the mirror image of one another. Here again, as is the case of the three preceding conic sections, it is possible to express this curve in the form of an equation that will permit us to sketch or plot the hyperbola whenever application

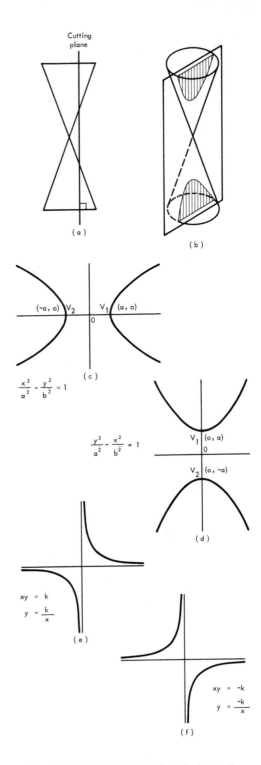

Fig. 4-27. Hyperbola is produced when cutting plane passes through both nappes of cone perpendicular to bases

requires. And again, as with the other conic sections, the equation can be made a relatively simple one by properly orienting the hyperbola with respect to the axes. Some strong similarities to a previous discussion will be noted here; but some significant and useful differences will also become apparent.

4.48. Equations of the hyperbola

If the hyperbola is oriented on the axes so that its vertices are on the X axis, a distance a on either side of the origin, then the equation of the hyperbola becomes

$$\frac{x^2}{a^2} - \frac{y^2}{b^2} = 1$$

The distance $2a$ between the two vertices is known as the *transverse axis* of the hyperbola and can be seen, from Fig. 4-27c, to be an axis of symmetry; that is, the curve on one side of this axis is the mirror image of the curve on the other side. Note that the equation given for the hyperbola is very similar to that of the ellipse. The only difference is the sign between the two terms. Recall that the ellipse has two axes of symmetry and one had a length of $2a$, as we have here with the hyperbola. The length of the second axis of the ellipse is $2b$ and is also an axis of symmetry for the ellipse. Since the equation of the hyperbola is very similar to that of the ellipse, does the hyperbola have a second axis?

Yes, the hyperbola does have a second axis, and its length is also $2b$, as in the case of the ellipse. It is known as the *conjugate axis* and, as in the ellipse, is perpendicular to the other axis at the origin. Figure 4-28 shows how the conjugate axis, together with the transverse axis, determines the hyperbola defined by a specific equation. To follow the procedure for producing the hyperbola from information contained within the equation let us start with the equation

$$\frac{x^2}{36} - \frac{y^2}{16} = 1$$

To put the equation in the form shown previously, we can write

$$\frac{x^2}{6^2} - \frac{y^2}{4^2} = 1$$

The equation tells us that the semitransverse axis a is 6 units long. Thus, one vertex is 6 units to the right of the origin, and the other is 6 units to the left, on the X axis. Note from Fig. 4-27 that the vertices V_1 and V_2 are so located. From the equation we can see also that the semiconjugate axis b is 4 units long. Thus, a distance of 4 units is marked off above the origin and below it to yield points $B_1(0, b)$ and $B_2(0, -b)$. The line drawn between these two points is the conjugate axis, $2b$ units in length. To draw the two nappes of the hyperbola, it is necessary first to draw a rectangle whose width is $2a$ and height $2b$. Thus, the rectangle shown in the figure is 12 units wide (2×6) and 8 units high (2×4). *The extended diagonals of this rectangle are the asymptotes of the hyperbola.* Since the hyperbola is known to approach its asymptotes rapidly, it is a simple matter to sketch the two nappes of the curve once the vertices are located and the asymptotes drawn. This was done to produce the curves of Fig. 4-28. The hyperbola is the only one of the four conics we have discussed that has asymptotes, and every hyperbola has two.

If Fig. 4-28 is examined again, it will be noticed that one feature of this diagram has not been discussed here as yet. The significance of the a and b values have been described as has the method for drawing the asymptotes and sketching the curve. However, the diagram also shows a c length. This length is half the length of the diagonals of the rectangle formed by the transverse and conjugate axes. Note also that c is the hypotenuse of the right triangle OSV_1, whose legs are the semitransverse axis a and the semiconjugate axis b. If this distance c is measured along the x axis to the right and to the left of the origin, it locates the two focal points of the hyperbola. These points will be referred to again when the hyperbola is redefined as a locus of a moving point and will be shown to be critically significant in many applications of the hyperbola. Since c is the hypotenuse of a right triangle, the sides of which are known, the value of c can be determined. From the Pythagorean

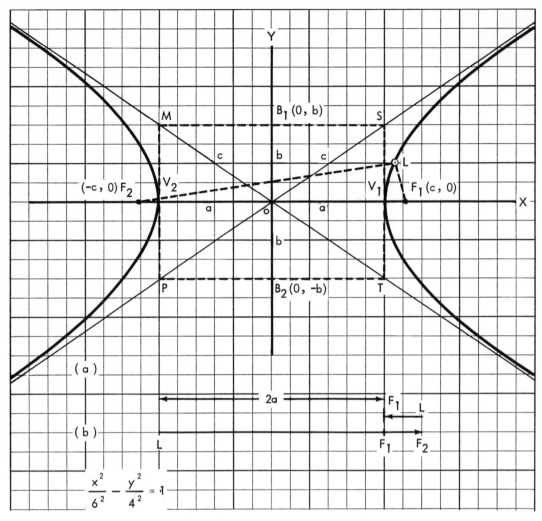

Fig. 4-28. Conjugate axis, together with transverse axis, determines hyperbola defined by a specific equation

Theorem we have $c^2 = a^2 + b^2$. Thus, for the hyperbola of Fig. 4-28,

$$c^2 = 6^2 + 4^2$$
$$c^2 = 36 + 16$$
$$c^2 = 52$$
$$c = 7.2$$

Thus, the *focal length* of the hyperbola shown is 7.2 units, measured from the origin. The foci can more accurately be located, however, if a compass or pair of dividers is opened to the length c shown in the figure and this distance marked off to the right and to the left

of the origin. This latter procedure was used in the figure to locate the focal points.

As with the other curves, the hyperbola can be oriented in several positions on the axes and still produce a relatively simple equation. Figure 4-27d shows a second position of the hyperbola. This position places the vertices on the Y axis. This means that the transverse axis $(2a)$ is along the Y axis. The equation incorporates this information by placing the a^2 below the y^2 and shows this term before the minus sign. The equation for this position of the hyperbola is

$$\frac{y^2}{a^2} - \frac{x^2}{b^2} = 1$$

4.49. The equilateral hyperbola

A special case of the hyperbola is produced when the transverse and conjugate axes are the same length. Under this condition the rectangle *SMPT* of Fig. 4-28 becomes square, since the width (2*a*) is now equal to the height (2*b*). Furthermore, the asymptotes, which are extensions of the diagonals of this rectangle, become perpendicular to one another because the diagonals of a square are known to be the perpendicular bisectors of each other. *A hyperbola with equal axes and thus with perpendicular asymptotes is known as an equilateral hyperbola.*

If an equilateral hyperbola is now rotated 45° counterclockwise from the curve position shown in Fig. 4-27*c*, its asymptotes coincide with the *X* and *Y* axes, and the hyperbola is positioned as shown in Fig. 4-27*e*. Note that the curve is now entirely in the first and third quadrants. Under this condition the equation of the hyperbola becomes

$$xy = K$$

where *K* represents the total distance between the two focal points and can therefore also be represented as 2*c*. If an equilateral hyperbola is rotated 45° in the clockwise direction from the curve position shown in Fig. 4-27*c*, its asymptotes will again coincide with the *X* and *Y* axes, but the nappes of the hyperbola will be in the second and fourth quadrants as shown in Fig. 4-27*f*. Under this condition the curve equation form becomes

$$xy = -K$$

where *K* again represents the distance between the two focal points, 2*c*.

4.50. The hyperbola as a reciprocal function

In many applications the hyperbola is considered a *reciprocal function*. This designation stems from the form of equation of the equilateral hyperbola. Starting with the equation $xy = K$ and dividing both sides of the equation by *x*, we obtain $y = K/x$. Since *x*

is in the denominator, we can say that *y* is proportional to the reciprocal of *x*. If we are dealing with the special case where $K = 1$, then the equation becomes $y = 1/x$. Here *y* is not only *proportional* to the reciprocal of *x*, it is *equal* to the reciprocal of *x*. In the same manner the equation $xy = K$ can be written $x = K/y$. Two equations of this form with which the reader may be familiar are (1) the Boyle's Law equation relating the pressure, *P*, and volume, *V*, of a gas under constant temperature conditions, $PV = K$ (Fig. 2-16); and (2) the expression that relates the reactance of a capacitor (X_c) to the frequency, *f*, of operation of the circuit, $X_c = 1/2\pi f C$. So many relationships of this type exist throughout technology that a special graph paper has been developed on which such relationships can very readily be plotted. The graph paper is known as "hyperbolic," or "reciprocal ruling," paper (Fig. 4-29) and is designed to yield a *straight line* when the equation of a hyperbola is plotted cn it.

The advantages of such graph paper become apparent when we consider the relative ease with which a straight line can be drawn as compared with a hyperbola. To draw an accurate straight line only two points are required. Certainly a plot of three points will verify graphically that the equation yields a true straight line. A hyperbola can either be sketched from the asymptotes and vertices and possibly one or two additional points from the equation, or it can be plotted out entirely by producing a table of values from the equation. In either case, less accuracy and more work results than in the accurate plotting of a straight line. Consider now reading information back from a plot. Certainly no curve yields information as readily and accurately as a straight line. Let us follow through one example of an application of hyperbolic paper to gain some insight into its use.

4.51. Use of the reciprocal ruling graph paper

The equation $PV = 100$ can apply to a cylinder and piston arrangement in which the

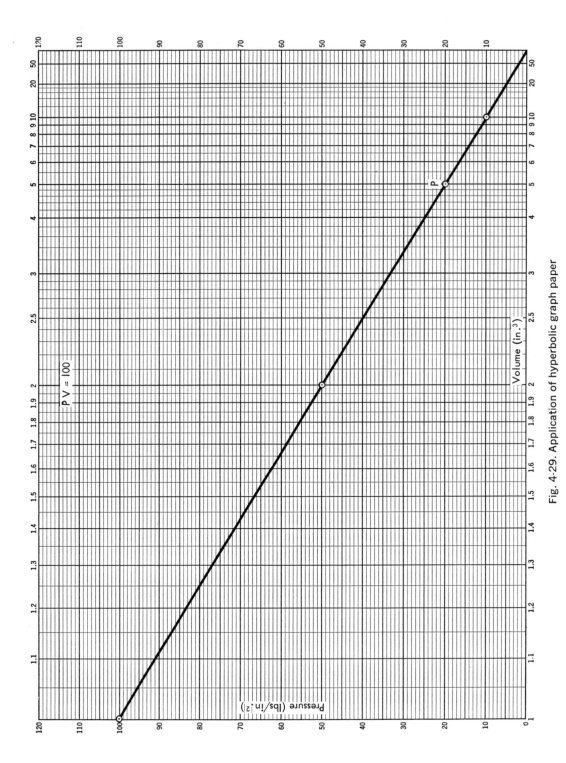

Fig. 4-29. Application of hyperbolic graph paper

volume is varied in order to produce different pressure conditions. Note that the temperature is not shown as such in the equation and is therefore considered to be constant and part of the K value of 100. Since the volume is varied in order to produce different pressure conditions, we can say that the volume is the independent quantity and will therefore appear on the horizontal axis. This makes pressure the dependent quantity, which will appear on the vertical axis. Now for a table of values to plot the curve. However, we are interested in using the reciprocal ruling paper, since it will yield a straight line for a reciprocal (hyperbolic) relationship. Therefore, our table of values will be a very short one. Two points are minimum, and we'll add one point for good measure. Starting with the equation $P = 100/V$, let us choose three values for V and calculate P. To make matters simple, let's choose 1, 2, and 10 for V, calculate P and put the results in tabular form as shown in Table 4-3.

Table 4-3.

V (in.^{3})	1	2	10
$P \dfrac{\text{lbs}}{\text{in}^2}$	100	50	10

Since we have determined which quantities to put on the horizontal axis and which on the vertical, and since we have a table of values, all that remains is the calibration of the axes and the plotting of the points that yield the graph. Carefully examine the hyperbolic paper (Fig. 4-29) to be used for this plot. Although it is called hyperbolic, or reciprocal ruling, paper we can see by looking along the axes that it is truly *semihyperbolic paper*. Only one of the two axes shows the nonuniform, reciprocal calibration; the other is linearly (uniformly) calibrated. For this plot let us choose the reciprocal ruling as the independent axis and put volume on this axis. The linear axis therefore becomes the dependent axis, and pressure quantities will be plotted on this axis. Note that the calibration numbers for both axes are printed on the paper by the manufacturer, and for this example they fit our

table of values most satisfactorily. (A case in which the calibration numbers provided are not so well suited to the problem will be discussed in a later paragraph.) Only one calibration number is missing on the paper as printed and that is the first calibration number of the nonlinear axis. This value cannot be zero, since we are dealing with a reciprocal equation. If we have an x value of 0, the y value is $1/0$, which is equal to infinity. No such value can be indicated on a scale. Therefore, since we are using the horizontal calibration numbers provided without change, this first calibration number of the horizontal axis should be 1, and was therefore so marked.

The next step is labeling the axes with names and units and then plotting the points. The three plotted points are marked with small location circles and are connected to yield the straight line of Fig. 4-29. This line will now readily yield information without the use of the equation. At what volume will the cylinder pressure be 20 psi (pounds per square inch)? To find the answer from the graph, locate a point on the line that has a vertical coordinate (pressure) of 20 psi and read the corresponding volume on the horizontal axis. This point, P, is marked on the plot, and its abscissa (volume) value is 5 in.^{3}. Other corresponding conditions of pressure and volume for the cylinder of our example can just as readily be found from the graph, even though they may involve decimal or fractional values of pressure or volume. Thus, this straight line plot will permit rapid prediction of conditions which could not be nearly so easily accomplished with the equation or with a plot of the hyperbola on uniformly calibrated graph paper.

4.52. Extending the use of reciprocal ruling

Hyperbolic papers are often precalibrated; that is, the calibration numbers are printed on the paper by the manufacturer. If these numbers are used as given, they will determine whether the reciprocal ruling will be the X or Y axis. Note that the direction increase of the calibration numbers in the graph paper of Fig. 4-29 requires that the horizontal axis be the reciprocal ruling and the vertical axis the linear one.

It is possible to reverse this arrangement by recalibrating the linearly ruled axis. If it is desired to treat the reciprocal axis as the vertical and the linear axis as the horizontal, then the printed numbers on the linear axis are disregarded or crossed out and the axis recalibrated with the numbers increasing in the reverse direction from that shown originally. This change is depicted in Fig. 4-30. *Only the uniformly calibrated axis can be treated in this manner.* No change in the direction of increase of the calibration numbers is possible for the hyperbolic ruling.

Figure 4-30 is a plot of the same relationship, $PV = 100$, that yielded the line of Fig. 4-29. Note the significant differences between the two plots. In Fig. 4-30 the independent axis on which volume is shown is the linear (uniform) axis. The vertical (pressure) axis is the one with hyperbolic ruling. In order to put the volume calibration numbers on the horizontal axis, it was necessary to cross out the calibration numbers printed on the graph paper and to put in the required range of from 0 to 10 in.[3] Note that the direction of increasing values for the newly calibrated horizontal axis is just the reverse of the calibration direction originally printed on the graph paper. Changes in calibration numbers were also necessary on the vertical axis. However, the change was only in the position of the decimal point or, if you will, in the power of 10. No change in the direction of increase of the calibration numbers can be made on the axis showing the reciprocal ruling. Each of the calibration numbers on the vertical axis is increased by a factor of 10 from that originally shown on the graph paper. To accomplish this change of scale, the first number on the reciprocal (vertical) scale is shown as 10 (instead of 1) and each printed number is shown increased by a factor of 10. The points plotted are taken from Table 4-3 and are therefore the same as those plotted in Fig. 4-29. The resulting line, shown in Fig. 4-30,

can be seen to provide the same information as that of Fig. 4-29 but with a line of seemingly larger negative slope. However, in this application there is no advantage to changing the axes, and this is often the case. Personal preference and special applications do require the change on occasion, and in such cases the outlined procedure should be followed. The change in the *magnitude* of the given calibration numbers is a common necessity and is not related to the interchange of the axes.

Figure 4-31 illustrates an important application of hyperbolic graph paper as a tremendous time-saving device. It is common knowledge that the cost for electrical energy is proportional inversely to the amount used in a specified period of time. Expressing this in equation form,

$$AR = K/DR$$

where

$AR =$ Average rate, in cents per kilowatt-hour

$DR =$ Demand rate, in hours use per month

$K =$ constant of proportionality.

We thus have a reciprocal relationship, which yields an equilateral hyperbola when plotted on linear paper. However, plotted on reciprocal ruling, the equation yields a straight line. Furthermore, as the number of hours of energy use increases per month, the constant of proportionality, K, changes at certain specified points. This means that each equation is valid for only a certain range of values. It is apparent that if monthly bills for each consumer of electrical energy are to be computed longhand, the amount of time involved for these calculations would be tremendous. Instead, a reciprocal ruling plot is used on which the several straight lines are drawn to represent the decreasing rates with use.

Using the assumed rates shown plotted in Fig. 4-31, let us determine the average rate per kilowatt-hour for a customer who used electrical energy for 150 hours in a particular month. To make this evaluation, follow the horizontal (Demand rate) axis to 150 and then the ordinate line to the plotted line. The

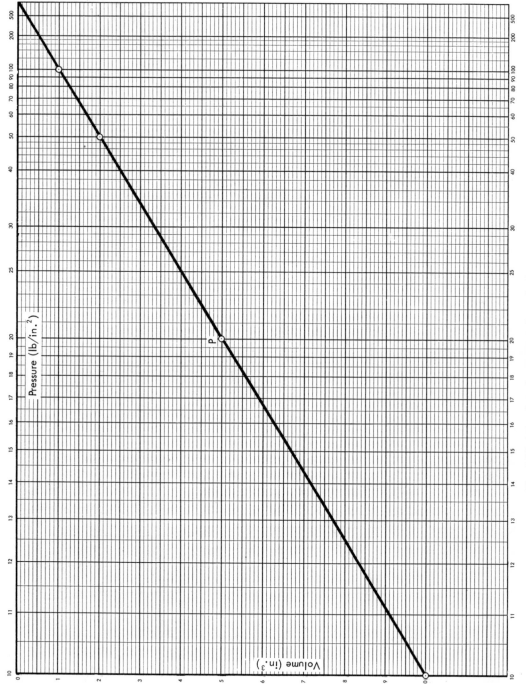

Fig. 4-30. Interchanging axes on hyperbolic graph paper

ENERGY RATE CALCULATION PLOT

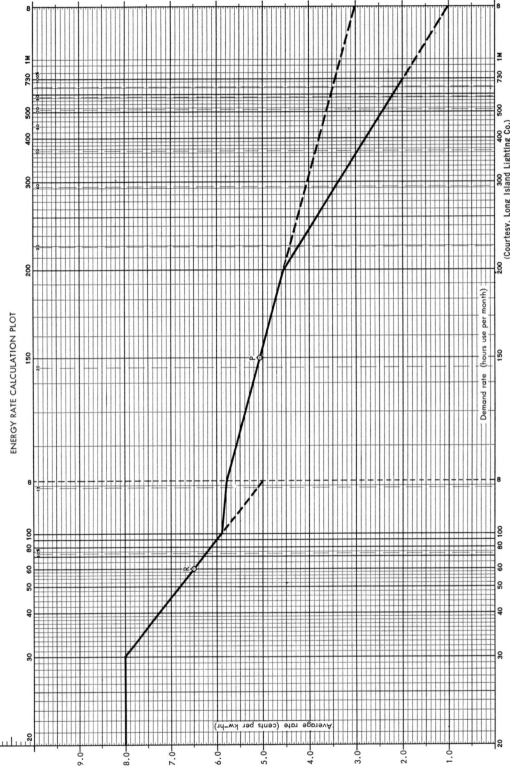

Fig. 4-31. Important application of hyperbolic graph paper (all rates and quantities shown are assumed values)

(Courtesy, Long Island Lighting Co.)

point thus found is specified as P on the plot. The ordinate value of this point is the desired rate, and it is read as 5.07 cents per kilowatt-hour. If this rate is multiplied by the actual number of kilowatt-hours, let us say 40 kilowatt-hours, we obtain a total cost of

$$\text{Cost} = 5.07 \, \frac{\text{cents}}{\text{kw-hr}} \times 40 \, \text{kw-hr}$$
$$= 202.80 \text{ cents}$$
$$= \$2.03$$

Let us use the plot to make the same type of evaluation for a consumer who uses 40 kilowatt-hours of electrical energy at a rate of only 60 kilowatt-hours for the entire month. His average rate is shown as point R on the plot of Fig. 4-31 and is read to be 6.5 cents per kilowatt-hour. Computing his cost,

$$\text{Cost} = 6.5 \, \frac{\text{cents}}{\text{kw-hr}} \times 40 \, \text{kw-hr}$$
$$= 260 \text{ cents}$$
$$= \$2.60$$

The 40 kilowatt-hour figure used in these calculations is the information read from the watt-hour meters installed in the home, office, or plant of each energy purchaser.

4.53. The hyperbola as the locus of a moving point

Our discussion of some of the applications of the parabola and ellipse centered around the focal points of these curves. The hyperbola is no exception. To appreciate many of its applications, particularly in the fields of acoustics, optics, and navigation, requires understanding the properties of the curve as related to its focal points. *For* these purposes *the hyperbola is defined as the path described by a point that moves so that the difference of its distances from two fixed points is a constant value.* The two fixed points referred to in this definition are the focal points (F_1 and F_2 of Fig. 4-28), and the constant value is the distance $2a$ between the vertices of the hyperbola. To apply the definition to point L on the right-hand nappe of the hyperbola of Fig. 4-28, the distance from focal point F_2 to point L on the curve is first measured off. This length is shown drawn below the hyperbola as the length of line between the point L at the left end of

the horizontal line and F_2 at the right end. Next, the distance from curve point L to focal point F_1 is measured. If this distance LF_1 is measured off on the horizontal line of Fig. 4-28b by starting from F_2 and measuring to the left, the point F_1 can be located on the line as shown in the diagram. By this procedure we have in effect subtracted the length LF_1 from length LF_2. The resulting length can readily be seen to be equal to the distance between the two vertices, since the line of Fig. 4-28b starts directly below vertex V_2 of the hyperbola, and the endpoint of the subtraction falls directly below the other vertex, V.

That the definition holds is most obvious when we consider one of the vertices as the point on the curve to be tested. If vertex, V_2, of Fig. 4-28a is taken as the point on the curve, then its two distances to the foci are subtracted from one another, the result will be the length of the line from V_1 to V_2. This means that distance V_2F_2 is to be subtracted from V_2F_1; but since V_2F_2 equals V_1F_1, the result of this subtraction is necessarily the distance V_1V_2 between the two vertices, most often designated as $2a$.

4.54. Constructing the hyperbola by applying the locus definition

The meaning of the locus definition and the significance of the focal points becomes readily apparent when we carry out a simple construction similar to that described for the ellipse in an earlier discussion. To carry out this construction, proceed as follows:

1. Place two tacks or nails into a piece of fiberboard or other rigid drawing surface, some inches apart. Permit a small space to remain between the tack head and the drawing surface. The tack position will become the focal points of the hyperbola; therefore, label them F_1 and F_2.

2. Obtain a long piece of string, and loop it around F_2.

3. Hold both free ends of the string in one hand, and place both strands of the string over the F_1 tack.

4. With the other hand, place a pencil point within the string loop and pull one strand of

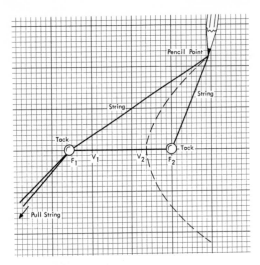

Fig. 4-32. Drawing a hyperbola using "locus definition" (materials needed are two thumbtacks, piece of string, and sheet of paper)

the string some distance away from the focal point. The string now forms the triangle F_1PF_2 as shown in Fig. 4-32.

5. Keep the string taut with the pencil point and slowly pull downward the two string strands that go over the F_1 tack. The pencil point will trace out half of one nappe of the hyperbola.

6. When the two strands of string come together, the pencil point will be at the vertex of the hyperbola nappe. Use the pencil point to pull the other strand of string some distance below the horizontal axis.

7. Pull the string taut again. Then pull slowly downward the two strands that slide over the F_1 tack. The second half of that same hyperbola nappe will be traced out.

8. How would you produce the second nappe of this same hyperbola?

9. Test any point on the hyperbola just completed by applying the "difference of distance" definition, described in the previous paragraph.

From this construction and check, it becomes apparent that the total length of string decreases continuously (unlike the construction of the ellipse), but the difference between F_1P and F_2P (where P is any point on the hyperbola) is always equal to the distance between the two vertices.

4.55. The hyperbola as a navigational aid

The properties of the hyperbola that show up in the construction described above are applied directly as a navigational aid in the American loran system and the British "gee" system, both of which are forms of *hyperbolic navigation*. In each case it is necessary to draw two sets of hyperbolas on a navigational chart. The two hyperbolas intersect at two different points. One of these points is the location of the ship or aircraft. The two points of intersection of the curves are so far apart that it is obvious to the navigator which of the two points represents his location.

To construct the two nappes of a hyperbola, we have seen that it is necessary to have two focal-point locations and a fixed distance $(2a)$, which is always the difference between the distance measured from a point on the curve to the two focal points. In navigation, the focal points are the positions of two radio transmitters that send out signals for hyperbolic navigation. These positions are accurately shown on the navigation charts. To determine its position, a ship receives signals from two different radio transmitters. The fixed distance, $2a$, can be found by the navigator if he accurately notes the time at which a signal is received from radio transmitter 1 and from radio transmitter 2. If the difference in these two times is multiplied by the travel speed of the radio signals in air, the result is the fixed difference distance, $2a$. Knowing the focal points and the fixed length $2a$, a hyperbola similar to that shown in Fig. 4-33a can be plotted on the navigation charts. However, this is insufficient, since the ship location could be at any point on either of the two nappes of the hyperbola. A second set of radio signals from the two transmitters of a second station can now be used in the same manner. The solid curve of Fig. 4-33b represents the curve drawn from the transmitter, 1' and 2' information. The ship is known to be located somewhere on this second curve also. If the two hyperbolas are drawn on the same navigational chart, as shown on Fig. 4-33b, then the points of intersection will give the desired location. Since

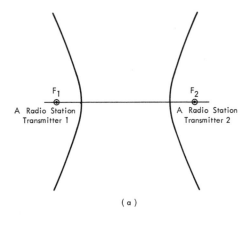

(a)

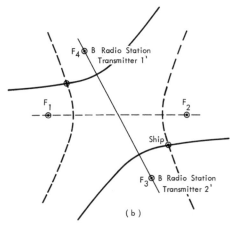

(b)

Fig. 4-33. Hyperbolic navigation depicted

the curves will intersect at two different points, it is necessary to determine which of the two is the correct location of the ship or aircraft. However, if the focal point stations are properly chosen, the two points of intersection will be so far apart that the selection of the proper point poses no problem at all.

It should be pointed out here that the difference between the loran system of hyperbolic navigation and the "gee" system is that the loran system uses two entirely different sets of focal-point stations to obtain the two hyperbolas. In the "gee" system, one of the two transmitters used to obtain the first hyperbola is used as part of a second pair of focal-point transmitters. In this manner, three focal points are required in order to draw the two sets of curves. Modern navigational systems provide charts with the hyperbolas already drawn for different focal point and $2a$ conditions as well

as overlays on which the proper curve lines can be traced. An example of a loran chart is shown in Fig. 4-34. Use of these improvements results in appreciable time savings in the application of the hyperbola to navigation.

4.56. Acoustical and optical properties of the hyperbola

Have you ever taken a careful look at the curved bandshell used in outdoor theatres or dance areas? If you have, the curved surface you saw was most probably hyperbolic in shape. The reason for this is that a hyperbolic surface causes divergence of rays or waves that emanate from its focus. The diagram of Fig. 4-35 will help clarify this property. If a sound wave or light ray is emitted from focal point F_1 of the diagram, it travels to a point on the inner surface of the hyperbola. The angle α shown is the angle of incidence that the wave direction makes with the normal line N at the surface of the hyperbola. Since the angle of reflection equals the angle of incidence, the sound (or light) bounces off the curved surface and makes an equal angle (α_r) with the normal, as shown in the diagram. *If this reflected ray line or wave direction is extended backwards, it will pass through the other focus of the hyperbola.* This construction holds for every point on the curve. In other words, if we look into the hyperbola from any point to the right of F_1, it will seem as if the sound (or light) is coming from the other focal point F_2. Obviously, therefore, any energy rays or waves, sound, light or others, will fan out and cover a large volume if they start at the focus of a hyperbolic shell. A bandshell hyperbolic in shape therefore causes the sound and light from its stage to reach a large or somewhat dispersed audience.

4.57. Other applications of the hyperbola

The previous discussions of the hyperbolic curve and its properties indicate the extent to which this curve is useful in science and technology. To accent further this wide range of applicability, note the funnel-shaped structure shown in Fig. 4-36a. These are hyperbolic out-

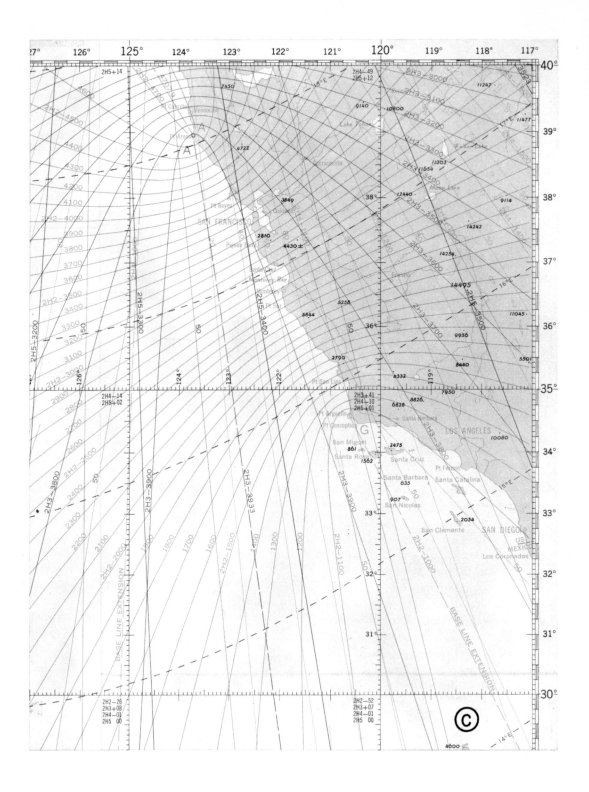

Fig. 4-34. Portion of typical Loran chart

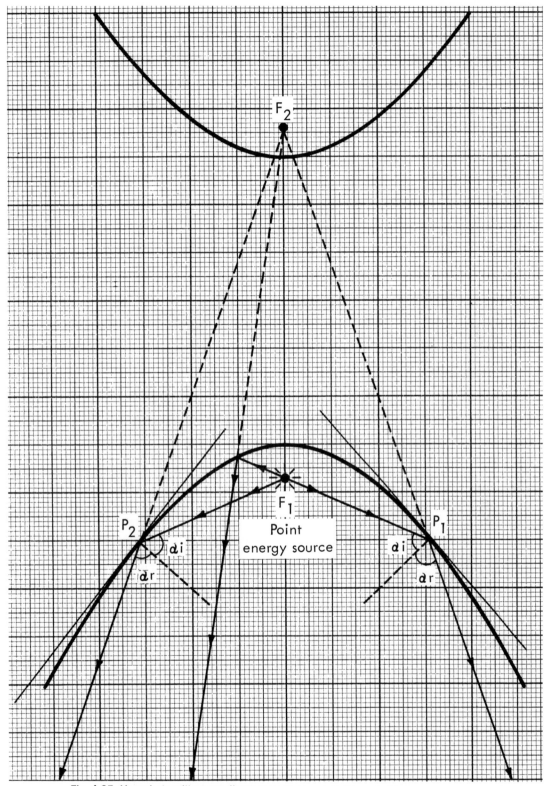

Fig. 4-35. Hyperbola will cause divergence of sound, light, and other energy rays
that start at focal point, F_1

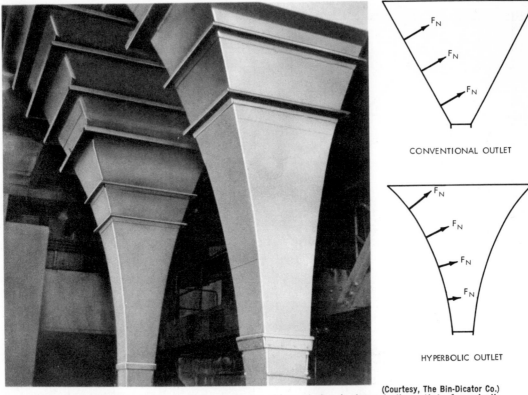

CONVENTIONAL OUTLET

HYPERBOLIC OUTLET

(Courtesy, The Bin-Dicator Co.)

Fig. 4-36. Application of asymptotic character of hyperbolas (a: hyperbolic outlets from bulk material hoppers; b: comparison of normal forces exerted by hyperbolic outlet and conventional one)

lets used to minimize flow restriction when granular or lump materials are transferred or emptied by gravity feed from storage hoppers or bins. A surface can only exert a nonfrictional force perpendicular or normal to itself. Therefore, a container exerts a restricting force on the material it contains which is proportional to the component of the material weight that is normal to the surface. Since the slope of the straight side of such an outlet is always the same, it exerts a constant restricting force on the material being emptied from the bin. The hyperbola, on the other hand, approaches an asymptote. Therefore, its slope approaches that of a vertical line, and its normal force decreases rapidly but smoothly to zero. Figure 4-36b shows this comparison diagrammatically. The length of the force arrows indicates the size of the normal restricting force.

We have already mentioned the "reciprocal" nature of one form of the equation of a hyperbola. The force exerted on an alpha particle

(helium nucleus) that is near the nucleus of an atom varies inversely as the square of its distance from that nucleus. This means that the orbital path of an alpha particle in the electric field of an atomic nucleus is hyperbolic. Certainly, this is a field that is considerably removed from the "hopper outlet" application shown above, yet the curves involved are the same.

4.58. The hyperbolic functions

It was mentioned early in this chapter that two of the conic sections yield a complete set of curves that are themselves widely applied. These two conics are the circle and the hyperbola. We have already treated the circular functions and their applications at some length. Now let us consider what is meant by the hyperbolic functions and where throughout technology we might expect to meet these curves.

A partial answer to where these curves are applied can be obtained from Fig. 4-37. The pictured monument to Thomas Jefferson is in

(Courtesy, St. Louis Chamber of Commerce)

Fig. 4-37. The St. Louis Gateway Arch—prime example of classic catenary (630-ft high)

the form of an inverted classical catenary, a shape that has both aesthetic value and structural stability. As will be shown in later paragraphs, the catenary is obtained directly from the hyperbola in much the same manner as the cosine curve is obtained from the circle. A catenary (hyperbolic cosine) can readily be seen by observing a suspended telephone cable or by freely suspending any uniform rope, wire, or chain from two points along its length. A bridge cable hangs from its supports in the form of a catenary before it is loaded with the roadway. In electronics, the hyperbolic functions are important in discussion of the commonly found effect of applying a step voltage (suddenly increased voltage) to a simple *RLC* circuit, as shown in Fig. 4-38, and in consideration of the impedance properties of a transmission line carrying energy to and from an antenna. The hyperbolic function curves are so prevalent that they are given special names, and their properties considered a part of basic knowledge.

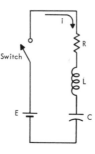

Fig. 4-38. Both hyperbolic sine and cosine required to discuss current and voltages produced in this common electronic circuit

4.59. The hyperbola and hyperbolic functions

In our earlier discussions we expressed the equation of the hyperbola as

$$\frac{x^2}{a^2} - \frac{y^2}{b^2} = 1$$

If we consider the special case of an equilateral hyperbola, where $a = b$, and set these constants equal to 1, we have the equation $x^2 - y^2$

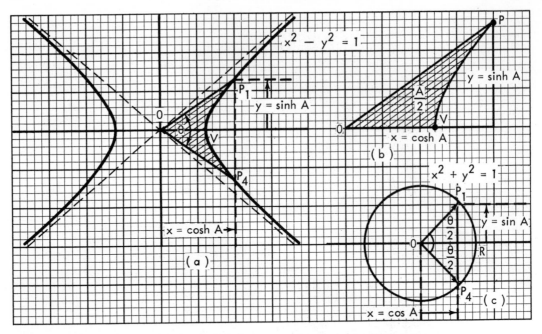

Fig. 4-39. Hyperbolic functions are analogous to circular functions

= 1. This curve is shown in Fig. 4-39a. If we now consider any point P_1 on this hyperbola, its ordinate value y represents the hyperbolic sine, and its abscissa value x represents the hyperbolic cosine. In other words, if we consider a vector of varying length, $0P$, pivoted at the origin, 0, and its other end, P, moving along the hyperbola, then its vertical projection yields the values of the hyperbolic sine and its horizontal projection yields the values of the hyperbolic cosine. A detail of the significant portion of Fig. 4-39a is shown in Fig. 4-39b. A comparison of Figs. 4-39a and b with Figs. 4-2 and 4-3 will readily show why the terms "hyperbolic sine" and "hyperbolic cosine" are used. Figure 4-2 shows the plot of the vertical projection of a rotating vector, and the resulting circular function is, of course, known as the sine. What is more logical, therefore, than to refer to the vertical projection of a vector moving along a hyperbola as the *hyperbolic sine* (abbreviated "sinh" and pronounced like the word "cinch"). Figure 4-3 shows the development of the circular function, the cosine, by plotting the horizontal projections of a rotating vector. Thus, the horizontal projections of the pivoting vector $0P$ when plotted are known as the *hyperbolic*

cosine (abbreviated "cosh" and pronounced as spelled).[9]

In the case of the circular function of Fig. 4-2 the values for the sine curve obtained from the vertical projections of the rotating vector are plotted against the angle that the rotating vector has swept through from its starting point. In other words, Fig. 4-2b, is a plot of the sine values along the dependent axis vs. the angle of the vector along the independent axis. In order to plot the hyperbolic sine curve, the values for the vertical axis are obtained from the ordinate values of sweeping vector, $0P$, but the horizontal axis coordinate is not the angle made by the vector, $0P$, with the horizontal. The horizontal axis coordinate values represent *twice the area of the sector* $0PV0$ of Fig. 4-39a. Note that this is the area bounded by the vector $0P$, by the hyperbola, and by the horizontal axis. Twice the area of sector $0PV0$ is the same as the area of the double sector $0P_1P_40$ of Fig. 4-39a. Thus, it

---

[9] The hyperbolic cosine is also so named because if in the expression $y = \cos \theta$, the θ is replaced by jA, then the resulting mathematics yields the equation of the catenary, a hyperbolic function. Since it was developed from the cosine, it is referred to as the *hyperbolic cosine* (cosh).

is often said that the horizontal coordinate values used to plot the hyperbolic sine represent the area of the double sector $0P_1P_40$, or its equal, twice $0PV0$.

4.60. Plotting hyperbolic functions

Since we are dealing with a curve produced by plotting the ordinate values of points on the hyperbola vs. the area of the sectors produced by a vector to these points, how is an accurate plot obtained? If we use A to represent the area of the sector $0P_1P_40$, then the equation of the abscissa values of point P becomes $x = \cosh A$, as shown in Fig. 4-39b. The question above then becomes, How is an accurate plot obtained of the equation $x = \cosh A$? There are at least two answers to this question.

The first method for obtaining the corresponding value of x and A for a plot of the cosh curve is to read these values directly from the hyperbola. For each position of P, its abscissa can be read directly from the horizontal axis of Fig. 4-39, and the corresponding area of the sector found by counting the graph paper squares within this area. The curve is then obtained by plotting the hyperbola abscissa values as the dependent (vertical axis) values against the sector area values as the independent (horizontal axis) values. For example, if we were to start this plot with point P at the vertex (V) position, then its abscissa value is 1 and the area under the vector $0P$ is 0. Thus, the coordinates of one point on the cosh A curve are (0, 1). This point is the vertical intercept point of the cosh A curve shown in Fig. 4-40. Now consider P_1 to be somewhat higher up on the hyperbola.

Its abscissa value is obviously greater than 1 (it is 1.66), but how accurately can the area of the sector $0PV0$ be obtained by counting the boxes? Twice this area is needed to produce the independent coordinate corresponding to the dependent coordinate 1.66. At best, the box-counting technique is a tedious operation, and without a planimeter it is not an accurate one. Therefore, although it is possible to obtain the independent coordinate values for the cosh plot in this manner, the tedium and inaccuracy makes its use infrequent.

4.61. Equations of hyperbolic functions

If this method is not often used then what method does yield a plot of the hyperbolic cosine and hyperbolic sine? It is possible to find the coordinates of all points that lie on the hyperbolic cosine curve by the use of an equation developed from the circular cosine. Thus,

$$\cosh A = \frac{\epsilon^A + \epsilon^{-A}}{2}$$

where ϵ is the natural number "epsilon," whose value is 2.71828, and A represents twice the area bounded by the vector $0P$, the hyperbola, and the horizontal axis. Thus, to plot the curve for cosh A, values for A can be substituted in this equation and the corresponding cosh A values obtained. The cosh A values are then plotted on the vertical axis and the corresponding A values on the horizontal. Table 4-4 gives some of these values, and Fig. 4-40 shows them plotted.

It can be seen from Fig. 4-39a that when the vector is in the first quadrant, its hori-

Table 4-4. The hyperbolic functions

A	sinh A	cosh A	tanh A	csch A	sech A	coth A
0	0	1.0				
0.5	0.52	1.13				
1.0	1.18	1.54				
1.5	2.13	2.35				
2.0	3.63	3.76				
2.5	6.05	6.13				
3.0	10.02	10.07				
3.5	16.54	16.57				
4.0	27.30	27.30				
4.5	45.00	45.01				
5.0	74.20	74.21				

zontal projections (the cosh values) are positive and the area $0PV0$ under the vector is considered positive, since it is above the horizontal axis. The resultant cosh plot is therefore entirely in the first quadrant of its axes (Fig. 4-40), since both the dependent and independent coordinates of all its points are positive. Consider now the position of the sweeping vector to be in the negative direction (its fourth quadrant), as is the case for $0P_4$ in Fig. 4-39a. Here again the horizontal projections of the vector are positive, but the area under the vector is now entirely below the horizontal axis and is considered negative. Thus, for each cosh value (horizontal projection of the vector) there is a positive and a negative area value. The positive area is produced when the sweeping vector is above the horizontal axis, and the negative area is produced when the vector is below the horizontal. But Table 4-4 shows only positive values, because the negative value for A for any one cosh value is equal in magnitude to the positive A value. The portion of the cosh curve in the second quadrant of Fig. 4-40 shows these points plotted. Note from this plot that every positive A value has a corresponding negative one for the same vertical axis (cosh) value.

Table 4-4 also shows values for the hyperbolic sine, obtainable from the vertical projections of the vector $0P$ of Fig. 4-39a. Here again the problem of plotting the curve involves the accurate determination of the area under the vector. Again the problem is usually solved not by counting boxes or measuring area with a planimeter but by the use of an equation. The equation for the hyperbolic sine can be obtained from that of the hyperbolic cosine by the use of a relationship described in the next paragraph. The resulting equation is very similar to that of the cosh, differing only by a minus sign. The equation for the hyperbolic sine is

$$\sinh A = \frac{\epsilon^A - \epsilon^{-A}}{2}$$

The sinh curve is also shown plotted in Fig. 4-40. Note from Fig. 4-39a that when the vector $0P$ sweeps below the horizontal, its vertical projection is negative and so is the area

bounded by that vector. Therefore, in a plot of the sinh curve negative sinh values appear and their corresponding area values are also negative. This accounts for the portion of the curve in the third quadrant of Fig. 4-40. The coordinates of the points shown in the third quadrant are equal in value to corresponding points in the first quadrant of Fig. 4-40. Only the sign is different. For this reason Table 4-4 gives only the positive values of A and sinh A.

4.62. Analogies between circular and hyperbolic functions

In our discussions of the development of the hyperbolic functions, we have shown that they are analogous to the circular functions, since in both cases we are dealing with vertical and horizontal projections of vectors that sweep out an angle. In the case of the hyperbolic functions, it was necessary to plot these values against the area under the vector. In the case of the circular functions the angle swept out by the vector served as the independent variable against which the function values were plotted. However, even this apparent difference can be eliminated, since it is also possible to consider the circular functions sine and cosine as being plotted against the area of the sector produced by the rotating vector.

If the rotating vector $0P$ of Fig. 4-39c were to sweep out a full $360°$, or 2π radians, then the area of this circular sweep would be

$$\text{Area} = \frac{2\pi r^2}{2}$$
$$= \pi r^2$$

which we know to be the area of a full circle. In general, therefore, we can say that the area of the sector of a circle is one-half the angle expressed in radians times the radius squared, that is, $A = \theta/2r^2$. Suppose we now consider a circle of radius equal to 1 as shown in Fig. 4-39c. The area of the sector $0P_1R0$ can now be considered equal to $\frac{1}{2}\theta$, since r equals 1, that is,

$$\text{Area} = \frac{\theta}{2}$$

If we let A represent the word "area," we have $A = \frac{1}{2}\theta$. Since the horizontal projection of

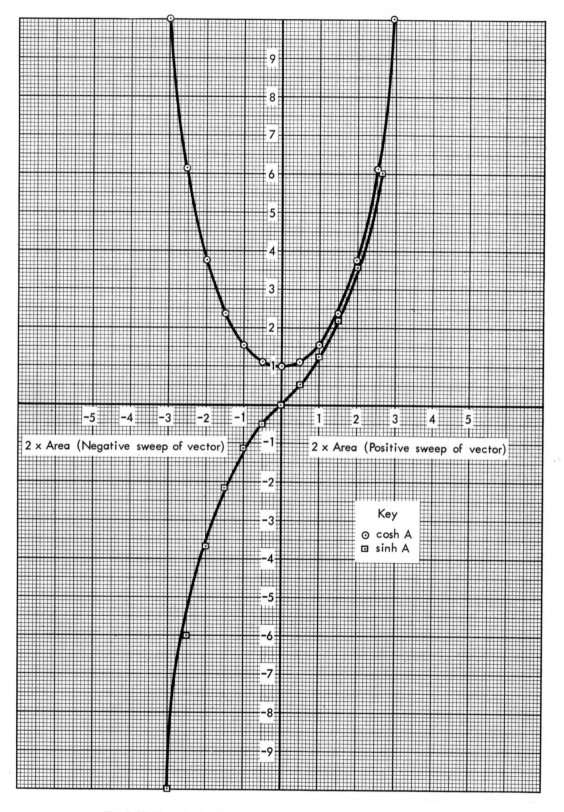

Fig. 4-40. Hyperbolic sine (sinh) and hyperbolic cosine (cosh) curves

the rotating vector is the cosine of the angle, we could write $x = \cos \frac{1}{2}\theta$. Since $A = \frac{1}{2}\theta$, we can also write $x = \cos A$. This usage is valid only if the value of the area of the sector is considered to be measured in radians squared. By the same token, we can state that $y = \sin A$. These equations are exactly analogous to those given for the hyperbolic functions, $x = \cosh A$ and $y = \sinh A$.

From the two circular functions sine and cosine that were obtained directly from the circle, four additional functions were obtained and plotted. In the case of the hyperbolics, the same is true. Four additional hyperbolic functions can be obtained from the sinh and cosh by using formulas analogous to those that applied to the sine and cosine. Table 4-5 repeats the trigonometric relationships and gives the corresponding hyperbolic ones. By means of these expressions, it is possible to fill in the columns left blank in Table 4-4 and to plot the four curves. The results you obtain should be similar to those shown in Figs. 4-41 and 4-42.

Table 4-5. Analogous trigonometric and hyperbolic relationships

$\tan A = \dfrac{\sin A}{\cos A}$	$\tanh A = \dfrac{\sinh A}{\cosh A}$
$\csc A = \dfrac{1}{\sin A}$	$\operatorname{csch} A = \dfrac{1}{\sinh A}$
$\sec A = \dfrac{1}{\cos A}$	$\operatorname{sech} A = \dfrac{1}{\cosh A}$
$\cos^2 A + \sin^2 A = 1$	$\cosh^2 A - \sinh^2 A = 1$

The first three hyperbolic relationships of Table 4-5 were probably anticipated, but where did the relationships of line 4 of Table 4-5 come from? An examination of Fig. 4-39 will readily show their origin.

The equation of the circle of Fig. 4-39c is $x^2 + y^2 = 1$, since we set the radius of that circle equal to 1. If the abscissa values (horizontal projections) represent the cosine, $x = \cos A$, then $x^2 = \cos^2 A$. Similarly, if the ordinates (vertical projections) represent the sine of $y = \sin A$, then $y^2 = \sin^2 A$. If now in the

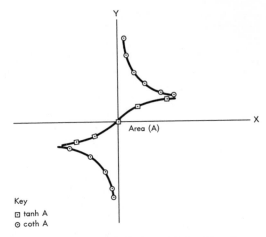

Key
□ tanh A
⊙ coth A

Fig. 4-41. Hyperbolic tangent (tanh) and hyperbolic contangent (coth) curves

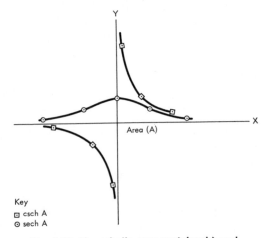

Key
□ csch A
⊙ sech A

Fig. 4-42. Hyperbolic cosecant (csch) and hyperbolic secant (sech) curves

equation of the circle we replace the x^2 and the y^2 by their equivalents, we obtain[10] $\cos^2 A + \sin^2 A = 1$.

From Figs. 4-39a and b we note that $x = \cosh A$, and therefore it is true that $x^2 = \cosh^2 A$. Similarly, since $y = \sinh A$, we can say that $y^2 = \sinh^2 A$. Substituting these equivalents in the equation for the hyperbola of Fig. 4-39a, $x^2 - y^2 = 1$, we obtain $\cosh^2 A - \sinh^2 A = 1$. These relationships, both the circular and hyperbolic, are basic and useful both in discussion of the graphs of these functions and in the analysis of information obtained from them.

---

[10] This equation is sometimes referred to as the trigonometric form of the Pythagorean Theorem.

REVIEW

Define concisely each of the following terms:

4-1. Sine wave motion

4-2. Displacement

4-3. Amplitude

4-4. Peak value

4-5. Wave crest

4-6. Wave trough

4-7. Positive direction of rotation

4-8. Sinusoid

4-9. Circular function

4-10. Cycle

4-11. Periodic motion

4-12. Period of a wave

4-13. Frequency

4-14. Corresponding points

4-15. Wavelength

4-16. Phase (phase angle, phase displacement)

4-17. Leading curve

4-18. Lagging curve

4-19. Similar waveshapes

4-20. Deci-trig system

4-21. Straight line

4-22. Slope of a *curve*

4-23. Secant line to a curve

4-24. Tangent line to a curve

4-25. Point of tangency

4-26. Point of inflection

4-27. Infinity

4-28. Magnitude bars about a number

4-29. Asymptote

4-30. Extent of a curve

4-31. Solid of revolution

4-32. Right circular cone

4-33. Lissajous pattern

4-34. Normal line at a point on a curve

4-35. Element of a cone

4-36. Beam-forming property of a parabola

4-37. (a) The volume of a sphere is a *function* of its _____. (b) The speed of a falling object is a *function* of the_____ through which it has fallen.

4-38. (a) When a stone is whirled in a vertical circle, it throws a shadow on the ground. Describe the motion of this shadow if the stone is being whirled with a constant angular speed of one revolution per second. (b) How is the motion of the shadow related to a sine wave?

4-39. What does the R represent in the equation $y = R \sin \theta$.

4-40. Describe the procedure for obtaining a negative sine wave from a rotating vector.

4-41. Use Fig. 4-2 to complete Table 4-1.

4-42. What are the similarities and differences between a sine waveshape and a cosine waveshape?

4-43. The frequency of middle C on a piano is 256 cps. What is the period of this note?

4-44. What is the frequency of a radio wave whose period is one microsecond?

4-45. (a) What is the equivalent in degrees of $T/6$? (b) Express, in terms of a fraction of T, the 240-deg position of a waveshape.

4-46. (a) A high pitched sound has a frequency of 10 kilocycles. Sketch its sinusoidal waveshape, and calibrate the horizontal axis in fractions of a second, every eighth of a period. (b) Repeat part (a) for a 440-cps sound.

4-47. Refer to Fig. 4-4. Are points (a) G and L, (b) K and M, and (c) K and L corresponding points? Explain.

4-48. (a) What is the relationship between the wavelength, frequency, and velocity of a wave? (b) If the speed of transmission of radio waves is $3(10^8)$ meters per second, what is the wavelength of a wave of 1-megacycle frequency? (c) Sketch this wave as a cosine waveshape and calibrate the horizontal axis in (1) meters, (2) fractions of a period, and (3) radians.

4-49. (a) Name a pair of curves that are out of phase by 90 deg and tell which leads. (b) Name a second pair of curves that are out of phase by 90 deg and tell which lags.

4-50. Explain how to determine the phase separation between two curves of different peak value.

4-51. (a) What two labeled points of Fig. 4-10 show a phase separation of 300 deg between curves 1 and 2? (b) Which curve leads?

(c) Give another statement of the phase separation between curves 1 and 2.

4-52. (a) How can an angle of 1 radian be produced? (b) Produce an angle of 1 radian using circles of 1-in. radius and 2-in. radius. (c) Measure both angles with a protractor, and show that they are the same. (d) What is the value in degrees of the angles measured in (c).

4-53. Why is radian measure considered a pure numeric, that is, it has no units?

4-54. (a) Convert to radian measure and express the results in terms of π: (1) 135 degrees, (2) 540 degrees, (3) 60 degrees. (b) Express the answers to (a) without the use of π.

4-55. Convert to degrees: (a) $3\pi/2$ radians, (b) $3/2$ radians, and (c) $\pi/6$ radians.

4-56. Explain the relationship between simple harmonic motion and a sinusoidal waveshape.

4-57. (a) Refer to Fig. 4-13. Draw four more tangent lines to the cosine curve of Fig. 4-13a. (b) Evaluate each of the four tangent line slopes. (c) Plot these slopes for the appropriate abscissa (time) on the axis of Fig. 4-13b. (d) Do these points fall on the curve of Fig. 4-13b? Explain.

4-58. Refer to Fig. 4-13. As you scan the curve from left to right, how do the slopes change in: (a) the concave downward region from point A to point B? (b) the concave upward region from point B to point D?, and (c) the concave downward region from D to E? (d) From these observations express the significance of the concavity of a curve as related to its slope.

4-59. Refer to Fig. 4-13, and (a) Draw several tangents to the acceleration vs. time curve. (b) Evaluate their slopes and plot these slope values vs. time. (c) Name the resultant waveshape. (The plot just produced shows the rate of change of acceleration. The term occasionally used to express such a rate of change is "jerk.")

4-60. What is the range of values of each of the six trigonometric functions?

4-61. Under what conditions is a curve considered to be discontinuous?

4-62. (a) List the primary trigonometric functions. (b) List the secondary trigonometric functions. (c) How are the primary and secondary functions related?

4-63. Use the relationship between the primary and secondary trigonometric functions to complete the last three columns of Table 4-2.

4-64. Explain how a circle is produced: (a) as a conic section and (b) as the path of a moving point. Repeat (a) and (b) for (c) an ellipse, (d) a parabola, and (e) a hyperbola.

4-65. (a) What is meant by the whispering gallery property of an ellipse? (b) Do you know of any room or structures in which this arrangement exists?

4-66. (a) Plot the equation, $x^2 = -5y$. (b) On the same set of axes, plot the equation, $x^2 = 10y$. (c) Point out two major differences between these two curves. (d) Explain how these differences are designated in the equation.

4-67. Construct a parabola of focal point F $(3, 0)$ and directrix $x = -3$. Show clearly the location of the vertex and at least five points on either side of the vertex.

4-68. Sketch (do not plot) the curves represented by each of the following equations: (a) $xy = 10$; (b) $x = 10y$; (c) $x^2 + y^2 = 10$; (d) $x^2/36 + y^2/25 = 1$; (e) $x^2/36 - y^2/25 = 1$; (f) $y^2/25 - x^2/36 = 1$; (g) $y = 10x$; (h) $y = -10x$; (i) $y = -10 \cos x$; and (j) $y = 10 \cosh x$.

4-69. Refer to the reciprocal ruling plot of Fig. 4-31 showing average rate vs. demand rate. Determine the cost for 100 kw-hr of energy used at a demand rate of 300 kw-hr per month.

4-70. Carry out the hyperbola construction procedure discussed in Section 4-54 on an 8½x11-in. sheet of paper. Complete both nappes of the hyperbola using this procedure.

4-71. (a) Use the relationships of Table 4-5 to complete the last four columns of Table 4-4. (b) Plot these values and compare the results to Figs. 4-41 and 4-42.

5 - LOGARITHMIC PLOTS –
RATIO CHARTS

Figures 5-1 and 5-2 are graphs obtained by plotting the data of Table 5-1. The data represent readings from a specific electronic circuit element operating under relatively high temperature conditions. There is obviously a drastic difference in the appearance of the two plots. Which would you prefer to plot? Which of the two curves can be read more accurately, particularly at the low and high ends of the voltage range? From which of the two plots would you prefer to make predictions on what the current readings will be if the voltage is increased beyond 10 volts? In general, which curve is more useful? The answer to each of these three questions is Fig. 5-1, the plot on the semilogarithmic paper. The reason for the answer is that the plot on the semilogarithmic paper (Fig. 5-1) produces a straight line, whereas the uniform calibration paper plot yields a very rapidly changing curve. The straight line is, of course, the easi-est of all curves to plot, read, and extend correctly for prediction purposes (dotted portion of Fig. 5-1). The type of curve shown in Fig. 5-2 is among the most difficult to read because, first of all, it converges with the horizontal axis. Therefore, for low values of voltage, the ordinate values (current) are so small that no distinctions in ordinate values can be made for abscissas between 0 and 2 volts. In addition, from 2 to 4 volts, the ordinate readings taken from the curve are highly inaccurate. Beyond 8 volts the curve slope increases so rapidly that very many plotted points are needed between 8 and 10 volts to provide a useful plot in this region. A curve drawn on the basis of two plotted points in a region of rapidly increasing slope is merely a good approximation of the correct curve and no more.

For these reasons, and others that will become apparent as our discussion progresses, the "semilog plot" is by far the more useful

Table 5-1. Laboratory data for a specific electric circuit

Applied voltage (volts)	0	1	2	3	4	5	6	7	8	9	10
Measured current (ma)	1	2.2	3.8	9	16	35	54	120	250	560	1,000

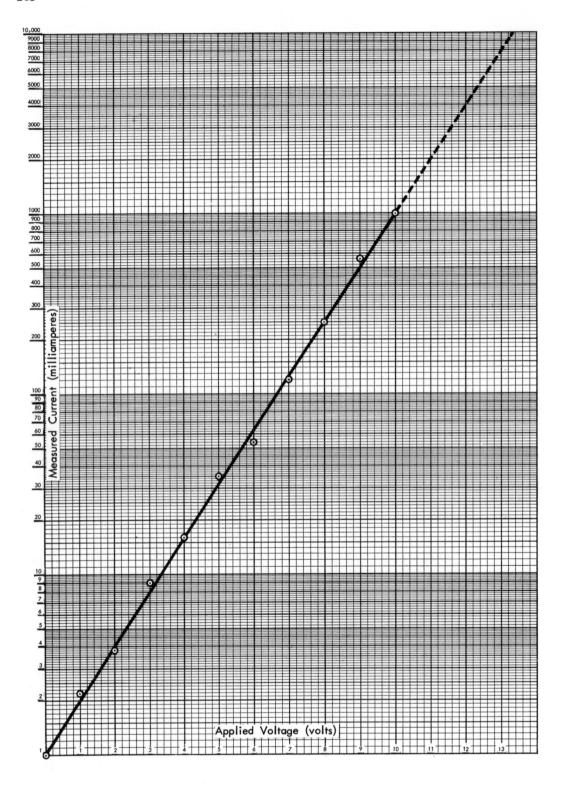

Fig. 5-1. Table 5-1 data plotted on semilogarithmic paper

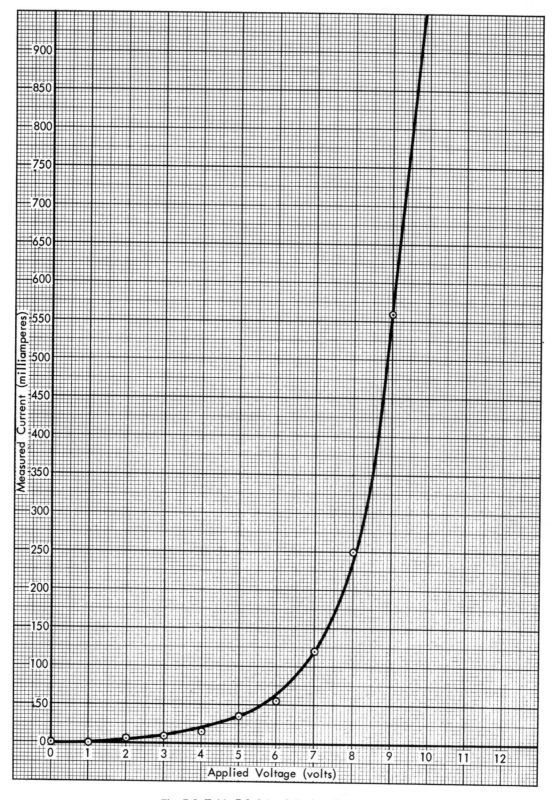

Fig. 5-2. Table 5-1 data plotted on linear paper

form of plotted data of this type and as such is quite prevalent throughout technology. It is also extensively used for economic and financial data. But, exactly what is a "semilog plot," and why does it differ so in appearance from a linear paper plot?

5.1. What is semilogarithmic paper?

The first step in determining just what semilogarithmic paper is requires a careful examination of the physical appearance of this type of graph paper. Note from the graph sheet of Fig. 5-1 that the vertical grid lines (calibration lines) are uniformly (linearly) spaced. However, the spacing between the horizontal calibration lines is far from being uniform. Note that the calibration lines extending to the left of the vertical axis are numbered starting from 1 at the bottom of the scale and increase consecutively to 10. *However, the spacing between successive calibration numbers is not equal throughout. The spacing decreases as the numbers go from 1 to 10 and then repeats.* This repetition occurs four different times on the graph sheet of Fig. 5-1. Each set or repetition is known as a *cycle*. Since four cycles appear on this sheet, it is known as *four-cycle semilogarithmic paper*. The term "semilogarithmic" will be defined in a later paragraph. For the present, we shall concern ourselves with the alternate name used for this type of paper—"ratio ruling."

Figure 5-3 is a four-cycle semilog graph sheet identical to that used for the Fig. 5-1 plot with the vertical axis calibration of this plot repeated. Note the distance marked *A* in the lowermost cycle of this sheet. This distance *A* starts at the 1 position and terminates at the 10. As such it represents a ratio of ordinate values of 10 to 1, *everywhere on the sheet*. For example, the distance *A* is again shown marked off somewhat higher up on the graph sheet. Note that it starts at the 300 line and terminates at the 3,000—a ratio of 10:1. Check this further by starting at any line and measuring off vertically the specified distance *A*. Note that it terminates at a line whose calibration value is 10 times the starting-line value.

Now refer to the distance marked *B* in the lowermost cycle. It starts at the 1 line and terminates at the 8, representing a ratio of 8:1. Thus, this particular length represents an 8:1 ratio of ordinate values *everywhere on the graph sheet*. A *B* distance is also shown marked off starting at the 50 line and terminating at 400. Similar specific lengths exist for every desired ratio, whether it be 2:1, 20:1, or any other ratio. Thus, we have the name—"ratio ruling."

On linear graph paper a specific distance (call it l) represents a definite quantity. Twice that distance ($2l$) is double the quantity and three times the distance is triple the quantity. On ratio-ruling paper, the *ratio* is taken twice (l^2) or three times (l^3). For example, if on linear paper (Fig. 5-1) a specific distance represents 50 units, then twice that distance represents 100 units. On ratio ruling paper (Fig. 5-3) if a specific distance represents 50, then twice that distance represents 2,500! Measure it off and see!

Now let's consider the effect of plotting on this kind of paper as compared to plotting on linear graph paper. When data points for a curve are plotted on *linear paper*, the resulting curve shows how the ordinate values *change in amount* from one point to another. When these same points are plotted on semilog paper, the resulting curve shows how the *ratio* of ordinate values changes. The fact that the semilog plot of Fig. 5-1 is a straight line indicates that the ratio of the ordinate values of the plotted points is constant. Checking the plot will show that the ordinate values of consecutively plotted points are in a ratio of 2 to 1. Since this ratio is the same (approximately) for every pair of consecutive points, the resultant plot is a straight line. Another manner in which the effect of a ratio-ruling plot can be expressed is to say that when points are plotted on semilog paper, the resulting curve shows the *percentage change* of each ordinate with respect to the previously plotted point. In the case of Fig. 5-1 the percentage change from one ordinate to the next is 100 per cent. This holds constant for all the plotted points of Fig. 5-1, thus yielding a

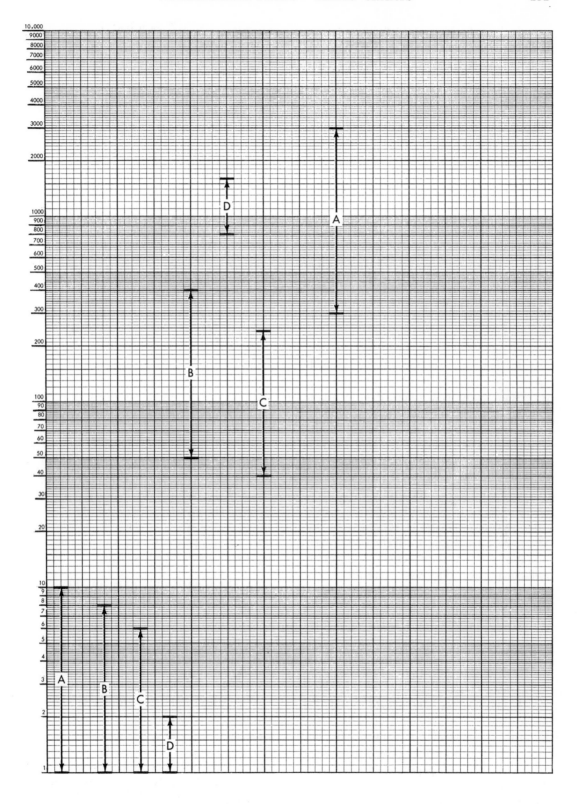

Fig. 5-3. Each vertical distance of "ratio ruling" represents specific ratio

straight line. To illustrate, let's consider the last three plotted points of Fig. 5-1. The point with abscissa 8 has an ordinate value of 250. If the next point had fallen directly on the line, its ordinate would be exactly 500. This represents a 100 per cent increase. The last plotted point has an ordinate of 1,000, again a 100 per cent increase over the previous ordinate of 500.

5.2. Advantages of using semilogarithmic paper

We can readily see that semilog paper (ratio ruling) should be used when it is desired to investigate how the ordinate values change in ratio (or per cent) rather than just in amount. The ratio change is usually far more significant than the change in amount. In addition, if amount change information is desired, it can still be obtained from a semilog plot by manually subtracting the ordinate value of one point from that of another. This is certainly more readily done than obtaining ratio information from a linear plot.

We mentioned earlier the relative ease with which the semilog plot (Fig. 5-1) could be read as compared with the linear paper plot (Fig. 5-2) of the same data. It is usually the case that the *ratio* of the ordinate values of points changes more slowly than the *differences* between ordinates of successive points. Therefore, a semilog plot will show less curvature than the same data plotted on uniformly calibrated paper. The less curvature a plot shows, that is, the closer it is to a straight line, the easier it is to read accurately.

Another decided advantage that semilog paper has over uniformly calibrated paper is its enormous range of values. Note, for example, the range of values on the vertical (logarithmic) scale of Fig. 5-1. The values range from 1 to 10,000. For the same length of axis the linear scale of Fig. 5-2 goes from 1 to 1,000. In terms of range of the vertical scale, our sheet of four-cycle semilog paper is equivalent to 10 sheets of linear paper, taped end to end. This very significant advantage is clearly accented by noting Fig. 5-4, which shows the characteristic curve of an often used electronic

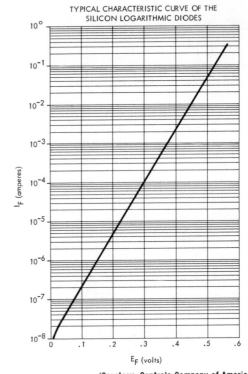

TYPICAL CHARACTERISTIC CURVE OF THE
SILICON LOGARITHMIC DIODES

(Courtesy, Controls Company of America)
Fig. 5-4. Enormous range of logarithmic scale is one of its primary advantages

component. Note that the range of values represented on the vertical axis of this eight-cycle semilog plot is the same as the range from 1 to 100 million. Any attempt to plot this curve on linear paper with any reasonable degree of accuracy would require about 100,000 sheets of linear graph paper, tacked end to end. This represents about 20 miles of paper!

5.3. The logarithmic axis for the independent quantity

Thus far we have considered the use of semilog paper only for cases where the logarithmic axis is held vertically, that is, used for plotting the dependent quantity. It is certainly conceivable that certain data will require the use of the logarithmic axis for the independent quantity. Note, for example, the plot of semiconductor surge-current ratings shown in Fig. 5-5. Here we see a plot on four-cycle semilog paper, where the ratio ruling appears along the horizontal axis. Well then, doesn't the use of semilog paper in this manner merely require turning the paper around so that the uni-

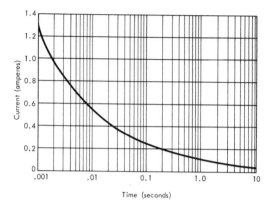

Fig. 5-5. Semilog paper used with logarithmic axis held horizontally

form axis is vertical and the logarithmic axis is horizontal? Yes, this is so, but note that there is a correct and incorrect way of turning the paper around. If the graph sheet of Fig. 5-3 is turned clockwise, so that the logarithmic scale numbers, printed by the paper manufacturer, appear at the top then the paper is being held correctly. If the position of these numbers is inconvenient, they may be recopied along the lower horizontal axis.

However, some logarithmic graph papers come without calibration numbers already printed along the logarithmic scale. What is the true guide for determining the correct position of the logarithmic scale? Note how the logarithmic spacing varies as the calibration numbers increase. *The spacing between calibration lines decreases as the calibration numbers increase.* Therefore, if the logarithmic scale is to be held horizontally, make certain that the *logarithmic spacing* between calibration lines *decreases* in the direction of *increasing X*-axis values. Note that this is the case in Fig. 5-5.

5.4. How is the logarithmic scale produced?

Although knowledge of the method for producing semilog paper calibration is not at all essential to the correct and effective use of this graph paper, it does help the understanding of why a plot on this type of paper behaves as it does. Furthermore, such knowledge permits the use of this graph paper for one additional,

although limited, application.

To start with, it would be helpful to refresh our memories on what logarithms mean. How would you algebraically solve the following equation for x?

(1) $$10^x = 17$$

Can the equation be solved by taking roots or powers of both sides of the equation? No. Can the equation be solved by multiplying or dividing both sides of the equation by anything? No again. Is there any algebraic operation that will result in the solution for x in the form

$$x = \text{combinations of 10 and 17}$$

Once again the answer is, No. Well then, is it possible to solve for x? Yes. We can solve for x by restating the equation in something like the following manner:

(2) x is the power of 10 that yields 17

This hardly looks like a "solution" for x. However, with a little abbreviation we obtain,

(3) $x = \text{pwr of 10 that yields 17}$

To abbreviate further, let's eliminate the word "of" and make the 10 a subscript. We then obtain

(4) $x = \text{pwr}_{10} \text{ that yields 17}$

If we now omit the words "that yields" and have them "understood" by the reader of the equation, the statement becomes:

(5) $$x = \text{pwr}_{10} \, 17$$

This last statement can certainly be considered a mathematical equation and can be left in this form. However the term "power" is usually replaced by its synonym "logarithm" in such applications. (Logarithm is a term derived from the Greek words *logos*, meaning "ratio," and *arithmos*, meaning "number.") By making the replacement and abbreviating the word logarithm, we obtain

(6) $$x = \log_{10} 17$$

Again we have a form that is perfectly usable, but as in any shorthand, mathematical or other, attempts are made to abbreviate as much as possible. The subscript 10 is therefore often omitted and also considered "understood" as being there. The initial statement (1) thus "boils down" to the much abbreviated statement

(7) $$x = \log 17$$

But every one of the seven statements means exactly the same thing.

We have obtained a logarithmic solution of the original equation. Let's follow through these steps once again for the equation below. This time we want to solve the equation for the exponent 2.

(1) $\qquad 10^2 = 100$

(2) $\qquad$ Two is the power of ten that yields one hundred

(3) $\qquad 2 = $ pwr of 10 that yields 100

(4) $\qquad 2 = \text{pwr}_{10}\ 100$

(5) $\qquad 2 = \log_{10} 100$

(6) $\qquad 2 = \log 100$

Using this mode of abbreviation, we can readily build up a table of exponents. In column 1 of Table 5-2 a list of powers of ten equations is given. In column 2, these equations are restated using the method of abbreviation just discussed.

Table 5-2. Powers of ten

Col. 1	Col. 2
$10^0 = 1$	$0 = \text{pwr}_{10}\ 1$
$10^1 = 10$	$1 = \text{pwr}_{10}\ 10$
$10^2 = 100$	$2 = \log_{10} 100$
$10^3 = 1{,}000$	$3 = \log_{10} 1{,}000$
$10^4 = 10{,}000$	$4 = \log 10{,}000$
$10^5 = 100{,}000$	$5 = \log 100{,}000$
$10^6 = 1{,}000{,}000$	$6 = \log 1{,}000{,}000$

We have here the powers of 10 that give us numbers from 1 to 1 million. But what about the intervening numbers? For example, what are the powers of 10 that yield 1, 2, 3, 4, 5, 6, 7, 8, and 9? We can see from Table 5-2 that the powers of 10 that yield these values must lie between 0 and 1. Table 5-3 fills in the

range between the first two lines of Table 5-2. It is the information from this second table, Table 5-3, that we need for the development of our semilog paper.

Table 5-3. Fractional powers of ten

Col. 1	Col. 2
$10^0 = 1$	$0 = \text{pwr}_{10}\ 1$
$10^{0.3010} = 2$	$0.3010 = \text{pwr}_{10}\ 2$
$10^{0.4771} = 3$	$0.4771 = \text{pwr}_{10}\ 3$
$10^{0.6020} = 4$	$0.6020 = \log_{10} 4$
$10^{0.6990} = 5$	$0.6990 = \log_{10} 5$
$10^{0.7781} = 6$	$0.7781 = \log 6$
$10^{0.8451} = 7$	$0.8451 = \log 7$
$10^{0.9030} = 8$	$0.9030 = \log 8$
$10^{0.9542} = 9$	$0.9542 = \log 9$
$10^{1.00} = 10$	$1.00 = \log 10$

Let us now plot the quantities of column 2 on a sheet of *linear* paper by plotting the fractional exponents from 0 to 1 as the dependent quantity (vertical axis) and the integral numbers from 1 to 10 as the independent quantity (horizontal axis). Since a high degree of accuracy is desired, the entire calibrated length of the graph paper is used for the exponents from 0 to 1. Figure 5-6 shows the plot. Note that the full length of the sheet is used for the vertical axis and that the width of the calibrated horizontal axis is not critical in this case. Note also that through each of the 10 plotted points a horizontal line was drawn and extended beyond the grid portion of the graph sheet. Note carefully the spacing between successive lines. *This is the logarithmic spacing that is seen on a sheet of semilog paper.* If we now ignore all the horizontal grid lines of the original graph sheet of Fig. 5-6, and consider only those drawn through the plotted points and include all the original vertical lines, we have a sheet of single-cycle semilog paper.

5.5. The significance of the numbers shown on graph paper

To complete our sheet of semilog paper, let us include the calibration numbers seen on

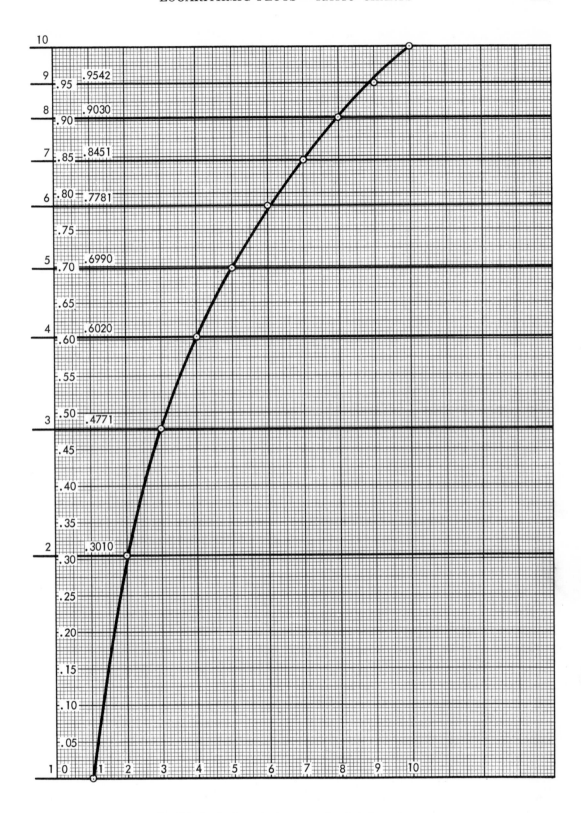

Fig. 5-6. Producing semilog paper by plot of **y** = log **x**

most graph-paper log scales. Note first that in Fig. 5-6 the ordinate values of each of the plotted points are given on the line we drew through that point. These numbers are shown on the grid portion of the graph paper. For example, the ordinate for the first plotted point is 0, for the second is 0.3010, and for the third is 0.4771. These quantities are the powers of 10 shown in Table 5-3. Now note the numbers we placed on the *extension* of the horizontal lines drawn through the plotted points. For the first plotted point, 1 is written on the extended line, for the second point, 2 appears on the line extension, for the third point, 3, and so on. These numbers 0, 1, 2, 3 etc. are the values obtained when 10 is raised to the corresponding fractional power shown. And these numbers shown on the extension of the horizontal lines through the plotted points are the numbers that the manufacturer prints on graph-paper log scales. In other words, *instead of the exponent (logarithm) of 10, the result of carrying 10 to that power is printed.* Thus 2 is placed where the 0.3010 should be, and 3 is placed where the 0.4771 should be, and so on all the way up to placing 10 where 1 should be. However, since 10 is different from 1 only by a matter of a decimal point, the 0 of the 10 is not shown (no zeros are shown on printed log scales), and the top calibration line of single-cycle semilog paper is marked 1.

But what is the purpose of so designating the numbers on the log scale? It can be seen by referring to Figs. 5-4 and 5-5 that the numbers along the logarithmic scale are treated like numbers along any other scale. When we plot,

no recognition is taken of the fact that these numbers are not uniformly spaced. *When plotted on semilog paper, under these conditions, the equation $y = 10^x$ appears as a straight line.* This equation was actually used as the basis for developing the semilog paper. The semilog plot of this equation is shown in Fig. 5-7.

Note the format of the equation $y = 10^x$. We are dealing here with a relationship in which a constant quantity (10 in this case) is raised to a variable power. On the plot (Fig. 5-7, line 1), the variable power is used as the abscissa. The ordinate values are those obtained by evaluating the constant carried to different powers. Further, *any equation that falls into this general format will appear as a straight line when plotted on semilog paper.* For example, the plot of $y = 2^x$ is also shown in Fig. 5-7 to be a straight line (line 2). Note that Fig. 5-1 is plotted as a straight line because the data fits roughly into the equation $I = 2^V$, where I represents the measured current in milliamperes and V represents the applied voltage. The third straight line shown in Fig. 5-7 is a plot of basically the same type of equation and therefore also yields a straight line. The equation is $y = (2)3^x$, and the values for the plotted points are shown in Table 5-4. In general, therefore, a *straight-line plot will be obtained on semilog paper if the data to be plotted falls into the form*

$$y = (K)N^x$$

where K and N are any constant values and x and y are, of course, the independent and dependent variables or contain these variables.[1]

---

[1] For those familiar with the theorems of logarithms, it can be seen that if we start with the equation $y = KN^x$ and take the logarithms of both sides, we obtain

$$\log y = \log K + x \log N$$

Since $\log y$ is a variable quantity, let us replace it by y'; and since $\log K$ is a constant quantity, let us replace it by K'; and since $\log N$ is a constant quantity, let us replace it by N'. With these substitutions made, the above equation becomes

$$y' = K' + xN'$$

Rewriting this into a more standardized form, we obtain

$$y' = N'x + K'$$

From our discussions in "The Straight Line" chapter it can be seen to be the equation of the straight line of the standard form

$$y = mx + b$$

where y' = dependent variable
x = independent variable
N' = slope of straight line
K' = vertical intercept

Bear in mind that when the y values are plotted on the vertical axis, we are in reality plotting the log y. This log y term is the dependent quantity (y') of the straight-line plot on semilog paper.

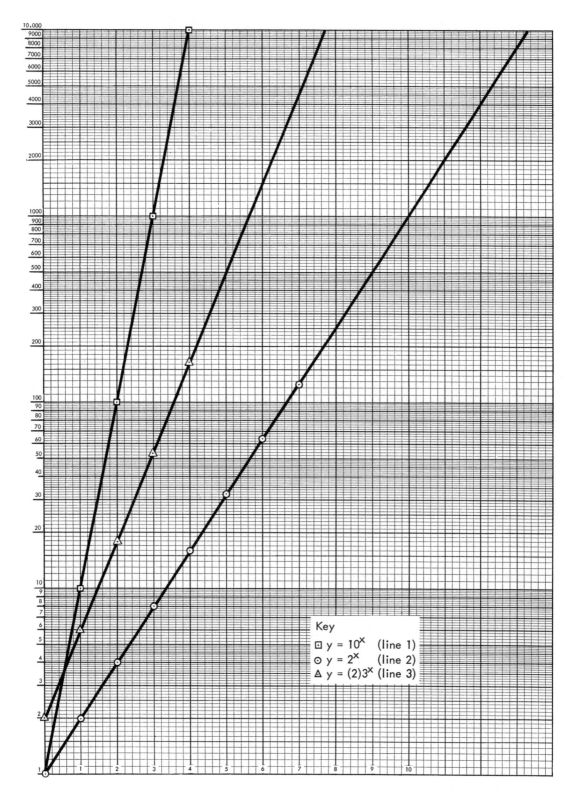

Fig. 5-7. Equation types that yield straight-line plots on semilog paper

Table 5-4. $y = (2)3^x$

x	0	1	2	3	4	6	6.6	7.2
y	2	6	18	54	162			10,000

Read missing values from graph

A commonly met example occurs in electronics in the circuit arrangement shown in Fig. 5-8. Here a battery is connected to a resistor (R), a capacitor (C), and a switch (SW). When the switch is closed, electrical current begins to flow and the capacitor begins to charge. The electricity flows rapidly at first, and as a result the voltage across the resistor is large at first. The current, however, decreases with time and, therefore, so does the voltage across the resistor. The equation that relates the resistor voltage to time is

$$V_R = E\epsilon^{-t/RC}$$

where $V_R =$ voltage across the resistor at any time t

$E =$ fixed battery voltage (10 volts for this example)

$R =$ value of the resistor (1.25 megohms)

$C =$ value of the capacitor (0.2 microfarad)

Does this equation fit the general form $y = KN^x$? Yes it does, even though the exponent of the N term ($\epsilon = 2.71828\ldots$) contains constant values (R and C) as well as a variable (t). This means that the equation will plot as a straight line on semilog paper. Time (t) is used as the independent variable and V_R as the dependent quantity. The result of this plot is shown in Fig. 5-8. Note that the dependent (voltage) values are plotted on the logarithmic axis, since the voltage values vary over a large range. The time values range from 0 to 1 sec (in steps of sixteenths of a second) and can thus readily be placed on the uniform (short-range) axis. Since we know that the result will be a straight line, only two points need be plotted to draw the line and a third plotted to verify that it falls on the same line. Plotting so few points is an obvious advantage in connection with an equation of the type shown for

V_R. Plotting this equation on linear paper will result in an asymptotic curve which required many plotted points in order to yield a fairly accurate curve. Since each point requires calculations, a linear paper plot is tedious to produce and results in a curve more difficult to read.

The equation for the second plot shown in Fig. 5-8 is

$$V_C = E - E\epsilon^{-t/RC}$$

and represents the voltage across the capacitor during the charging time. Is this equation of the general format $y = KN^x$? No, it is not. The second term of the equation may be of this form, but the entire equation is not. Therefore, the resultant plot on semilog paper will *not* be a straight line. The curve that is produced is also shown in Fig. 5-8. Its general appearance is similar to what it would be if plotted on linear paper. Since the curve is not a straight-line plot, many points were plotted to insure an accurate result. It can be seen from the equation and from Table 5-5 that to obtain the V_C values, it is necessary to compute the V_R values first. All the V_R values of the table are shown plotted on the V_R line and can be seen to fall on that line.

Table 5-5. Coordinate values for the curves of Fig. 5-8

Time (seconds)	V_R (volts)	V_C (volts)
0	10	0
¼ (¼₆) = 0.0156	9.42	0.58
¹⁄₁₆ = 0.0625	7.78	2.22
²⁄₁₆ = ⅛ = 0.125	6.06	3.94
⁴⁄₁₆ = ¼ = 0.25	3.68	6.32
⁸⁄₁₆ = ½ = 0.5	1.35	8.65
¹²⁄₁₆ = ¾ = 0.75	0.49	9.51
¹⁶⁄₁₆ = 1	0.18	9.82

5.6. Using semi-log paper as a log table

It was mentioned in an earlier paragraph that a knowledge of the method for producing the logarithmic calibration on semilog paper would permit an additional use to be made of this paper. That additional application is the

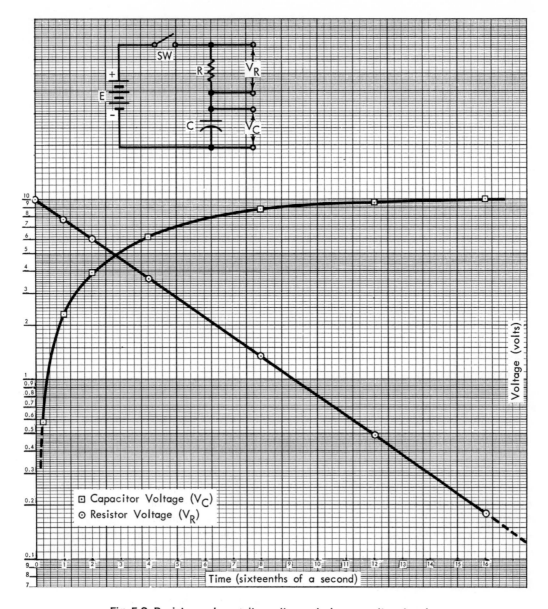

Fig. 5-8. Resistor and capacitor voltages during capacitor charging

use of a sheet of semilog paper as an emergency two-place table of logarithms.

It is only necessary to refer to Fig. 5-6 to recall that the semilog calibration is produced by plotting the logs of numbers from 1 to 10 on a linear scale. In other words, the vertical scale of Fig. 5-6 is truly a linear scale, with the logarithms of the numbers 1 to 10 indicated by a horizontal line (extended), with the proper number shown on the appropriate line. If now we wish to know the actual deci-mal number that yields each of the lines, all that need be done is to place a linearly calibrated scale alongside the logarithmic scale of a sheet of semilog paper. The step-by-step procedure for accomplishing this is as follows:

1. Obtain a sheet of one- or two-cycle semilog paper of the type shown in Fig. 5-9. Paper with a large number of cycles would yield results of poor accuracy.

2. Obtain a uniformly calibrated sheet of

graph paper. Use an axis length equal to the length of one log cycle of the semilog paper. On this length of linear axis, calibrate uniformly from 0 to 1.

3. Place this uniformly calibrated axis beside the logarithmic axis of the semilog paper. Make certain that the 0 of the linear axis corresponds with the 1 of the log axis and that the 1 of the linear axis corresponds to the 10 of the log axis.

4. Beside the 2 line of the logarithmic axis, read the log of 2 on the linear axis. Beside the 3 line of the log axis read the log of 3 on the linear axis. The first decimal place of these readings is accurate, and the second place is reasonably so.

5. Continue this process up to the log of 10. The log of 10 is obtained by noting where the 10 line of the logarithmic axis meets the linear axis. The linear axis reading will be 1 if the linear axis was properly produced and used.

6. Compare the values thus obtained with the information of Table 5-3 to determine the accuracy of this method. Maximum accuracy is obtained when a sheet of single-cycle semilog paper is used.

The procedure described above is effective and can serve as an emergency table if none other is available. However, it requires the use of two sheets of graph paper, one semilog and one linear. It is readily possible to avoid the use of the linear graph sheet by utilizing the linear scale of the semilog paper. To accomplish this proceed as follows:

1. Calibrate the linear axis of the semilog paper from 0 to 1, as shown on the horizontal axis of Fig. 5-9.

2. Draw a straight line from the $(0, 1)$ point of these axes to the $(1, 10)$ point, as shown in Fig. 5-9.

3. The numbers on the horizontal scale are the logarithms of the quantities shown on the vertical (logarithmic) scale. The diagonal line drawn will permit you to use this sheet as a log table.

For example, to determine log 2, locate 2 on the vertical (logarithmic) scale, read over to

the diagonal line, and then down to the horizontal axis. Note that the horizontal axis reading is 0.30. The log 2, expressed to four places is 0.3010; thus, the accuracy of this method is reasonable. Now read the log 4. The plot of Fig. 5-9 yields 0.60. Actually, log $4 = 0.6020$. Log 9 shows here as 0.955. Expressed to four places, log $9 = 0.9542$. It can therefore be seen that this procedure is accurate to at least two decimal places and requires only a single sheet of semilog paper.

Note that in Fig. 5-9, the line drawn for log-reading purposes is extended into the second cycle. The extended portion is shown in a broken line. What is the purpose of this extension and how is it used? Since this line extends into the second cycle, it permits us to read the logarithms of numbers above 10 if the horizontal calibration is extended. The size of this sheet permits the line to extend to only 25 on the vertical scale, but double sheets are readily available. The logarithm of 25 read from the horizontal scale is 1.40. Expressed to four decimal places, log 25 is actually 1.3980. Log 20 appears on the horizontal scale as 1.3. More accurately, log $20 = 1.3010$. This method of obtaining logs is limited only by the size of the sheet used.

By comparing the diagonal line drawn in Fig. 5-9 with line 1 of Fig. 5-7, we can see that the equation of the line of Fig. 5-9 is $y = 10^x$. Thus, with a thorough knowledge of logarithms, it is possible to develop extensions of this method that will permit direct readings of the logarithms of numbers to any base at all, and therefore also to convert from any one base to any other log base. If you feel that you are familiar with logs, use the above described method to read the logarithms of numbers to the base 2 from line 2 of Fig. 5-7.

5.7. What is log-log paper?

The general physical appearance of this type of graph paper can be determined by a glance at Fig. 5-10, which shows a sheet of 2-by-2-cycle log-log paper, or at Fig. 5-11, which shows a plot of the output power vs. frequency

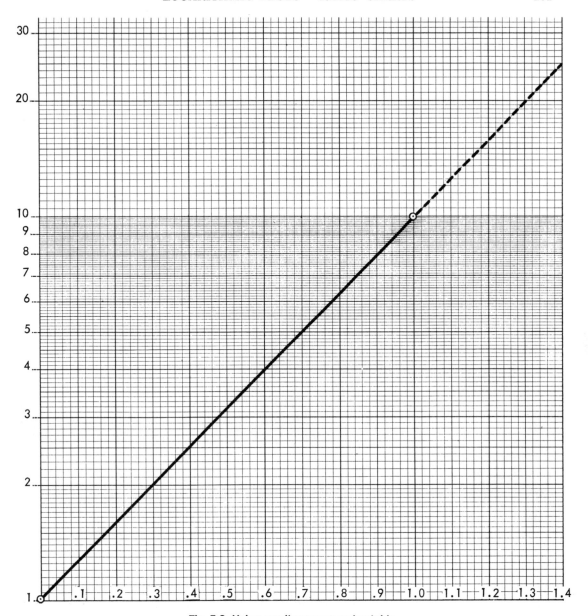

Fig. 5-9. Using semilog paper as log table

of a specific microwave tube on 4-by-3-cycle log-log paper, or at Fig. 5-12, which shows the straight-line plot of an exponential equation on a sheet of 3-by-5-cycle log-log paper. Examination of any one of these sheets shows that one of the axes is calibrated logarithmically exactly as on the semilog paper already discussed. The difference is, however, that on log-log paper the second axis also has the same type of calibration, that is, logarithmic and not linear as is the case with the semilog papers. Furthermore, it can be seen from the three samples of Figs. 5-10, 5-11, and 5-12 that almost any combination of cycles (repetitions of logarithmic scales) can be obtained for the two axes of a single sheet of log-log paper. Special combinations can be obtained, when necessary, by tacking together two or more sheets of log-log paper. For example, if two sheets of the 2-by-2-cycle log-log paper shown in Fig. 5-10 were taped together to extend the horizontal axis, the result would be a large

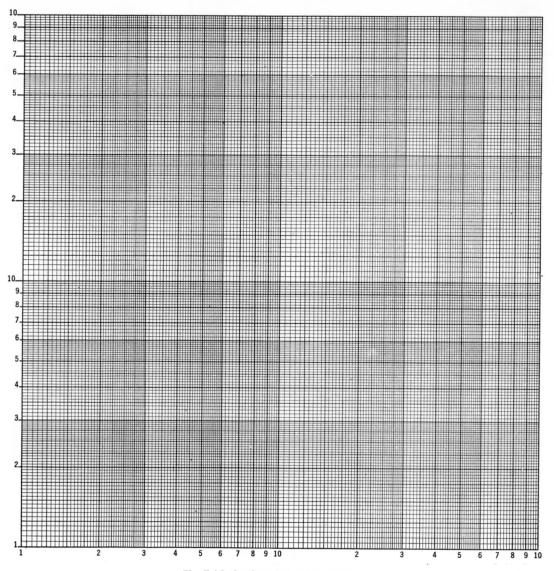

Fig. 5-10. 2 x 2 cycle log-log paper

log-log sheet of 2 cycles for the vertical axis and 4 cycles for the horizontal. The reverse arrangement could also be produced readily. Two graph sheets of the type used for Fig. 5-12 could be used to yield one sheet of 6-by-5-cycle log-log paper or one sheet of 10-by-3-cycle log-log paper.

5.8. One important application of log-log paper

One of the applications discussed for semi-log paper applies, in an extended manner, to the log-log paper. It was pointed out in the earlier discussion that the logarithmic axis pro-

vides a means of plotting a wide range of values on a scale of reasonable length. Thus, if one variable that has a very wide range of values is to be plotted against another, the range of which is far more limited, then semi-log paper is called for and the wide-range variable is put on the logarithmic axis. Suppose, however, that the two variables involved in a plot both have a wide range such as 1,000 to 1 for one of the quantities and several hundred to one for the other. Under such conditions log-log paper is in order merely because it permits plotting these wide ranges of values on a single sheet of graph paper. An example

AVERAGE POWER OUTPUT AS A FUNCTION OF FREQUENCY FOR MICROWAVE TUBES.

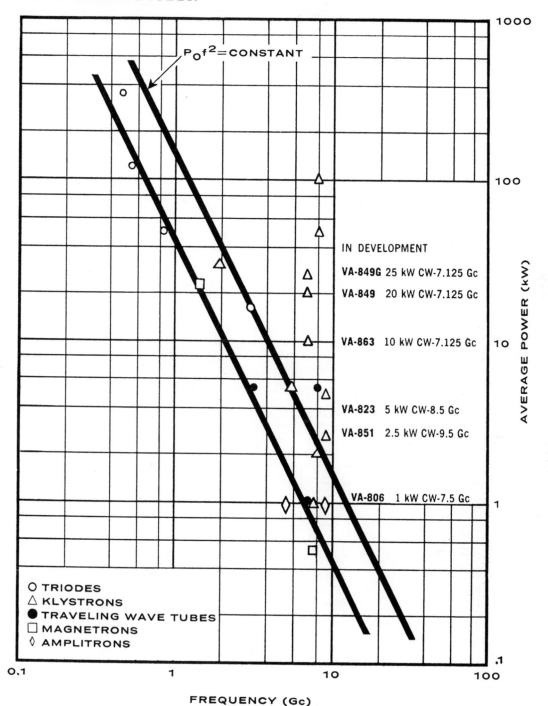

(Courtesy, Varian Associates)

Fig. 5-11. 4 x 3 cycle log-log grid used to present power output vs. frequency characteristic of specific microwave tube

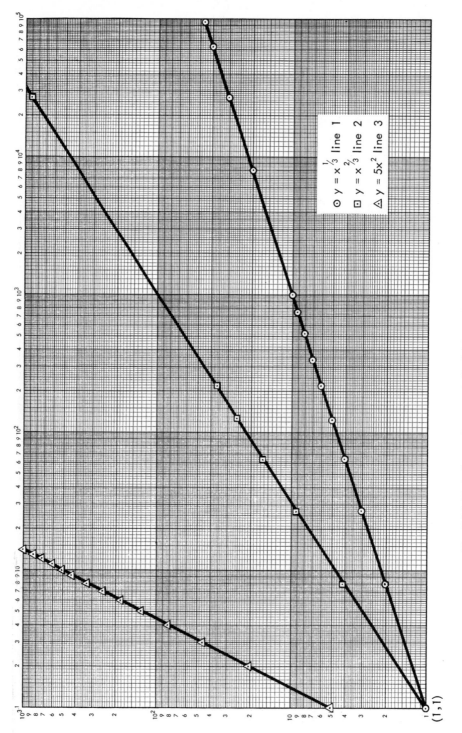

Fig. 5-12. Plot of equation, $y = kx^N$, yields straight line on log-log paper

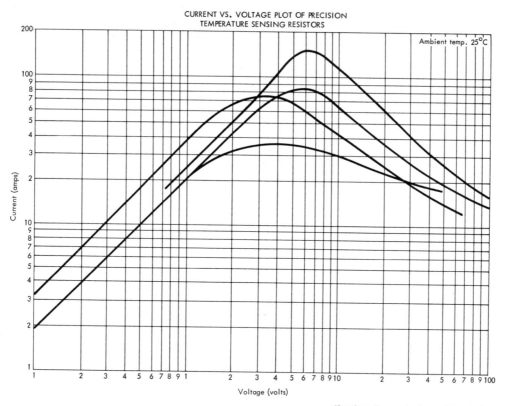

Fig. 5-13. Log-log paper provides expanded axis in both directions

(Courtesy, Ferroxcube Corp. of America)

of this application of log-log paper is shown in Fig. 5-13, which is a current-vs.-voltage plot of precision temperature-sensing resistors. Note that a 200:1 range of values is shown on the vertical axis calibration and a 1,000:1 range on the horizontal axis calibration.

In our earlier discussions of the use of semilog paper, it was pointed out that some care in the proper use of this paper is necessary when the logarithmic axis is to be used for the independent variable. Most semilog graph papers are printed so that the numbers on the logarithmic axis are oriented for easy reading when the log axis is held vertically. When the log axis is held horizontally, care must be taken to hold the paper in the correct manner, that is, so that the spacing between the logarithmic calibration lines decreases as the calibration numbers increase. How does this apply to log-log paper? Is it possible to turn log-log paper around and use it in a manner different from that intended by the manufacturer of this paper? To answer this ques-

tion, refer to Fig. 5-12, in which a sheet of 3-by-5-cycle log-log paper is used. Note that when the paper is held so that the 5-cycle axis is horizontal, then the numbers increase from left to right along the horizontal axis and from bottom to top along the vertical axis. This, therefore, is the direction in which the manufacturer intended the paper to be held. However, suppose the values to be plotted show a much wider range for the dependent quantity, and the 5-cycle direction is therefore desired for the vertical axis. Is it possible merely to turn around the graph sheet so that the numbers increase from bottom to top as the 5-cycle axis is held vertically? If this is done, then what is true of the numbers along the now horizontal 3-cycle axis? Note that they read *downscale* when the horizontal axis is read from left to right. This is obviously incorrect. The final answer is that *it is not possible to turn the log-log sheet around in any manner other than that intended by the manufacturer of that paper.*

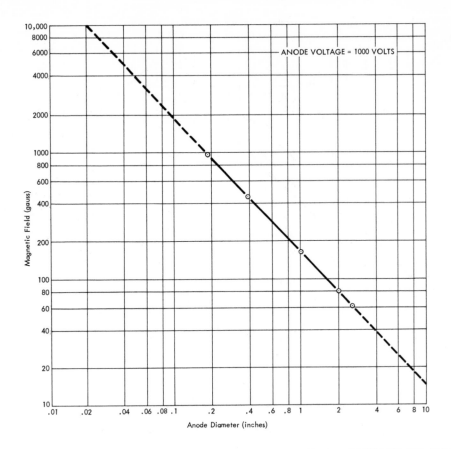

Fig. 5-14. Relation between anode diameter and cut-off field yields straight line when plotted on log-log paper

As in the case with some semilog papers, log-log papers exist on which no calibration numbers are shown. In such a case, be careful to hold the sheet so that the spacing between logarithmic calibration lines decreases as the horizontal scale is read from left to right, that is, in the increasing direction, and also so that the spacing between the logarithmic calibration lines decreases when reading the vertical axis from bottom to top.

5.9. A second important application of log-log paper

In our earlier discussions it became apparent that data showing a fixed proportional change of one of the variables, as the other varies linearly, plot as a straight line on semilog paper. It is apparent from Figs. 5-11, 5-12, 5-14, and 5-15 that certain relationships between the independent and dependent data values yield a straight line when plotted on log-log paper. As previously mentioned, the straight line is by far the simplest curve to plot, the one most readily and accurately read, and the curve type most easily extended into the region of predicted values. It is consequently of considerable advantage to recognize what data will plot as a straight line on log-log paper. The three straight-line plots of Fig. 5-12 can serve as a guide. Line 1 is a plot of the equation $y = x^{1/3}$, line 2 a plot of $y = x^{2/3}$, and line 3 a plot of the equation $y = 5x^2$. Table 5-6 lists the coordinate values for the points shown in Fig. 5-12. Note that in each of the three cases we are dealing with relationships containing constant exponents. These constant exponents can be fractions, whole numbers and either positive or negative. Note from the equation of line 3 that the variables can also have coefficients. In general, *a straight-line plot will be obtained on log-log paper if the relationship between the dependent and independent variable is of the form*

$$y = Cx^A$$

where C and A are any constant values and x and y are the independent and dependent variables.[2]

An often met example in electronic technology of this type of relationship involves the amount of power that must be supplied to the cathode of an electron tube in order to bring it up to the several thousand degrees Kelvin (°K) required to cause emission of electrons. The equation is known as the Stefan-Boltzmann relationship and states that

$$P = KeT^4$$

where P = power that must be supplied per unit surface area of electron-emitting surface, in watts per square meter

K = Stefan-Boltzmann constant
$\quad = 5.67(10^{-8})$

e (often shown as e_T) = a constant that we will take as 0.3 and that differs for different materials

T = temperature of electron emitter, in °K

Does this equation satisfy the form $y = Cx^A$? Yes, it does, if we consider the product of Ke as being the constant preceding the variable (T) carried to a power (4). Since the given equation does fit our general form, it will plot as a straight line on log-log paper. Thus, a complete plot can be accomplished with the coordinates of only two or three points that satisfy the equation as in the following example.

A particular diode (two-element electron tube consisting of an electron emitter called

Table 5-6. Coordinates for Fig. 5-12

(a) $y = x^{1/3}$		(b) $y = x^{2/3}$		(c) $y = 5x^2$	
x	y	x	y	x	y
1	1	1	1	1	5
8	2	8	4	2	20
27	3	27	9	3	45
64	4	64	16	4	80
125	5	125	25	5	125
216	6	216	36	6	180
343	7	343	49	7	245
512	8	512	64	8	320
729	9	729	81	9	405
1,000	10	1,000	100	10	500
8,000	20	8,000	400	11	605
27,000	30	27,000	900	12	720
64,000	40			13	845
				14	980

the "cathode" and an electron collector called the "plate" or "anode") has an electron-emitting surface area of 60×10^{-6} square meters. The measured amount of power supplied to this surface and the corresponding temperature produced are given in columns 1 and 2 of Table 5-7.

Table 5-7. Power-temperature data for a given diode

Power, watts	Temperature, °K	Power/area, watts/meter^2
40	2,440	0.66×10^6
20	2,120	0.33×10^6
5	1,600	0.084×10^6

If each of these power values is divided by the surface area of the emitter, the P (power per unit area) term of the Stefan-Boltzmann equation is obtained. The values resulting from this operation are listed in column 3 of Table 5-7 alongside the corresponding temperature values.

---

[2] For the reader familiar with the theorems of logarithms it can be seen that if we start with the equation $y = Cx^A$ and take logarithms of both sides of the equation, we obtain

$$\log y = \log C + A \log x$$

Note that in this equation *both* the log y and log x terms appear. Thus, if on a sheet of log-log paper we plot both the x and the y coordinate values on logarithmic scales, we are in reality plotting log x rather than x and log y rather

than y.

Let us replace the log y variable term by y', the log x term by x' and the log C constant term by C'. With these substitutions made, the above equation becomes

$$y' = C' + Ax'$$

Rewriting this slightly so that it conforms to the standardized form, we obtain $y' = Ax' + C'$. From our discussions in "The Straight Line" chapter, we recognize this as the equation of the straight line.

Since temperature is the independent variable, a plot of the power per unit area values vs. temperature on log-log paper should yield the expected straight line. Note that the range of values of P requires two cycles for the vertical axis, whereas the T range requires only one cycle for the horizontal axis. The log-log paper thus chosen is 2-by-1-cycle log-log paper and the resultant plot is shown in Fig. 5-15. Note that the portion of this line drawn between the data points is shown solid and the "predicted" region, that is, the portion drawn by extending the known line is shown in broken-line form.

A careful check of the plotted points will show that they do not all fall on a perfect straight line. Such a condition should be carefully investigated to yield the reasons for the discrepancy, since according to our discussion, a perfect straight line should be obtained. The discrepancy could be due to slight errors in taking the data. In this particular instance, however, the discrepancy is more likely the result of our assumption that the e_T term of our equation remains absolutely constant at 0.3. Actually, this quantity changes somewhat with temperature. Thus, a plot of this nature can and often does serve to point out discrepancies in the laboratory data, since deviations from a straight line are very readily apparent to the reader of the graph. Such deviations must always be investigated and a satisfactory explanation obtained.

5.10. Graph papers designed to yield straight-line plots

As we know, the advantages of the straight-line plot are many. Therefore, several types of graph papers have been developed that will yield a straight line for a curve or function that is inconvenient to plot or read on linear graph paper. Such a paper can be developed for almost any function. However, those that are available commercially have been designed against equation types that are very commonly found in technology. We have already discussed three such graph paper types.

The reciprocal ruling or hyperbolic graph paper is illustrated and described in Chapter 4. Since the reciprocal relationship is met so often in technology, a graph paper has been designed that will permit the equilateral hyperbola (reciprocal function) to plot as a straight line. Examples of the use of this paper are shown in Chapter 4, and its many advantages are discussed.

Semilog and log-log graph papers have several distinct advantages, as described earlier, but their primary purpose is to yield a straight line plot for a specific, commonly met, type of curve or function.

In laboratory work in general and in reliability and basic research work in particular, the probability function plays a particularly important role in determining conclusions and making predictions from the data yielded by the test equipment. This curve of error, or normal distribution curve as it is often called, can be represented by the equation

$$y = \frac{1}{\sqrt{2\pi}}\, \epsilon^{-x^2/2}$$
$$= 0.4\epsilon^{-x^2/2}$$

and is shown in Fig. 5-16. From the equation and curve it is obvious that a graph paper that could convert this curve into a straight line would be a definite aid. Such a graph paper has been developed and will plot the normal distribution equation as a straight line.

Normal distribution applies to many random measurements as much as it does to occurrence of error in a series of data readings. For example, Table 5-8 shows the effect of applying an increasing voltage to a specific type of electronic circuit component after many hours of continuous operation. Table 5-8 shows the number of units that failed as the voltage was increased from 0 to 10 and also the number of failure occurrences as the voltage was decreased from 10 to 0.

From Fig. 5-17, on which these data are plotted, it can be seen that the failure rate for both the increasing and decreasing voltage tests follows a normal distribution curve. Since this is the case, the data from Table 5-8 should plot as a straight line on probability paper.

This plot is shown in Fig. 5-18. Note that it was necessary to use the right-hand probability axis for the dependent quantity. This is

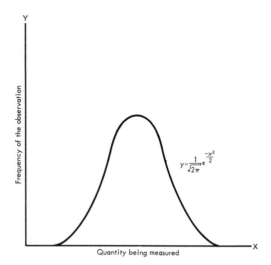

Fig. 5-16. Normal distribution curve

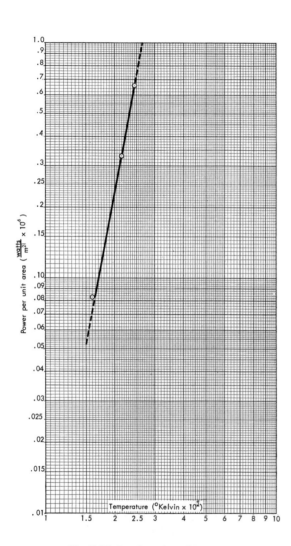

Fig. 5-15. Log-log plot of P = Kϵ_TT^4
yields straight line

Table 5-8.

No. of failures (units)	Applied voltage (volts)
1	0.01
3	1
5	2
11	3
19	4
30	5
42	6
58	7
71	8
84	9
90	10
80	9
68	8
52	7
36	6
23	5
13	4
6	3
3	2
1	1

so, since probability graph paper is precalibrated by the manufacturer and when the paper is held vertically as in Fig. 5-18, the right-hand axis shows increasing quantities from bottom to top, whereas the left-hand axis shows decreasing quantities in this direction. In this application it was necessary to hold the graph paper vertically, since the applied voltage is the independent quantity and the quantity that varies linearly.

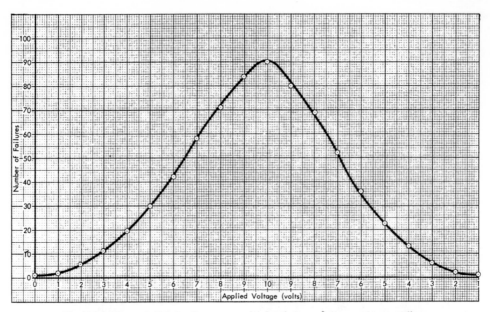

Fig. 5-17. Normal distribution curve obtained from failure rate sampling

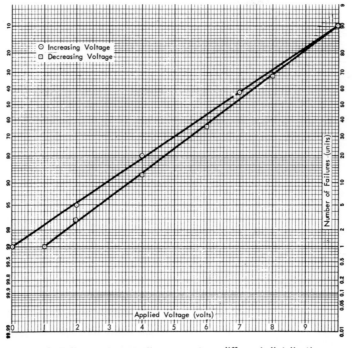

Fig. 5-18. Failure rate samplings showing different distributions

Examination of Fig. 5-18 shows clearly several advantages of the probability paper plot. First of all, the plot on this graph paper is the expected straight line. Thus, it was necessary to plot only a few points in order to obtain the entire curve. Note also that the line representing the frequency of failure as the voltage is increased is different from that obtained with decreasing voltage. This is not readily apparent from the linear paper plot or from the numerical data. Thus, predictions and conclusions based on breakdown of this sampling are not the same for increasing as for decreasing voltages, although the voltage range is the same in both cases.

The reader should compare the linear plot of Fig. 5-18 and the distribution curve of Fig. 5-17 with the histogram type of bar graph discussed in Chapter 2, since the three curves are closely interrelated.

Other special graph papers are commercially available that are designated to produce a straight-line plot of a commonly used function. One such paper is sinewave paper. However, since the sine curve itself is so readily sketched and the curve equation and values are so readily available, sinewave graph paper finds far less application in technology than do the log papers and probability papers. Nevertheless, the development of a sheet of sine wave paper using a variation of the procedure described for making semilog paper is an interesting challenge.

REVIEW

5-1. Explain why semilog paper is often referred to as ratio ruling paper.

5-2. (a) Under what conditions will data plotted on semilog paper yield a straight line? (b) Make up a sample table of such data. (c) Plot your data on semilog paper and verify that they produce a straight line.

5-3. What other types of data, in addition to the type shown in problem 5-2, are best plotted on semilog paper?

5-4. (a) What type of equation will plot as a straight line on semilog paper. (b) Does the equation $y = 5^x$ fall in this category? (c) Check your answer by producing a semilog paper plot of this equation.

5-5. (a) Will the equation $y = 5^{(x+1)}$ plot as a straight line on semilog paper? (b) Check your answer by carrying out the plot.

5-6. (a) Fill in the missing quantities in Table 5-4. (b) Check to determine whether these points fall on line 3 of Fig. 5-6.

5-7. (a) Plot the data of Table 5-5 on linear paper. (b) Compare your result to the graphs of Fig. 5-7. Explain the differences and similarities.

5-8. Refer to Fig. 5-7. (a) Which of the lines shown can provide information for a log table to the base 2? (b) Use this line to complete the table in the right-hand column.

Number	Log to the base 2
1	
2	
3	
4	
5	
6	
7	
8	
9	
10	
20	
25	
30	
35	
40	
45	
50	
60	
100	
500	
1,000	
2,000	
5,000	
10,000	

5-9. (a) On a sheet of semilog paper, (a) draw a straight line for the equation, $y = N^x$, where N is the number of letters of your surname. (b) From this line develop the _____ Table of logarithms for which
(your surname)
the base number is _____. Extend
(N)
the table from at least 1 to 1,000.

5-10. (a) On the same sheet of graph paper as problem 5-9, plot the line $y = 10^x$. (b) From these two plots determine which is the larger quantity, the common log of 50 (base 10) or the _____ log of 50 (base N).
(your surname)
Explain your answer.

5-11. Under what two different conditions would you use log-log paper for plotting a graph?

5-12. The amount of current flowing in an electron tube depends upon the voltage applied between the cathode (electron emitter) and the anode (electron collector). The relating equation is known as the 3/2 Power Law since $I_b = KE_b^{3/2}$ where $I_b =$ anode current, $E_b =$ applied voltage, and $K = 15(10^{-5})$ for a particular tube. (a) Plot this equation on log-log paper. (b) Plot this equation on linear paper. (c) Compare the results of the two plots and comment on the significant differences between them.

5-13. In Chapter 4, the equation $PV = 100$ is shown plotted as a straight line on reciprocal ruling paper. (a) Plot this equation on log-log paper. (b) Compare the resultant plot to that shown on the hyperbolic paper. Explain the similarities and differences.

5-14. (a) Refer to Fig. 5-6 and review the procedure for producing a sheet of semilog paper. (b) Develop a modification of this procedure that will yield a sheet of *sine wave paper*, that is, a sheet of graph paper that will cause the sine curve (the equation $y = \sin \theta$) to plot as a straight line. (c) Plot $y = \sin \theta$ on this sheet, and verify that it produces a straight line. (d) What are the advantages and disadvantages of a graph paper of this type?

5-15. $X_c = 1/2\pi f C$ is the equation for the reactance of a capacitor (useful in electronic circuit calculations) where $X_c =$ capacitive reactance (ohms), $C =$ capacitance (farads), and $f =$ frequency (cycles per second, or cps). If for a particular unit, C equals 10 microfarads (10×10^{-6} farads), (a) Plot X_c versus frequency if frequency varies from 10 cps to 1 million cps. What conditions of this problem determine what graph paper should be used? (b) What would this plot look like on hyperbolic paper? Explain. (c) What would this plot look like on linear paper? Explain.

5-16. Joules Law of heating due to an electric current states that $P = I^2R$, where $P =$ power (watts), $I =$ current (amperes), $R =$ resistance (ohms). (a) If R equals 100 ohms, produce a straight line plot of this equation by plotting power versus current on the appropriate type of graph paper. Let current vary from 1 to 1,000 milliamperes (1 milliampere $= 10^{-3}$ amperes). (b) On the same set of axes, replot this equation but with a value of R of 50 ohms. (c) How do the (a) and (b) plots compare? What is the major difference between them? (d) What would be the result of a plot of this same equation on the same set of axes if R is given a value of 200 ohms? *Sketch* (do not plot) your prediction on the same sheet of graph paper. (e) Check your sketch by plotting several points and notice that they fall on your graph sketch.

5-17. Solve graphically with the use of the appropriate graph paper: If the bacterial count in a container of stagnant liquid doubles every four hours, by what factor would the count increase in 35 hours? In 100 hours?

5-18. Radioisotopes vary in the rate at which they decay, that is, lose their radioactivity. This decay rate is commonly measured in terms of the time required for *half* of a given sample of the material to decay away. This time is known as the *half-life* of the radioactive material. The radioactive decay pattern

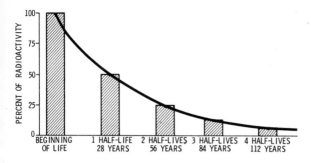

(Courtesy, U.S. Atomic Energy Commission)

Fig. 5-19. Radioactive decay pattern of Strontium-90

following table of values:

P_{out} (milliwatts)	1	2	5	10	20	30	50	100
db								

(b) Choose a graph paper so that these data will plot as a straight line. (c) From the plot obtained for part (b) above determine: (1) the value of output power that corresponds to 25 decibels; (2) the power output from the system that will give db readings of 5 and 15.

of strontium-90 is shown in Fig. 5-19 in both bar graph and curve form. (a) Plot the information obtainable from Fig. 5-19 so that it will yield a straight line. Use the appropriate graph paper and plot percentage of radioactivity vs. time in years. (b) Explain your choice of graph paper type. (c) If the original sample of this material has a mass of 10 grams, determine from your plot how much material has decayed away after (1) 10 years, (2) 40 years, (3) 120 years.

5-19. The decibel (db) is a convenient means of measuring increase or decrease in power level and is commonly used in high-fidelity audio systems and in many other applications. The decibel can be defined by the equation, $db = 10 \log P_{out}/P_{in}$, where db represents the increase in decibels, P_{out} represents the amount of power output from system in milliwatts (1 milliwatt = 10^{-3} watts), and P_{in} represents the input power to the system. For the purposes of this problem, consider the input power (P_{in}) to be 1 milliwatt. (a) Use the above information and complete the

5-20. The piezoelectric effect describes the ability of certain crystals to convert a mechanical stress into a voltage. Through the joint efforts of Bell Telephone Laboratories, Brush Development Company, and the U.S. Naval Research Laboratory, a crystal having desirable properties was developed. It is known as the ADP (ammonium dihydrogen phosphate) piezoelectric crystal. One of the properties of this crystal, its volume resistivity (ohms/cm³), varies with temperature. Some of the measured data are listed below:

Temperature (°C)	45	60	78	90
Resistivity (ohms/cm³)	10^{10}	$4(10^9)$	10^9	$4(10^8)$

(a) Plot these data on the appropriate type of graph paper. (b) What is the value and direction of the slope of this plotted curve? (c) What is the resistivity of the ADP crystal at 100°C and at 50°C? (d) At what temperature is the volume resistivity of the ADP crystal $6(10^{10})$ ohms/cm³; $6(10^9)$ ohms/cm³?

6 - POLAR COORDINATE PLOTTING

Figures 6-1, 6-2, 6-3, and 6-4 show, to some extent, what coordinate plots are and how they are used. The diagram of Fig. 6-1 is the result of studies made of the radiation belts that surround the earth. Figure 6-2 shows the regions and levels of effectiveness of a microwave antenna. Figure 6-3 is a plot of the level of illumination provided by a specific lighting fixture at a distance of 25 ft measured at different angles from the fixture. Figure 6-4 shows that a certain solid-state photocell provides maximum effectiveness when the light source is directly in front of the cell and that the per cent effectiveness drops sharply when the light source is moved off at an angle to one side or another. Thus, we see here four widely diverse areas of application of the polar-coordinate type of graph.

What are the similarities between these four plots, and how do we recognize a polar-coordinate plot when we see one? It is apparent that the gridwork on which these four graphs are plotted is not made up of straight lines as in the graph papers of the previous chapters. In each of the first four figures of this chapter, the graph paper on which the curves are plotted is made up of a series of concentric circles as well as a series of radial lines emanating from the common center of these circles. A graph paper showing this type of gridwork is known as *polar coordinate paper,* and *the center of the concentric circles is called the pole.* Figure 6-6 shows the most commonly used type of polar coordinate paper, or circular paper, as it is often called. However, there are other types of circular graph papers that are more convenient in certain applications. "Fluxolite" paper is one of these and is shown in Fig. 2-45. The photometric data plot of Fig. 6-3 is done on a similar type of paper, which is used primarily in lighting studies. The paper shown in Fig. 6-5 is known as trigonometric function data paper and is seen to be a combination trigonometric function table and polar coordinate graph paper. As will be seen later in this chapter, such a combination is an extremely useful one when polar plotting is carried out.

6.1. Terms and conventions

In order to locate a point on each of the graph papers discussed in previous chapters two pieces of information are necessary. These are, of course, the abscissa and the ordinate

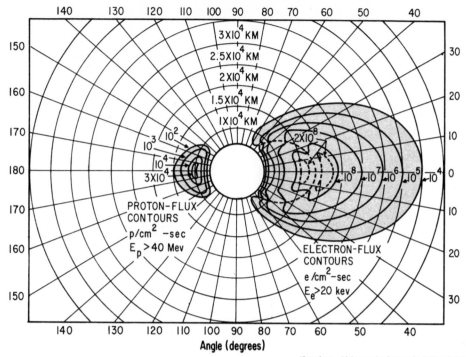

Fig. 6-1. Quiet-day electron fluxes as function of distance from center of earth and degree of earth latitude

(Courtesy, Airborne Instruments Laboratory)

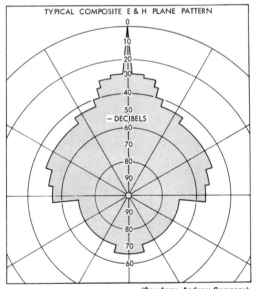

(Courtesy, Andrew Company)

Fig. 6-2. Antenna performance characteristic

values, and both are distances. Plotting a point on polar coordinate paper also requires that two pieces of information be known. However, only one is a distance. The other is a direction, or angle with respect to a standard reference line. Examine carefully the polar coordinate paper of Fig. 6-6. Note that the primary (heavy) radial line positions are calibrated in degrees, starting at zero and going completely around to 360 deg. The 0 deg line is equivalent to the positive X axis of the cartesian coordinate system, and thus, the polar graph sheet is correctly oriented *when the 0° line extends to the right* from the pole. Note also that the paper is ruled with primary and secondary (light) circles and that these are not precalibrated as are the radial lines. Before any points can be plotted, a length calibration must be provided for the radii of these circles. This calibration is placed along the 0-deg line and nowhere else on the sheet. For the purpose of point-location practice, let us call each major circle radius one unit. For this particular plot the units will not be named. This calibration is shown on the graph sheet of Fig. 6-6. Note, as in the case of the true X axis, the calibration numbers are placed directly below the 0° line. If the line and units are to be named, the wording would appear below the calibration numbers as is done on the cartesian pa-

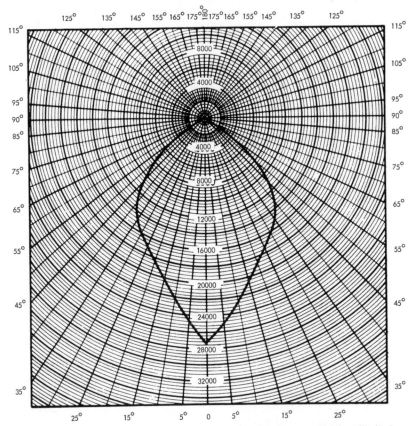

PHOTOMETRIC TEST DATA
Candlepower Measured at 25 Feet

(Courtesy, Westinghouse Electric Corp.)

Fig. 6-3. Photometric test data plot of specific lighting fixture

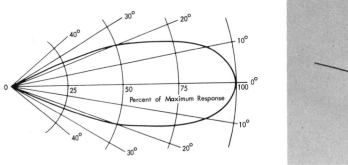

Percent of Maximum Response

(Courtesy, Solid State Products, Inc.)

Fig. 6-4. Angular response characteristic of solid-state photocell shown

per and as is shown in Fig. 6-4.

As Fig. 6-6 is now calibrated, every point on the circle of radius 1 is 1 unit from the pole, every point on the circumference of the 2 circle is 2 units from the pole, and so on out to the 10 circle. It should be noticed that not all the circles have their entire circumference shown.

Every circle, on this paper, of radius greater than 7.3 intersects the boundaries of the grid portion of the paper, and only a portion of their circumferences is shown. Thus, we see that the "distance information" referred to earlier is the distance from the pole. The "direction information" required for every point

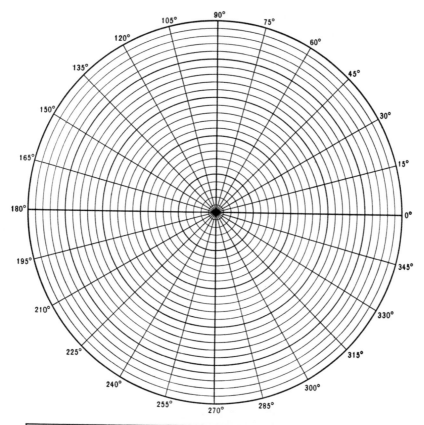

θ, Rad.	θ, Deg.	Sin θ	Cos θ	Tan θ			
0	0	0.00	1.00	0.00			
$\frac{1}{12}\pi$	15	0.26	0.97	0.27			
$\frac{1}{6}\pi$	30	0.50	0.87	0.58			
$\frac{1}{4}\pi$	45	0.71	0.71	1.00			
$\frac{1}{3}\pi$	60	0.87	0.50	1.73			
$\frac{5}{12}\pi$	75	0.97	0.26	3.73			
$\frac{1}{2}\pi$	90	1.00	0.00	- - - -			
$\frac{7}{12}\pi$	105	0.97	−0.26	−3.73			
$\frac{2}{3}\pi$	120	0.87	−0.50	−1.73			
$\frac{3}{4}\pi$	135	0.71	−0.71	−1.00			
$\frac{5}{6}\pi$	150	0.50	−0.87	−0.58			
$\frac{11}{12}\pi$	165	0.26	−0.97	−0.27			
π	180	0.00	−1.00	0.00			
$\frac{13}{12}\pi$	195	−0.26	−0.97	0.27			
$\frac{7}{6}\pi$	210	−0.50	−0.87	0.58			
$\frac{5}{4}\pi$	225	−0.71	−0.71	1.00			
$\frac{4}{3}\pi$	240	−0.87	−0.50	1.73			
$\frac{17}{12}\pi$	255	−0.97	−0.26	3.73			
$\frac{3}{2}\pi$	270	−1.00	0.00	- - - -			
$\frac{19}{12}\pi$	285	−0.97	0.26	−3.73			
$\frac{5}{3}\pi$	300	−0.87	0.50	−1.73			
$\frac{7}{4}\pi$	315	−0.71	0.71	−1.00			
$\frac{11}{6}\pi$	330	−0.50	0.87	−0.58			
$\frac{23}{12}\pi$	345	−0.26	0.97	−0.27			
2π	360	0.00	1.00	0.00			

(Courtesy, Keuffel and Esser Co.)

Fig. 6-5. Trigonometric function data paper

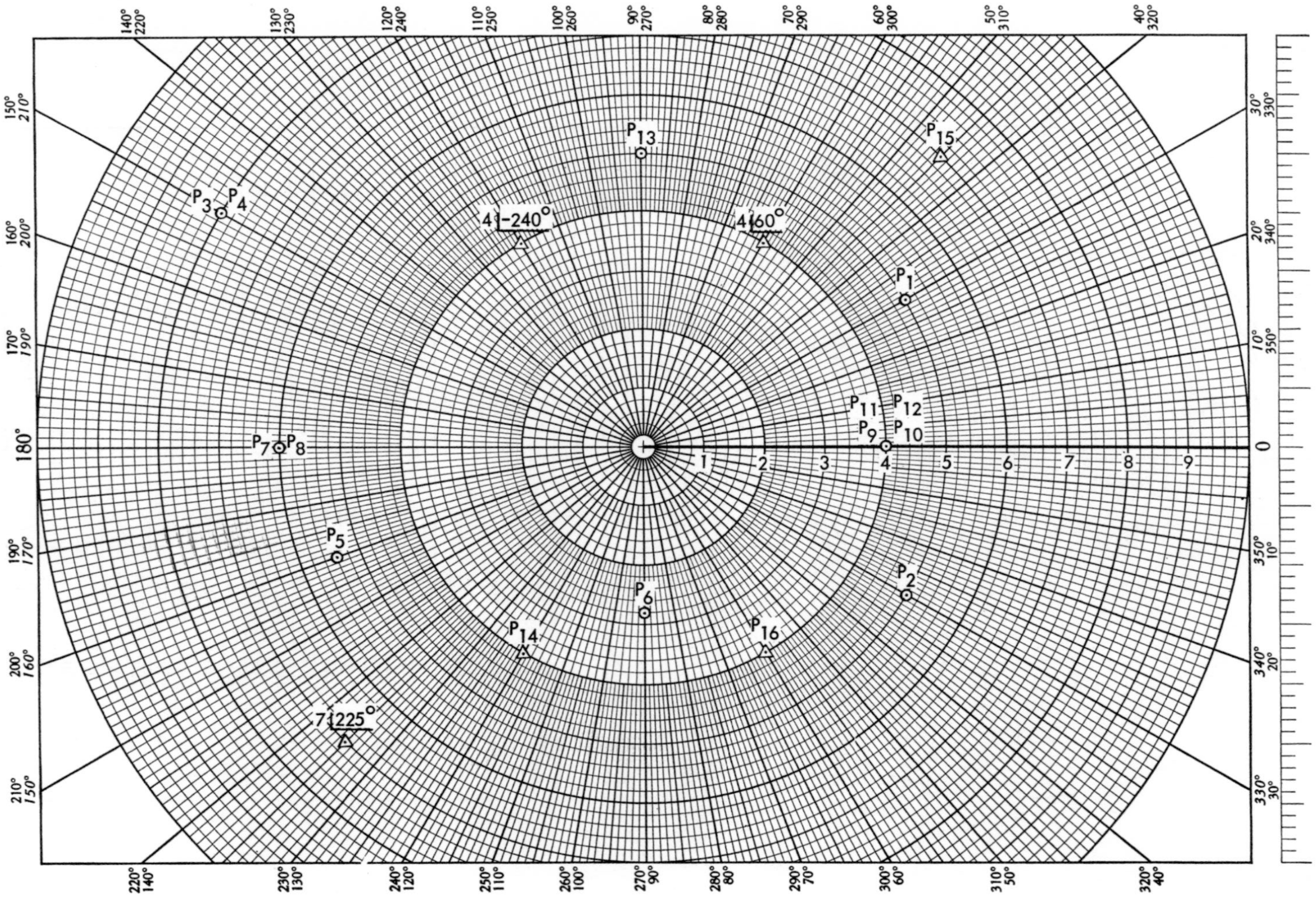

Fig. 6-6. Plotting points on polar coordinate paper

refers to the angle measured from the 0-deg line. As mentioned earlier, these angles are already marked on the graph paper from 0 to 360 deg, and the calibration is such that an angle can be measured accurately to one-half of a degree. However, two sets of angle calibrations are shown printed at the end of the major radial lines. One set of these angles goes counterclockwise around the paper from 0 to 360 deg and the second set covers the same range clockwise. These two calibrations are given to facilitate reading angles in the positive and negative directions. In a polar coordinate system, *the counterclockwise direction is standardized as the positive direction, and the clockwise direction is set as the negative direction of angle measurement.*

The distance from the pole is most commonly symbolized by the Greek letter *rho* (ρ) and is the *dependent* quantity of the two. The distance from the pole, in addition to being called "polar distance," is often referred to as the *magnitude* of the quantity being plotted. In mathematics *rho* is also referred to as the *modulus*. The angle with respect to the 0-deg line is symbolized by the Greek letter *theta* (θ) and is the *independent* of the two quantities. θ is either known as the direction or the angle, but in mathematics is often referred to as the *argument*. In the cartesian coordinate system, when the two coordinates of a point are specified, the independent variable is placed first and the dependent second, and the two are separated by a comma and enclosed in a pair of parentheses. In the polar coordinate system the reverse order is used. The magnitude (dependent variable) is shown first, and the angle value, enclosed in what is known as an angle bracket, appears second. Thus, if the coordinates ρ and θ of a given point P are stated, they appear in the following form:

$$P = \rho \angle \theta$$

6.2. Plotting points on polar coordinate paper

We are ready now to try our hand at plotting points. Let's refer to the first point to be plotted as P_1, the coordinates of which are $P_1 = 5 \angle 30°$. As described in the previous paragraph, this notation means that point P_1 is 5 distance units from the pole and appears on the +30-deg line. Notice that the coordinates given for point P_1 show no sign in front of the angle. If no sign is shown, a plus sign is understood and the angle is thus to be measured in the counterclockwise (positive) direction from the 0-deg line. To plot point P_1, therefore, locate the +30-deg line and follow it out to the 5-unit circle. The point P_1 is shown plotted in Fig. 6-6. (It is recommended that you plot these points on a sheet of polar paper of your own and use Fig. 6-6 as a check on your own work.) With P_1 successfully plotted, where should $P_2 = 5 \angle -30°$ be located? Since the minus sign in front of an angle means that the angle should be measured clockwise from the 0° line, the point P_2 appears on the 5-unit circle but falls in what would be the fourth quadrant of a cartesian coordinate system, as shown in Fig. 6-6. Where should point P_3 be located if its coordinates are $P_3 = 8 \angle -210°$?

Traveling clockwise 210° from the 0° line on the circle of 8 units radius, brings us to the point P_3 as shown in Fig. 6-6. Now plot point $P_4 = 8 \angle 150°$. This point is located by following the 8-unit circle counterclockwise to the 150° line. Point P_4 has the *same* location as point P_3. In other words, more than one designation exists for any one location on polar coordinate graph paper. Neither one of the two designations given for point P_3 or P_4 is better than the other or more nearly correct than the other. The positive designation, however, is more commonly used. We will see in the next few paragraphs that *four different designations are possible for any one location on polar coordinate graph paper.* Before continuing any further in polar discussions, plot each of the points designated in Table 6-1 and verify your plot by checking it against Fig. 6-6.

Note that points P_7 and P_8 are the same point, since a 180-deg counterclockwise (positive) rotation and a 180-deg clockwise (negative) rotation both bring us to the same line, the 180-deg line. Similarly, points P_9, P_{10}, and

Table 6-1. Polar coordinate designations

Point	Coordinates	
	ρ	θ
P_5	5.4	200°
P_6	2.8	−90°
P_7	6	180°
P_8	6	−180°
P_9	4	0°
P_{10}	4	360°
P_{11}	4	−360°

P_{11} are superimposed on one another, since no rotation (0 deg) or a complete counterclockwise rotation (+360 deg), or a full clockwise rotation (−360 deg) all bring us to the same position, the 0-deg line. Where does point $P_{12} = 4\angle 720°$ fall? Since 720 deg represents two complete revolutions, the point P_{12} also designates the same location as points P_9, P_{10}, and P_{11}. Although most polar plots require plotting points within the first 360 deg only, there are important exceptions to this statement, as will be seen in our discussion of spiral curves, later in the chapter. Thus, as a practice point locate on your polar graph sheet $P_{13} = 5\angle 450°$ and verify your plot by checking the location of P_{13} on Fig. 6-6.

6.3. Four polar designations for the same location

From the above discussions we see that each point can be given two different designations. Each of the two has the same magnitude, but one is shown with a positive angle θ, and the second is shown with a negative angle of 360 deg minus θ. Thus, points P_4 and P_3 show two different designations for the same location because point P_4 is on the circumference of the 8-unit circle and is located by traveling 150 deg counterclockwise (positive) from the 0-deg line. Point P_3 is also on the 8-unit circle and is located by traveling clockwise (negative) 210 deg. The two points fall one on the other, since they are at the same polar distance, and the negative angle of one (−210 deg) equals 360 deg minus the positive angle of the other point (360 deg − 150 deg).

But these are only two designations for the same location. How do we obtain four different designations for the same location and within the first 360 deg? The answer to this question involves learning how to plot points that have the type of designation shown for point $P_{14} = -(4\angle 60°)$. We are already familiar with the type of notation that appears within the parentheses above, but what is the significance of the parentheses and of the minus sign in front of the parentheses?

Let us consider the minus sign first. We have already used a minus sign in our discussion of polar coordinate notation and plotting, but that sign referred to the angle and indicated a clockwise direction of rotation. Certainly the polar distance cannot be considered as either negative or positive since it refers to a radial distance from the pole. This polar distance can be measured in any one of an infinite number of directions, and it is the angle that specifies the desired direction. What then is the meaning of the minus sign in front of the parentheses? This minus sign refers to the entire point contained within the parentheses and is also a means of indicating direction. *A minus sign in front of a point designation means that 180 deg is to be added to the angle shown.* Another manner in which the meaning of this minus sign can be explained is to say that a minus sign in front of a parentheses containing a point designation means that we are plotting a point that is in a *direction opposite to the point within the parentheses.* Thus, in order to locate point $P_{14} = -(4\angle 60°)$, it is necessary first to locate the point shown within the parentheses and then to plot the point P_{14} 180 deg away from (opposite to) that located point. Point $4\angle 60°$ appears in the first quadrant as shown in Fig. 6-6 emphasized by a triangle. Point P_{14} is 180 deg away from $4\angle 60°$, as also shown in Fig. 6-6, emphasized by a triangle around the plotted point.

Before going any further in this discussion, let us plot another one or two points showing this minus sign. Without reference to Fig. 6-6, plot point $P_{15} = -(7\angle 225°)$. The point $7\angle 225°$ is located in the third quadrant; thus, the point P_{15}, which is 180 deg away, is a first quadrant point. Both points P_{15} and $7\angle 225°$ are shown plotted in Fig. 6-6, and the plotted points are accented by a triangle around them. Now plot point $P_{16} = -(4\angle -240°)$. The point within the parentheses is one that is located on the 4-unit circle and along the radial line located by traveling 240 deg in the clockwise (negative) direction. This point thus falls in the second quadrant as shown in Fig. 6-6. The point P_{16}, which is the negative of the point within the parentheses, is located 180 deg away from the second-quadrant point just plotted and is therefore on the 4-unit circle in the fourth quadrant, as shown in Fig. 6-6. It is called out by a locating triangle around the plotted point.

Can point P_{16} be designated by polar coordinate notation in any manner other than $P_{16} = -(4\angle -240°)$? Since the plotted point, P_{16}, falls on the 300-deg line, the point can also be designated as $P_{16} = 4\angle 300°$, but the 300-deg line and the —60-deg line are the same line. Thus, the point P_{16} can also be expressed with the notation $P_{16} = 4\angle -60°$.

One more designation is made possible by again using the minus sign outside the parentheses. Since initially the angle within the parentheses was shown as $\angle -240°$, it can be replaced by $\angle 120°$, since the two notations refer to the same radial line. Thus, a fourth polar designation for P_{16} is $P_{16} = -(4\angle 120°)$.

This negative notation, which usually results from some operation or calculation, adds two polar designations to those previously discussed for each point. Consequently, each loca-

tion on a polar coordinate graph sheet can be designated in four different ways. The four designations for points P_{14}, P_{15}, and P_{16} are shown in Table 6-2. In addition, one designation is given for four other points that appear plotted in Fig. 6-6. It is strongly recommended that you fill in the blank spaces of Table 6-2 before proceeding any further.

The columns of Table 6-2 have been arranged so that the notation patterns that yield the four different designations for each point become evident. Note that each point can be designated with a positive angle and with the corresponding negative angle designation of the same radial line. This is true again for the notation involving the minus sign outside of the parentheses, yielding a total of four different designations for each location. Either one of the first two column notation methods is commonly used to designate a point.

The notations of the third and fourth columns often develop during plotting procedures, as will be seen later, and are otherwise not commonly used. Since they contain more symbols than their equivalent notations in the first two columns, they are usually replaced by the simpler notation. As a matter of fact, the clumsy notations of columns III and IV are very often written without the parentheses. This is done only to save some time and effort in the writing of these notations and should not be construed as having a different meaning. The minus sign in front of the entire number still means an addition of 180 deg (a subtraction of 180 deg yields the same result) to the angle of the given point.

Table 6-2. Four polar designations are possible for each plotted point
(The points listed in this table are plotted in Fig. 6-6.)

Point	Designations			
	I	II	III	IV
P_{16}	$4\angle 300°$	$4\angle -60°$	$-(4\angle 120°)$	$-(4\angle -240°)$
P_{15}	$7\angle 45°$	$7\angle -315°$	$-(7\angle 225°)$	$-(7\angle -135°)$
P_{14}	$4\angle 240°$	$4\angle -120°$	$-(4\angle 60°)$	$-(4\angle -300°)$
P_5	$5.4\angle 200°$			
P_4		$8\angle -210°$		
P_2			$-(5\angle 150°)$	
P_1				$-(5\angle -150°)$

The origin of the minus sign, meaning an addition (or subtraction) of 180 deg, or meaning a reversal in direction, can be traced back to the cartesian coordinate system. If the abscissa $+5$ is plotted along the X axis, it appears on the axis 5 units to the right of the origin. The abscissa -5 when plotted on the axis appears 5 units to the left of the origin. The only difference between the two quantities when written is that one is preceded by a minus sign. The effect of this minus sign is to cause the point to which it refers to be plotted 180 deg away from the $+5$ point. Another way of expressing the same thing is that the point with the minus sign is plotted in a direction opposite to that of the positive number. Thus, the minus sign actually refers to direction, and its effect is to add 180 deg to the angle of the polar notation. It is apparent from what has been said thus far that an addition or subtraction of 180 deg is equivalent to a reversal of direction, and the minus sign is used in this sense in polar coordinate notation.

6.4. Trigonometric functions on polar coordinate paper

Our discussions thus far have centered around conventions and notations associated with polar coordinate plotting and with becoming familiar with how points are located on the polar gridwork. We are at a stage now where this background can be applied to plotting curves on polar paper. In addition to gaining practice in plotting curves, it will be interesting to note the effect that polar paper has on the shape of familiar curves, and several significant comparisons between rectangular and polar plots will be made as we progress.

6.5. The sine function

Probably the most useful curve in technology is the sine waveshape. Since ρ (rho) is the dependent variable and θ (theta) is independent, the equation of the sine function in polar coordinates becomes $\rho = k \sin \theta$, where k represents any constant. To simplify the calculations and plotting, let us take the value of k as 10. Thus, the equation to be plotted is $\rho = 10 \sin \theta$.

Whenever an equation is to be plotted, regardless of whether it is in the cartesian coordinate system, polar coordinate system, or any other, it is necessary to prepare a table of values. Table 6-3 is the required table of values. Note that the independent quantity (θ) is shown every 15 deg from 0 to 360 deg. The values for ρ are obtained by determining the sine of the appropriate angle θ and multiplying that value by 10 as called for by the equation. Reference to the trigonometric function data paper in Fig. 6-5 shows the usefulness of this paper in an application of this type, since the required $\sin \theta$ values from 0° to 360° are listed.

Table 6-3 gives the coordinates of 25 points to be plotted. The first of these is $0 \angle 0°$. Since the distance from the pole is 0, the point appears at the pole. In other words, $0 \angle \theta$ are the coordinates of the pole, regardless of the value of the angle. This point is shown as P_1 in Fig. 6-7. Point P_2 is $2.6 \angle 15°$. To locate P_2, follow the 15° radial line out to a distance

Table 6-3. Coordinates for the equation $\rho = 10 \sin \theta$

θ	0°	15°	30°	45°	60°	75°	90°	105°	120°	135°	150°	165°	180°
ρ	0	2.6	5.0	7.1	8.7	9.7	10	9.7	8.7	7.1	5.0	2.6	0
Plotted point	P_1	P_2	P_3	P_4	P_5	P_6	P_7	P_8	P_9	P_{10}	P_{11}	P_{12}	P_{13}

θ	195°	210°	225°	240°	255°	270°	285°	300°	315°	330°	345°	360°
ρ	−2.6	−5.0	−7.1	−8.7	−9.7	−10	−9.7	−8.7	−7.1	−5.0	−2.6	0
Plotted point	P_{14}	P_{15}	P_{16}	P_{17}	P_{18}	P_{19}	P_{20}	P_{21}	P_{22}	P_{23}	P_{24}	P_{25}

of 2.6 and locate the point P_2 as shown in Fig. 6-7. It should be noted here that the calibration of the 0° line of Fig. 6-7 is such that each major circle is taken as 2 units instead of 1. This was done to permit the use of only those circles that show complete circumferences on the paper. If each major circle were taken as 1 unit, the 8, 9, and 10 circles would not show complete circumferences, and some of the points to be plotted would not fall on the graph sheet.

The plot is continued by locating points P_3 to P_{12} inclusive as shown in the plot of Fig. 6-7. Point P_{13}, $0 \angle 180°$, is another point that falls on the pole, since, as for P_1, the distance from the pole is 0. Thus, P_1 and P_{13} are the same point, and are so indicated in the diagram. When the 13 plotted points are connected by a smooth curve in the order in which they were plotted, the circle shown in Fig. 6-7 results. Note that the diameter of the circle is 10 units, which is the coefficient of the sin θ term in the equation of the curve.

But this curve was drawn with only 13 of the 25 points plotted. What happens when the next 12 points are plotted? The first of these is P_{14}, which from Table 6-3, has the coordinates $-2.6 \angle 195°$. Here we see an application of the polar coordinate notation type shown in Column III of Table 6-2, except that the parentheses are not shown. In order to plot point P_{14}, it is necessary first to locate $2.6 \angle 195°$ and then to find the point, P_{14}, which is 180 deg away from this location. The point $2.6 \angle 195°$ is shown located in Fig. 6-7. The point, P_{14}, which is 180 deg away from this location, falls directly on the point P_2, already plotted. By the same token, point P_{15} superimposes on plotted point P_3. Thus, because of the minus sign that precedes each of the ρ values for the angles from 180 to 360 deg, each of the last 12 points of Table 6-3 falls directly on a point already plotted. The resultant curve is, therefore, still the circle drawn through the first 12 points, as shown in Fig. 6-7. Recalling the sinusoidal waveshape produced when the equation $y = \sin \theta$ was plotted on cartesian coordinate paper, we can appreciate the drastic change produced by

plotting a given equation on polar coordinate instead of rectangular coordinate paper.

In our discussions in Chapter 4 we considered the equation of the circle with its center at the origin. Recall that the equation of a circle so oriented is $x^2 + y^2 = r^2$. In rectangular coordinates, the equation of a circle whose center is shifted upward from the origin is $x^2 + (y - k)^2 = r^2$. This equation is certainly more involved than the polar equation, $\rho = 10 \sin \theta$. For this and several other curves, the polar coordinate equation is far simpler than the corresponding rectangular coordinate equation and for that reason is often preferred. As another example, consider the polar equation $\rho = 5$. This equation states that, regardless of the value of θ, ρ is 5 units from the pole. If for every angle we plot a point, on polar paper, that is 5 units from the pole, the result will be a circle, with its center at the pole having a radius of 5 units. This is, therefore, the equation of the 5-unit circle that forms part of the gridwork of a sheet of polar coordinate paper. As discussed in the previous paragraph, the rectangular coordinate equation for such a circle is $x^2 + y^2 = 5^2$. No argument exists that the polar equation for this curve is far simpler.

6.6. The cosine function

In cartesian coordinates, the cosine curve has the same shape as the sine curve and differs from it only in phase. Let's plot the cosine curve in polar coordinates and determine whether the same holds true. In order to permit a ready comparison between the two curves, we will plot a cosine equation containing the same coefficient used in the sine plot of Fig. 6-7. Thus, the equation to be plotted is $\rho = 10 \cos \theta$, and Table 6-4 is the table of coordinates for this plot.

When the first seven points of Table 6-4 are plotted and connected, they form the semicircle shown in the first quadrant of Fig. 6-8. Now let's consider point P_8. The coordinates for this point are $P_8 = -2.6 \angle 105°$. It is understood that a pair of parentheses should separate the minus sign from the rest of the quantity, but, since the parentheses are not

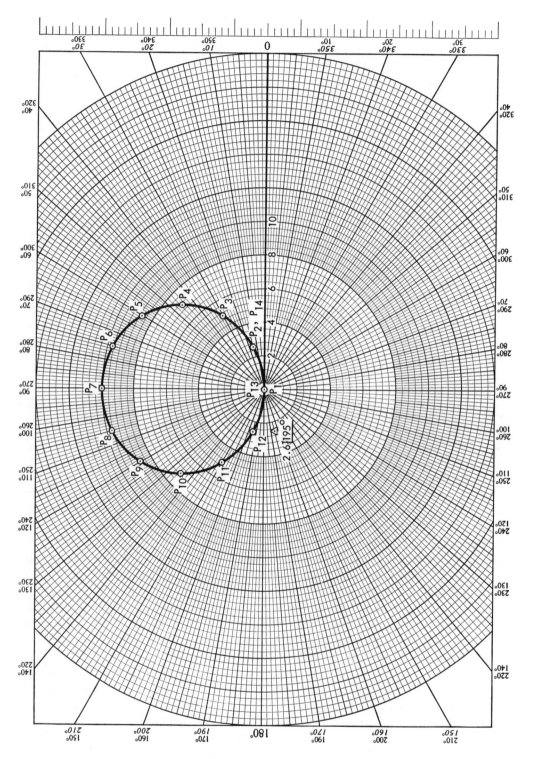

Fig. 6-7. Polar coordinate plot of $\rho = 10 \sin \theta$

Table 6-4. Coordinates for the equation $\rho = 10 \cos \theta$

θ	0°	15°	30°	45°	60°	75°	90°	105°	120°	135°	150°	165°	180°
ρ	10	9.7	8.7	7.1	5.0	2.6	0	−2.6	−5.0	−7.1	−8.7	−9.7	−10.0
Plotted point	P_1	P_2	P_3	P_4	P_5	P_6	P_7	P_8	P_9	P_{10}	P_{11}	P_{12}	P_{13}

θ	195°	210°	225°	240°	255°	270°	285°	300°	315°	330°	345°	360°
ρ	−9.7	−8.7	−7.1	−5.0	−2.6	0	2.6	5.0	7.1	8.7	9.7	10.0
Plotted point	P_{14}	P_{15}	P_{16}	P_{17}	P_{18}	P_{19}	P_{20}	P_{21}	P_{22}	P_{23}	P_{24}	P_{25}

shown in Table 6-4, they are omitted in the above notation also. The polar notation for point P_8 indicates that this point is 180 deg away from the location 2.6 $\angle$ 105°. This location is shown plotted in Fig. 6-9 and is called out by a locating triangle. Thus, the point P_8, which is 180 deg away from this plotted location, falls in the fourth quadrant of the Fig. 6-9 plot. A similar condition exists for points P_9 through P_{13}. Thus, a smooth curve drawn through the first 13 plotted points produces a circle of 10 units diameter.

As in the case of the sine plot, this circle was produced by plotting just over half of the points shown in the table of values. What does the plot look like when all the points are plotted? To answer this question, let's consider the next point in the table, $P_{14} = -9.7 \angle 195°$.

Figure 6-8 shows the location 9.7 $\angle$ 195°. Since P_{14} is the plotted on the opposite side of the pole from this location and the same distance (9.7 units) from the pole as this location, it is apparent that P_{14} is superimposed on P_2. A plot of the next four points of Table 6-4 shows that each falls on a point already plotted in the first quadrant of Fig. 6-8. Point P_{19} has a polar distance of 0 and is therefore plotted at the pole itself. The remaining six points shown in the table of coordinates are not preceded by a minus sign. How do these affect the curve produced by the points already plotted? Note that all of these six points are located at angles greater than 270 deg and are therefore all in the fourth quadrant. A plot of these six points shows that they each fall on a point already plotted and consequently do not alter

the curve at all.

Hence, as expected, the cosine plot in polar coordinates produces the same shape curve as does the sine plot. In cartesian coordinates the two waveshapes are 90 deg out of phase, and the cosine curve leads the sine. Is the same true in polar coordinates? Note from Fig. 6-8 that the center of the cosine circle is on the 0-deg line and has coordinates 5 $\angle$ 0°. Figure 6-7 shows that the center of the sine circle is on the 90-deg line, and its coordinates are 5 $\angle$ 90°. Since the positive direction of rotation is counterclockwise, we can say that the 90-deg line lags the 0-deg line by 90 deg. Extending this idea to the curves, we can say that the sine circle lags the cosine circle by 90 deg. It can be seen that this is so by recognizing that a 90-deg clockwise rotation of the sine circle will cause it to coincide with the cosine circle.

Another comparison of these two polar plots that is often made is a comparison of the rho values of the two curves when θ equals 0 deg. Note from the sine circle plot of Fig. 6-7 that when $\theta = 0$ deg, then $\rho = 0$. However, from the cosine circle plot of Fig. 6-8, notice that at $\theta = 0$ deg, $\rho = 10$, its maximum value. This arrangement, the sine curve at zero when the cosine curve is at its maximum value, was also clearly seen in the rectangular-coordinate plots of Chapter 4.

The circle produced by plotting the equation $\rho = 10 \cos \theta$ can also be expressed in rectangular coordinates by the equation

$$(x - h)^2 + y^2 = r^2$$

where for this particular case (Fig. 6-8) both h and r have a value of 5. Here again, it can be

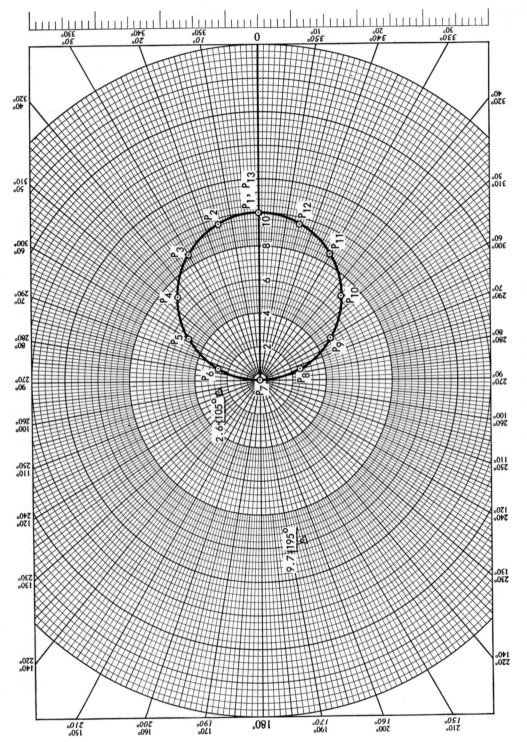

Fig. 6-8. Polar coordinate plot of $\rho = 10 \cos \theta$

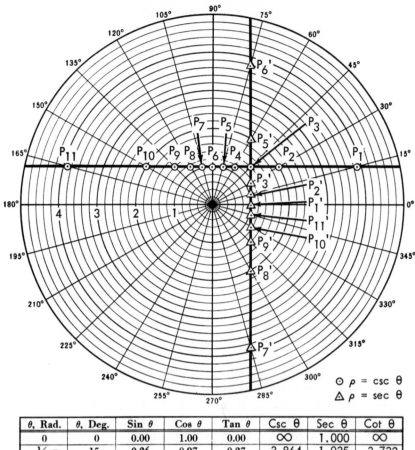

θ, Rad.	θ, Deg.	Sin θ	Cos θ	Tan θ	Csc θ	Sec θ	Cot θ
0	0	0.00	1.00	0.00	∞	1.000	∞
$\frac{1}{12}\pi$	15	0.26	0.97	0.27	3.864	1.035	3.732
$\frac{1}{6}\pi$	30	0.50	0.87	0.58	2.000	1.155	1.732
$\frac{1}{4}\pi$	45	0.71	0.71	1.00	1.414	1.414	1.000
$\frac{1}{3}\pi$	60	0.87	0.50	1.73	1.155	2.000	0.577
$\frac{5}{12}\pi$	75	0.97	0.26	3.73	1.035	3.864	0.268
$\frac{1}{2}\pi$	90	1.00	0.00	- - - -	1.000	∞	0.000
$\frac{7}{12}\pi$	105	0.97	-0.26	-3.73	1.035	-3.864	-0.268
$\frac{2}{3}\pi$	120	0.87	-0.50	-1.73	1.155	-2.000	-0.577
$\frac{3}{4}\pi$	135	0.71	-0.71	-1.00	1.414	-1.414	-1.000
$\frac{5}{6}\pi$	150	0.50	-0.87	-0.58	2.000	-1.155	-1.732
$\frac{11}{12}\pi$	165	0.26	-0.97	-0.27	3.864	-1.035	-3.732
π	180	0.00	-1.00	0.00	∞	-1.000	∞
$\frac{13}{12}\pi$	195	-0.26	-0.97	0.27	-3.864	-1.035	3.732
$\frac{7}{6}\pi$	210	-0.50	-0.87	0.58	-2.000	-1.155	1.732
$\frac{5}{4}\pi$	225	-0.71	-0.71	1.00	-1.414	-1.414	1.000
$\frac{4}{3}\pi$	240	-0.87	-0.50	1.73	-1.155	-2.000	0.577
$\frac{17}{12}\pi$	255	-0.97	-0.26	3.73	-1.035	-3.864	0.268
$\frac{3}{2}\pi$	270	-1.00	0.00	- - - -	-1.000	∞	0.000
$\frac{19}{12}\pi$	285	-0.97	0.26	-3.73	-1.035	3.864	-0.268
$\frac{5}{3}\pi$	300	-0.87	0.50	-1.73	-1.155	2.000	-0.577
$\frac{7}{4}\pi$	315	-0.71	0.71	-1.00	-1.414	1.414	-1.000
$\frac{11}{6}\pi$	330	-0.50	0.87	-0.58	-2.000	1.155	-1.732
$\frac{23}{12}\pi$	345	-0.26	0.97	-0.27	-3.864	1.035	-3.732
2π	360	0.00	1.00	0.00	∞	1.000	∞

Fig. 6-9. Application of trigonometric function data paper

seen that the polar coordinate equation is by far the simpler of the two and is often preferred for this reason.

6.7. The cosecant and the secant

In Chapter 4 we defined the cosecant as the reciprocal of the sine and the secant as the reciprocal of the cosine. Plotting these curves on the basis of this definition permitted us to determine the general shape of these significant curves and their properties. In addition, it permitted us to determine what kind of a curve is produced when we plot the reciprocal of a sinusoid.

The same two purposes can be served in connection with polar coordinate plots of the cosecant and secant variations. The plots will show us how these two functions appear in polar coordinates as compared with their rectangular coordinate shapes. In addition, since these functions are reciprocals of variations that yielded circles, we will in effect determine what curve is produced when the reciprocal of a circle is plotted in polar coordinates. If for the cosecant plot we use the equation, $\rho = \csc \theta$, with a coefficient of 1, then the values for ρ can be read directly from the trigonometric tables of Fig. 6-9. These corresponding values for θ and ρ, as well as the numbers of the plotted points, are given in Table 6-5.

Since at 0 deg, ρ is infinite, the first point is plotted at 15 deg at a polar distance of 3.86. This is the point P_1 shown in the first quadrant of the polar grid portion of Fig. 6-9. If the plot is continued up to point P_{11} of Table 6-5 and the points connected, they form a straight line parallel to the 0 deg line and at a

perpendicular distance of 1 unit from it. Since ρ is infinite when θ is 180 deg, we have another point that cannot be plotted. Table 6-5 shows that the coordinates for all the points from P_{12} to P_{22} inclusive are preceded by a minus sign. Thus, when these points are plotted 180 deg away from the indicated angle, they each fall on a point already plotted and in no way alter the straight-line locus. Consequently, the complete csc θ plot is the horizonal straight line shown in Fig. 6-9. The curve is certainly drastically different, and far simpler, than the discontinuous, asymptotic cosecant curve of the rectangular coordinate system.

Furthermore, this straight-line plot is the result of plotting the reciprocal of a circle. It is an interesting relationship that is put to good use. One application occurs in the discussion and plotting of admittances and impedances in connection with electrical circuit calculations.

In cartesian coordinates the secant curve is very similar in shape to the cosecant curve. The only difference between the two is that the secant curve leads the cosecant curve by 90 deg. The circle plots for the sine and cosine were proven to be similar to one another in polar coordinates and also maintained the same phase relationship to one another that the functions exhibited in the rectangular system. On the basis of this, it seems safe to predict that the secant will plot as a straight line, but how is the phase relationship shown graphically?

Again, as in the case of the cosecant curve, we will use the simplest form of the equation $\rho = \sec \theta$, so that the values for ρ can be read

Table 6-5. Coordinates for the equation $\rho = \csc \theta$

θ	0°	15°	30°	45°	60°	75°	90°	105°	120°	135°	150°	165°	180°
ρ	$\pm\infty$	3.86	2.0	1.41	1.16	1.04	1.0	1.04	1.16	1.41	2.0	3.86	$\pm\infty$
Plotted point	..	P_1	P_2	P_3	P_4	P_5	P_6	P_7	P_8	P_9	P_{10}	P_{11}	..

θ	195°	210°	225°	240°	255°	270°	285°	300°	315°	330°	345°	360°
ρ	−3.86	−2.0	−1.41	−1.16	−1.04	−1.0	−1.04	−1.16	−1.41	−2.0	−3.86	$\pm\infty$
Plotted point	P_{12}	P_{13}	P_{14}	P_{15}	P_{16}	P_{17}	P_{18}	P_{19}	P_{20}	P_{21}	P_{22}	..

directly from the table of Fig. 6-9. The corresponding values of ρ and θ are given in Table 6-6 as well as the numbers of the plotted points. Since the cosecant and secant plots are simple curves, and since we are interested in comparing them with one another, the two are plotted on the same polar grid, and both appear in Fig. 6-9. To permit us to refer to the plotted points of each of the two curves without confusing one with the other, the points of the secant plot are marked with a prime (') symbol.

Points P_1' through P_6' inclusive plot directly on the first quadrant and when connected form a straight line extending upward from the 0-deg line. At 90 deg ρ is infinite and therefore cannot be shown. However, the line is extended to indicate that it continues in the same manner beyond the plotted point P_6'. This extension of the secant line is parallel to the 90-deg line, since, like all parallel lines, they are known to meet at infinity. (Another way of saying that the two are parallel.) The angles for points P_7' through P_{11}' are second-quadrant angles. However, as can be seen from Table 6-6, each of these points is preceded by a minus sign. Hence, when they are plotted, they fall in the fourth quadrant, as shown in Fig. 6-6. Point P_{12}' superimposes on the already plotted point P_1'. When these last six plotted points are connected they form a straight line that connects to the line formed by the first six plotted points. This line is parallel to the 90- and 270-deg lines and is 1 unit from them, measured on a perpendicular between the parallel lines. The angles shown for the next five points of Table 6-6 are third-quadrant angles. However, each of the points

P_{13}' to P_{17}' inclusive is preceded by a minus sign. Consequently, when these points are plotted, they fall in the first quadrant and are superimposed on the points already plotted there. At 270 deg, ρ is infinite and the line is extended below P_7' as well as above P_6' to indicate this. The angles for the last six points of Table 6-6 are seen to be fourth-quadrant angles. Thus, when these points are plotted, they fall on the points already shown in this quadrant. The resultant plot is therefore the vertical line produced by plotting the first half of the table.

As expected, therefore, the secant function produces a straight line in polar coordinates, and since the line is vertical, it makes a 90-deg angle with the horizontal line of the cosecant plot. It is possible to compare the two curves point by point to show that one leads the other, but that portion of the relationship is not critical, since each curve is a limitless straight line. Also, as in the case of the cosecant we see again that a straight line is produced by plotting the reciprocal of a circle.

6.8. The tangent and the cotangent

One primary and one secondary trigonometric function remain to be observed in the polar coordinate system. These are, of course, the tangent and cotangent curves. If, as in the case of the two previous plots we use the simplest form of the equation containing the desired functions, then we can obtain the values for ρ directly from the tables of Fig. 6-9. These values are repeated for the tangent curve in Table 6-7 along with the corresponding θ values and the plotted point numbers.

Table 6-6. Coordinates for the equation $\rho = \sec \theta$

θ	0°	15°	30°	45°	60°	75°	90°	105°	120°	135°	150°	165°	180°
ρ	1.0	1.04	1.16	1.41	2.0	3.86	$\pm\infty$	−3.86	−2.0	−1.41	−1.16	−1.04	−1.0
Plotted point	P_1'	P_2'	P_3'	P_4'	P_5'	P_6'	..	P_7'	P_8'	P_9'	P_{10}'	P_{11}'	P_{12}'

θ	195°	210°	225°	240°	255°	270°	285°	300°	315°	330°	345°	360°
ρ	−1.04	−1.16	−1.41	−2.0	−3.86	$\pm\infty$	3.86	2.0	1.41	1.16	1.04	1.00
Plotted point	P_{13}'	P_{14}'	P_{15}'	P_{16}'	P_{17}'	..	P_{18}'	P_{19}'	P_{20}'	P_{21}'	P_{22}'	P_{23}'

Table 6-7. Coordinates for the equation $\rho = \tan \theta$

θ	0°	15°	30°	45°	60°	75°	90°	105°	120°	135°	150°	165°	180°
ρ	0	0.27	0.58	1.00	1.73	3.73	$\pm\infty$	−3.73	−1.73	−1.00	−0.58	−0.27	0
Plotted point	P_1	P_2	P_3	P_4	P_5	P_6	..	P_7	P_8	P_9	P_{10}	P_{11}	P_{12}

θ	195°	210°	225°	240°	255°	270°	285°	300°	315°	330°	345°	360°
ρ	0.27	0.58	1.00	1.73	3.73	$\pm\infty$	−3.73	−1.73	−1.00	−0.58	−0.27	0
Plotted point	P_{13}	P_{14}	P_{15}	P_{16}	P_{17}	..	P_{18}	P_{19}	P_{20}	P_{21}	P_{22}	P_{23}

The first plotted point of the tangent curve, P_1, is seen in Fig. 6-10 to be the pole, since its polar distance is shown to be 0 in Table 6-7. The next five points, to P_6 inclusive, are first-quadrant points and are shown plotted as such. The scale of Fig. 6-10 is such that no first-quadrant points beyond 75 deg are shown plotted. However, between 75 and 90 deg the values for ρ approach infinity very rapidly. The effect on the curve is to cause it to become asymptotic to a vertical line perpendicular to the 0-deg line. This property is the same as that exhibited by the tangent curve plotted in rectangular coordinates, since it too is asymptotic at 90 deg.

The angles for points P_7 through P_{11} are second-quadrant angles. Since each of these points is preceded by a minus sign, they plot in the fourth quadrant, as shown in Fig. 6-10. Point P_{12} is superimposed on P_1, since its polar distance is also 0. The next five points in the plot are third-quadrant points and plot as such. Here again the limits of the scale of Fig. 6-10 make the 255-deg point the last third-quadrant point that can be shown. However, in polar as in rectangular coordinates, the plot of the tangent curve becomes asymptotic to a vertical line at 270 deg. The balance of the plot appears in the second quadrant, since each of the next five points to be plotted is preceded by a minus sign and the angles associated with these points are fourth-quadrant angles. The last point, P_{23}, has the coordinates of the pole and is therefore also superimposed on point P_1.

Of the five trigonometric functions plotted so far, the tangent curve is the first to show any similarity to its shape in cartesian coordinates. The asymptotic property and the general shape of each quarter of the curve compares favorably to the tangent shape we are familiar with from our earlier discussions. The over-all curve is, however, not by any means the same as the $y = \tan \theta$ plot of Chapter 4, since the parts of the curve connect together differently.

In rectangular coordinates the cotangent curve was quite similar to the tangent curve in general shape and properties. Recall, however, that the cotangent curve was not merely the tangent curve displaced by 90 deg. As a matter of fact, it was not possible to obtain a phase relationship between the two curves, regardless of their generally similar shape. Let us then obtain the polar plot of the cotangent curve and determine whether a similar condition exists in this coordinate system. The equation to be plotted is $\rho = \cot \theta$, and Table 6-8 provides the coordinates as well as the numbers for the plotted points.

The procedure for plotting the points of Table 6-8 is very much the same as that for the previously considered polar plots, and the result is shown in Fig. 6-11. Note that the general shape of each of the four sections of the curve is the same as that of the tangent curve sections. The cotangent curve, however, is generally horizontal as compared with the generally vertical nature of the tangent curve. This comparison seems to indicate that the two curves are out of phase with one another by 90°. This would mean that each point on one of the curves is 90° away from its corresponding point on the other curve. Note carefully,

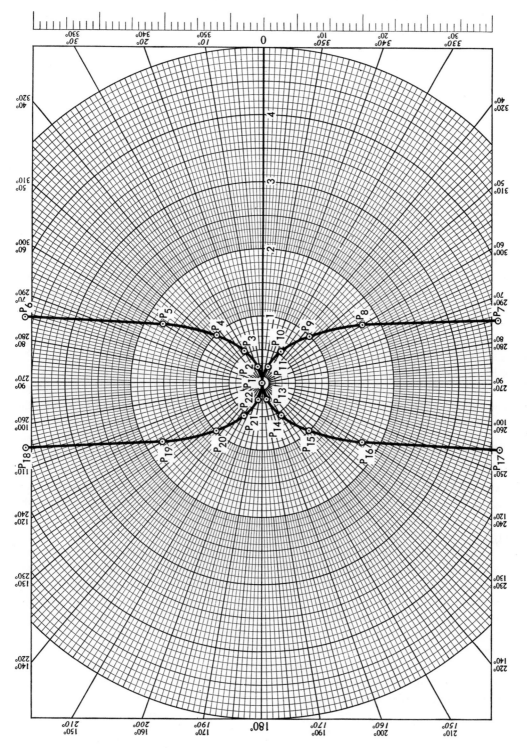

Fig. 6-10. Plot of $\rho = \tan\theta$

Table 6-8. Coordinates for the equation $\rho = \cot \theta$

θ	0°	15°	30°	45°	60°	75°	90°	105°	120°	135°	150°	165°	180°
ρ	$\pm\infty$	3.73	1.73	1.0	0.58	0.27	0	−0.27	0.58	−1.00	−1.73	−3.73	∞
Plotted point		P_1	P_2	P_3	P_4	P_5	P_6	P_7	P_8	P_9	P_{10}	P_{11}	P_{12}

θ	195°	210°	225°	240°	255°	270°	285°	300°	315°	330°	345°	360°
ρ	3.73	1.73	1.00	0.58	0.27	0	−0.27	−0.58	−1.00	−1.73	−3.73	$\pm\infty$
Plotted point	P_{12}	P_{13}	P_{14}	P_{15}	P_{16}	P_{17}	P_{18}	P_{19}	P_{20}	P_{21}	P_{22}	

on Fig. 6-10 and 6-11, the order in which the points are plotted for the two curves. Observe from this order of plotting that no fixed phase relationship can be established between the points of one curve and that of the second. Consequently, an analogous situation exists between the polar plots of the tangent and cotangent curves and their plot in rectangular system form. At first glance the curves seem to show a specific phase relationship, but careful investigation shows this not to be the case.

The polar cotangent curve is asymptotic at 0° and 180° as in the rectangular system. However, the asymptotes are horizontal lines, not vertical ones as seen in the rectangular system.

6.9. Spirals and roses

Figures 6-1, 6-2, 6-3, and 6-4 are all plotted on polar coordinates rather than rectangular coordinates, since in each case the technical application required showing how a specific quantity, or magnitude, varied as the angle from a reference direction changed. Certainly any plot is made to order for polar coordinates if it is designed to show an effective or operating region defined by angles from a specific reference direction. We have also shown that a polar coordinate plot of familiar rectangular curves can yield shapes drastically different from the rectangular plot. Further, the polar equation yielding a specific curve can be far simpler than the rectangular equation required to yield the same curve.

There is, in addition, an entire series of useful curves that lend themselves to polar coordinate plotting. Two of the most common sets of these curves are the "spirals" and the

"roses." The spiral known as Archimedes' spiral is probably the most well-known of these. Its equation is $\rho = k\,\theta$, where k is any constant value. Not only is the shape of this curve an interesting and useful one (an application is the basic shape of centrifugal pump casings), but the method for plotting this curve is somewhat different from any of the polar plots we have done so far. For purposes of simplicity, let's set the constant k equal to 1, making the equation for our plot $\rho = \theta$.

In each of the previous equations we dealt with a trigonometric function of θ, and it was either the sine or the cosine or some other function of θ that gave us the value of ρ to be plotted—and this is true for most polar equations. But our equation of the spiral states that the polar magnitude, ρ, at every value of the angle θ, is to be *equal* to θ. The question therefore is, "How can we express an angle so that it can be used as a magnitude?" And the answer is, "Use radian measure."

In other words, in order to plot an equation of this type, we can express θ in degrees to determine the position, or angle from the 0 line of the point to be plotted. However, when the angle θ is to be used to provide the polar distance ρ, it is expressed in radian measure, and this polar distance is plotted at the appropriate angle. The table of values for this plot, Table 6-9, shows the angle θ expressed in degress, and the polar distance ρ expressed first in terms of π and then in fractional form. The numbers of the plotted points are also shown.

The 30 points given in Table 6-9 are plotted in Fig. 6-12, and its spiral nature is evident at a glance. It should be noted that the points

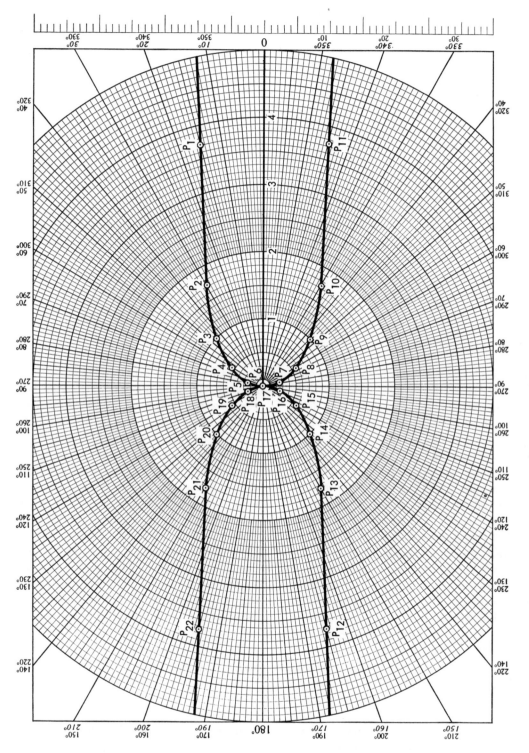

Fig. 6-11. Plot of $\rho = \operatorname{ctn} \theta$

Table 6-9. Coordinates for the equation $\rho = \theta$

θ	0°	15°	30°	45°	60°	75°	90°	105°	120°	135°
ρ	0	$\dfrac{\pi}{12}$	$\dfrac{\pi}{6}$	$\dfrac{\pi}{4}$	$\dfrac{\pi}{3}$	$\dfrac{5\pi}{12}$	$\dfrac{\pi}{2}$	$\dfrac{7\pi}{12}$	$\dfrac{2\pi}{3}$	$\dfrac{3\pi}{4}$
	0	0.26	0.52	0.79	1.05	1.31	1.57	1.83	2.10	2.36
Plotted point	P_1	P_2	P_3	P_4	P_5	P_6	P_7	P_8	P_9	P_{10}

θ	150°	165°	180°	195°	210°	225°	240°	255°	270°	285°
ρ	$\dfrac{5\pi}{6}$	$\dfrac{11\pi}{12}$	π	$\dfrac{13\pi}{12}$	$\dfrac{7\pi}{6}$	$\dfrac{5\pi}{4}$	$\dfrac{4\pi}{3}$	$\dfrac{17\pi}{12}$	$\dfrac{3\pi}{2}$	$\dfrac{19\pi}{12}$
	2.62	2.88	3.14	3.40	3.67	3.93	4.20	4.46	4.72	4.98
Plotted point	P_{11}	P_{12}	P_{13}	P_{14}	P_{15}	P_{16}	P_{17}	P_{18}	P_{19}	P_{20}

θ	300°	315°	330°	345°	360°	375°	390°	405°	420°	435°
ρ	$\dfrac{5\pi}{3}$	$\dfrac{7\pi}{4}$	$\dfrac{11\pi}{6}$	$\dfrac{23\pi}{12}$	2π	$\dfrac{25\pi}{12}$	$\dfrac{13\pi}{6}$	$\dfrac{27\pi}{12}$	$\dfrac{7\pi}{3}$	$\dfrac{29\pi}{12}$
	5.24	5.50	5.76	6.02	6.28	6.54	6.81	7.07	7.33	7.59
Plotted point	P_{21}	P_{22}	P_{23}	P_{24}	P_{25}	P_{26}	P_{27}	P_{28}	P_{29}	P_{30}

from P_{25} on are points in the second revolution of the spiral, that is, the angles for these points are 360 deg and greater. The only limit to the number of points that can be plotted for this (and any other) spiral is the size of the graph paper and the calibration scale chosen for the polar distances. However, regardless of whether the plot of Fig. 6-12 had been carried through the second or third revolution or more, it would still show only half of the spiral curve. Note that Table 6-9 considers positive angles only. Suppose, for example, we consider a point plotted at an angle of -30 deg. Such a point should fall in the fourth quadrant, since -30 deg is a fourth-quadrant angle. But according to the equation, the polar distance, ρ, equals the radian equivalent of the angle and it is therefore also negative. Thus, the coordinates of the point are -0.524 $\angle -30°$, and the point falls in the second quadrant 180 deg away from the -30 deg position. This point is shown plotted in Fig. 6-12 and is called out by a locating triangle. A second point of negative angle is also shown plotted in Fig. 6-12. For this second point θ is taken as -60 deg. The coordinates of the

point are therefore $-1.05 \angle -60°$, and it too plots in the second quadrant, as shown. With these two points as a start, it may be possible to visualize the appearance and location of the negative half of Archimedes' spiral. Before proceding further, complete the curve directly on Fig. 6-12. All the required numerical values appear in Table 6-9. Only the negative signs need be included for the second half of the curve.

At the beginning of this discussion it was stated that the properties of the spiral make it particularly adaptable to a polar plot. After tracing out the curve and noting how directly the location of each point is dependent upon its angular position from the 0-deg line, you can see why this statement was made.

It was also stated earlier that a second group of curves particularly adaptable to polar coordinate plotting are the "roses." This is a set of curves containing two, three, four, and more loops, referred to as "leaves," and the entire curve is named after the rose flower. Figure 6-13 shows examples of two-, three-, four-, and eight-leaved roses, and the polar equation for each curve is given below the

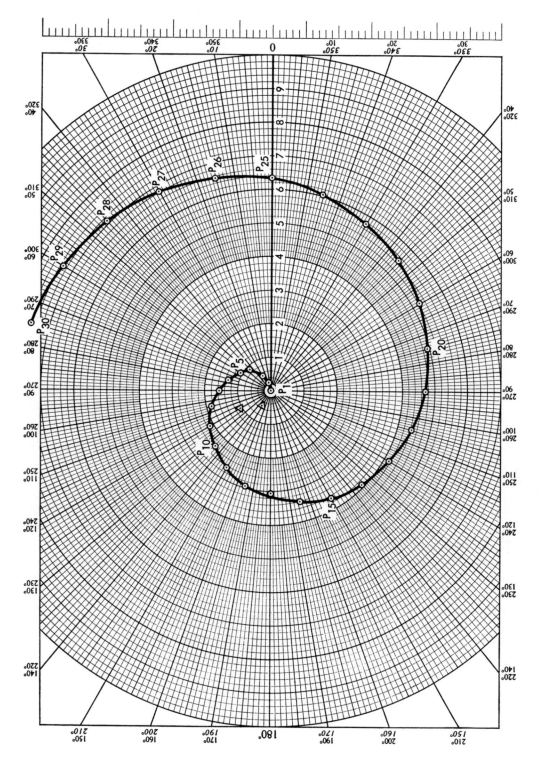

Fig. 6-12. Archimedes' spiral, positive portion

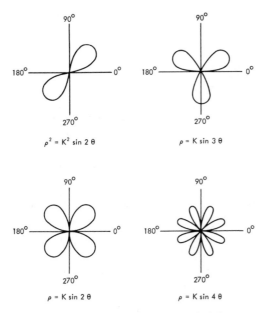

Fig. 6-13. Two-, three-, four-, and eight-leaved "roses"

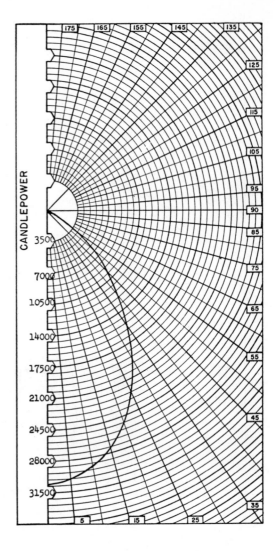

Fig. 6-14. Candlepower distribution semiplot

curve itself. The coefficient k in each of the equations is any constant, and for purposes of simplicity can be set equal to 1. It should also be noted that in the given equations the angle θ also has a coefficient of 2, 3, or 4. Thus, for example, in the case of the four-leaved rose ($\rho = k \sin 2\theta$), each angle must be doubled before the sine function is evaluated. If k is set equal to 1 in this equation, the coordinates of the point plotted at 30 deg are 0.866 $\angle$ 30°, the 0.866 being obtained by finding the sine of 60°, that is, the sine of twice 30 deg. The additional techniques required for plotting these equations have already been discussed in detail in connection with the other curves plotted in this chapter. From the shape of the "roses," and certainly from carrying out a plotting procedure, it is apparent that this set of shapes is also particularly adaptable to a polar system. The loop of Fig. 6-4 approximates very closely the leaf shape of the "roses" we have been discussing. Note also the candlepower distribution semiplot of Fig. 6-14. The second half of this plot is identical to the portion shown. If the second half of the plot is sketched in (or visualized), it becomes apparent that the shape of the total curve is very similar to that of the rose leaf.

6.10. Polar coordinates aid in the understanding of a-c circuits

For the reader interested in electric circuits, an important application of polar coordinates exists that incorporates directly the polar plots we have carried out for two of the trigonometric functions. We shall touch here only on the technique of analyzing an a-c circuit using the method of "current loci," but it will suffice to show the value of polar coordinates in this application.

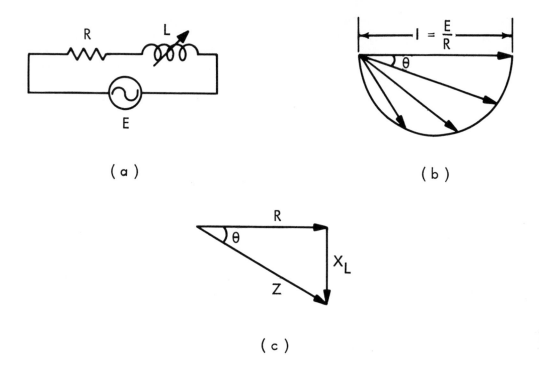

Fig. 6-15. Current locus of R-L circuit, with variable L

Let us consider a simple series a-c circuit made up of a resistor, R, an inductor, L, and a sinusoidal generator supplying the voltage, E. The circuit arrangement is shown in Fig. 6-15a. In a practical situation these quantities, R and L, are not maintained fixed or static but are continuously changed to produce desired results. In order to follow the changes in current as, let us say, L changes in value, a graphical approach is very effective. The arrow shown drawn through the inductor, L, of Fig. 6-15a indicates that the L (inductance) value changes. For simplicity everything else shown in the diagram will remain constant in value. The range of L values will be taken from 0 to infinity, thus encompassing all possible conditions.

When the value of L is 0, its "a-c resistance" (reactance) X_L is also equal to 0, and at this time the current, I, is at its maximum value of

$$I = E/R$$

This value of current, I, is represented in Fig. 6-15b by the horizontal arrow marked E/R.

It is the value of X_L that determines the angle θ of the current I, and since X_L is 0, the current I is shown at the 0-deg position. As L, and therefore X_L, increase, the value of I becomes smaller. In addition, the negative angle θ increases in value. Three additional current I arrows are shown drawn in Fig. 6-15b, each the result of a larger L value. Each is smaller than the preceding one, and each makes a larger clockwise angle with the horizontal. If a large number of these current-value arrows are computed and drawn and the ends of these arrows joined, a curve or locus (path) is obtained. This curve is called the "current locus." It would be extremely helpful to know if this is a regular, simple curve or some odd, irregular shape. If in all cases a simple curve is produced, and we can determine what it is, then accurate predictions can be made for current values and angles for any value of L. Let us investigate further.

From Ohm's Law the expression for current in an a-c circuit is

$$I = E/Z$$

Figure 6-15c shows how Z (impedance) is related to R and X_L. Trigonometry applied to this diagram tells us that

$$\cos \theta = R/Z$$

Rearranging this equation, we obtain

$$Z = R/\cos \theta$$

Now, if in the Ohm's Law equation above, we replace Z by its equivalent in terms of R and $\cos \theta$, we obtain

$$I = \frac{E}{R/\cos \theta}$$

This, when rearranged, becomes

$$I = \frac{E}{R} \cos \theta$$

Let us compare this with an equation of a type already plotted in Fig. 6-8, $\rho = k \cos \theta$. Obviously, the two equations have the same format. Thus, the current locus under conditions of varying L is a circle of diameter equal to E/R and with its center on the 0° line!

The above graphical approach to an a-c circuit is not limited to the simple series circuit shown. It is applicable to many circuit arrangements with one or more circuit quantities considered as varying. For our purposes here, however, we shall consider only one more simple series circuit. This second circuit is shown in Fig. 6-16a and is seen to contain a resistor, R, a capacitor, C, and the sinusoidal generator that supplies the voltage, E. In this circuit we shall consider that the resistor, R, changes value and that everything else remains constant. To indicate these conditions, an arrow is drawn through the R of Fig. 6-16a. We shall consider that R/C varies from 0 to infinity, again to include all possible conditions.

As before, let us start by setting R at a value of 0. Under this condition, the value of current, given by Ohm's Law is

$$I = E/X_C$$

and it is shown in Fig. 6-16b as a vertical arrow appropriately marked. The current is drawn at an angle of 90 deg since the circuit now contains only a capacitor, C, and no R,

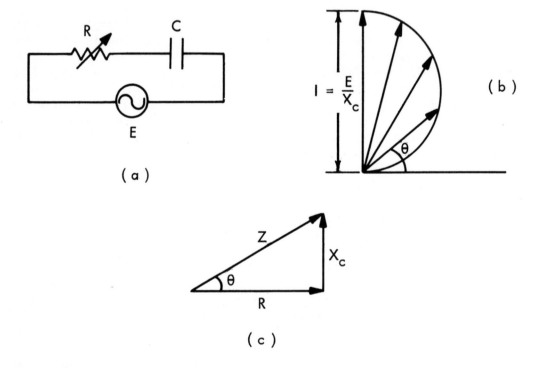

Fig. 6-16. Current locus of R-C circuit, with variable R

resulting in the 90-deg current direction. As R increases toward infinity, the value of the current, I, becomes smaller and so does the angle, θ. The three successive current arrows shown are each due to increased values of R. Each current arrow is smaller than the previous one, and each makes a smaller angle with the 0-deg line. The curve shown in Fig. 6-16b is obtained by connecting the tips of a large number of current arrows and is the current locus. We can again determine whether or not this is a regular curve by developing its polar equation as we did for the above case. Consequently, starting again with Ohm's Law for an a-c circuit, we have

$$I = E/Z$$

The relationship between R, X_C, and Z is shown in the triangle of Fig. 6-16c. Trigonometry applied to this triangle tells us that

$$\sin \theta = X_C/Z$$

Rearranging this equation, we have

$$Z = X_C/\sin \theta$$

If this expression for Z is put in the place of the Z in the Ohm's Law equation above, we obtain

$$I = \frac{E}{X_C/\sin \theta}$$

When this is rearranged it becomes

$$I = \frac{E}{X_C} \sin \theta$$

Now let us compare this expression with an equation of a type already plotted in Fig. 6-7, $\rho = k \sin \theta$. The I and ρ equations are, again, obviously of the same format. In other words the current locus is a circle of diameter equal to E/X_C, and its center lies on the 90° line. Thus, we again have a completely predictable and therefore usable circuit.

REVIEW

Define the following terms:

6-1. Polar coordinate paper

6-2. Pole

6-3. Fluxolite (luminous intensity) graph paper

6-4. Trigonometric function data paper

6-5. Zero-degree line

6-6. Positive direction of angle measurement

6-7. Negative direction of angle measurement

6-8. Standard reference line for angle measurement

6-9. Complete Table 6-2 by filling in three additional designations for points P_5, P_4, P_2, and P_1.

6-10. (a) Plot point $-5 \angle -220°$ on the polar sheet of Fig. 6-6. (b) List three additional designations for the same point.

6-11. When plotted on polar coordinate paper, (a) the angle between points A $= 5 \angle 30°$ and B $= -5 \angle 30°$ is _____ deg. (b) The angle between point C $= -3 \angle 30°$ and D $= -3 \angle -30°$ is _____ deg. (c) The distance between points E $= 6 \angle 60°$ and F $= -6 \angle 240°$ is _____ distance units. (d) The distance between point G $= 10 \angle 10°$ and H $= -10 \angle 10°$ is _____ distance units. (e) Of the eight point designations given above, those that fall in the fourth quadrant are _____.

6-12. (a) On a sheet of rectangular coordinate paper, sketch (do not plot) the curve whose equation is $y = -10 \sin \theta$. (b) On a sheet of polar coordinate paper, sketch (do not plot) the curve whose equation is $\rho = -10 \sin \theta$. (c) Give one advantage of the polar curve over the cartesian coordinate one.

6-13. Repeat problem 6-12 for the equations $y = -10 \cos \theta$ and $\rho = -10 \cos \theta$.

6-14. (a) On the same sheet of polar coordinate paper, sketch the curves, $\rho = -\csc \theta$ and $\rho = -\sec \theta$. (b) What is the phase relationship between these two plots? (c) How do these curves compare to the curves plotted in Fig. 6-9?

6-15. Determine carefully the order in which the points are plotted to produce the $\rho = \tan \theta$ curve of Fig. 6-10 and the $\rho = \cot \theta$ curve of Fig. 6-11. Compare the two, and comment on the phase relationship between the two curves.

6-16. (a) On the same sheet of polar coordinate paper sketch (do not plot) the curves $\rho = \cot \theta$ and $\rho = -\cot \theta$. (b) How do the two curves compare?

6-17. Use the numerical values of Table 6-9, and complete the plot of Archimedes' spiral on the graph sheet of Fig. 6-12. Let θ vary from 0 to -360 deg in multiples of 30 deg.

6-18. (a) Plot the curve of $\rho = -\theta$ on polar coordinate paper. (b) How does this plot compare to Archimedes' spiral? (c) Describe the graph that would be obtained by plotting $\rho = -\theta$ (ρ vs. θ) on rectangular coordinate paper.

6-19. (a) The equation $\rho = K/\theta$ yields a curve known as the reciprocal spiral. It is sometimes known as the hyperbolic spiral. Can you explain why? (b) Plot this curve on polar paper. (c) How does this plot differ from Archimedes' spiral?

6-20. (a) Plot the equation $\rho = \cos 3\theta$. (b) How does the plot compare to the three-leaved rose shown in Fig. 6-13?

6-21. Refer to the semi-plot of Fig. 6-14. What is the advantage of using a polar coordinate paper with the pole located at one border of the grid-work?

6-22. (a) Sketch the curve whose equation is $\rho = 10$. (b) What is the rectangular coordinate equation of this curve?

7 - GRAPHICAL SOLUTIONS
TO TECHNICAL PROBLEMS

If we are looking for a verbal definition of "twenty-five words or less," we can say that *a graphical solution is one in which plots, diagrams, and charts are used to supply data and conclusions in connection with a technical or mathematical problem.* The alternate to a graphical solution is an analytic or mathematical one, in which the techniques of the various branches of mathematics are applied to the problem. However, the verbal definition does not fully describe this area of graphical solution. Indeed, volumes have been written describing different aspects of this broad area, and many more will appear as the different technologies advance. It is the purpose of this chapter to give the reader an insight into this engineering technique and to cite some examples of graphical solutions in present use. The examples themselves are chosen to point up common types of graphical solutions and to indicate the broad range of application of these graphical techniques.

7.1. Each plot a "solution"

From what we know already of graphs and plots, we can say that each plot is a problem solution in itself, since it can provide considerable information to an experienced reader. Consider, for example, the distance-vs.-time plot of Fig. 3-1. The slope of this curve yields the velocity of the moving object. The fact that the plot is a straight line, that is, it has a

fixed slope throughout, tells us that the velocity of this moving object is constant for the time period in question. Similarly, the slope of the speed-vs.-time plot of Fig. 3-8 gives us the acceleration of this object, and the area under the curve supplies distance covered information.

A plot may permit predictions as indicated by the plot of Fig. 3-2. A plot may permit identification of specific conditions and properties of a material or device by noting changes of slope of a curve, as seen in Fig. 7-1. If we are looking for data or a pattern of behavior, we can utilize our knowledge that a straight line is the simplest to extend for predictions and to read for slope, area, and data points. There-

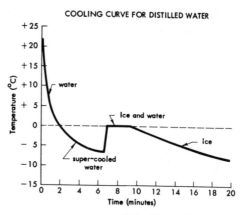

COOLING CURVE FOR DISTILLED WATER

Fig. 7-1. Changes in slope or character of plot permits identification of specific conditions

fore, as described in Chapter 5, we can often choose a graph paper that will yield a straight-line plot for the data or equation involved (see Figs. 5-7, 5-11, and 5-17). Thus, even the choice of graph paper for a specific plot is a step in a graphical solution.

In our discussions of multiple plots on the same set of axes, we used a technique of graphical solution to obtain answers to certain questions. The example of Fig. 3-5 shows us how to determine the distance between two vehicles at any time, and the discussion relating to Fig. 3-4 describes the many pieces of information available from the slopes and intercepts of the curves, their points of intersection, and their different abscissas for a common ordinate.

It is readily apparent whether two predictions give the same result if the plots appear on the same set of axes. This is illustrated in the approximate determination of absolute 0 temperature of Fig. 7-2. As another example, consider the value to a businessman of the multiple straight-line plots of Fig. 7-3. This simple break-even chart is a plot of costs-vs.-sales volume and income-vs.-sales volume on the same set of axes. On separate axes the shaded areas shown would have little significance. No explanation is needed of the significance of these axes as they appear on the multiple plot of Fig. 7-3.

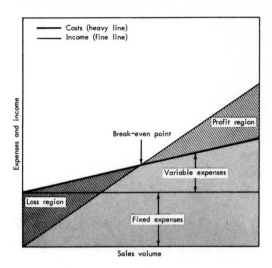

Fig. 7-3. Simple break-even chart clearly shows value of graphical solutions obtainable from multiple plots

Countless other examples can be given of significant information being available from a single plot and certainly from several plots on a common set of axes, and many not cited above appear in this text. However, this is only one type of graphical solution. Other common types are of equal importance.

7.2. Graphical addition and subtraction

The operation of any device, electrical, mechanical, or other, often requires that more than one input be supplied to the system simultaneously. The net effect is that the input to the device "sees" the *sum* of the two or more variations (often referred to as "signals" or "waveshapes"). How then does the user of the device determine in advance how the total input waveshape will appear? In other words, how does he carry out the addition of waveshapes? An addition of waveshapes is nothing more than an addition of ordinates. Reference to Fig. 7-4 will help clarify this statement. Note that Fig. 7-4a contains two waveshapes. The y_1 curve is a sine wave of amplitude 10 units, and its equation is therefore $y_1 = 10 \sin \theta$. y_2 shows no variation at all; that is, it is fixed at one value and does not vary with θ. Since its fixed value is 4, the equation for this quantity is $y_2 = 4$.

ABSOLUTE ZERO APPROXIMATION

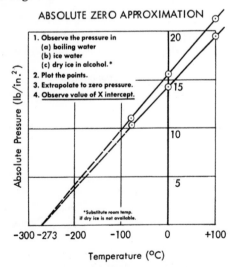

Fig. 7-2. Comparison of predictions made graphically is simplified when multiple plot is made on common set of axes

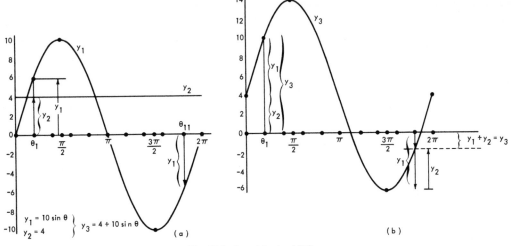

Fig. 7-4. Graphical addition

The sum of these two variations appears in Fig. 7-4b. How are the various ordinates of Fig. 7-4b obtained? Let's consider first the ordinates of the two curves when θ equals 0. At this abscissa $y_1 = 0$ and $y_2 = 4$. The sum of the two is 4. Therefore, on the sum curve of Fig. 7-4b the first plotted point is $(0, 4)$. At $\pi/2$ radians the y_1 ordinate $= 10$ and that of $y_2 = 4$. The sum, 14, is plotted in Fig. 7-4b at the abscissa $\pi/2$. At π radians the sum of the two ordinates is 4, yielding the coordinates $(\pi, 4)$ for a point on the b plot. Consider now the ordinates of the two curves of Fig. 7-4a at the abscissa value $3\pi/2$. y_2, of course, shows the fixed positive value of 4. The sine curve, y_1, has a negative ordinate of 10 at this point. The "sum" of these two values is actually an arithmetic subtraction. Thus, the ordinate plotted for y_3 at $3\pi/2$ is

$$y_3 = y_1 + y_2$$
$$y_3 = -10 + 4$$
$$= -6$$

At 2π radians, the y_3 ordinate is 4, since it is the sum of the y_1 ordinate, 0, and the y_2 ordinate, 4. We have considered the ordinates of the y_3 curve at only five different abscissa points. However, in order to obtain the y_3 curve, many more points on the curve must be obtained. By comparing the y_1 and y_2 curves with that of the y_3 plot, it can be seen that

this same procedure was carried out for the ordinates at many abscissa values chosen at regular intervals along the X axes. Actually a total of 13 such summations was obtained. The abscissa for each is indicated by dots along the horizontal axes.

Since these two curves are regular ones, a small number of plotted points for the y_3 summation is sufficient. But what would happen if two or more irregular curves had to be added? Is it necessary to determine the ordinate value for each abscissa point, first of curve 1 then of curve 2, then to add the two ordinates (being careful to consider their signs) arithmetically on paper, and finally to plot the sum obtained? This is a somewhat tedious procedure since often 20 points or more will have to be considered. It is also an inaccurate procedure, since not only is it necessary to estimate each of the ordinates to at least one decimal place from the given scale, but it is then necessary to plot the result of the summation to scale. Is it possible to eliminate the tedium and inaccuracy by carrying out the entire summation procedure graphically, without resorting to reading, adding, and replotting numerical values?

Yes, it certainly is possible to carry out the entire procedure graphically and thus minimize the difficulties described above. All that is needed is a pair of dividers. If you are not already familiar with the instrument, a divider is nothing more than a compass with the pencil lead replaced by a metal point. The resultant instrument thus has two metal points but no pencil lead with which to draw an arc. If a pair of dividers is not readily available, a compass will serve if the pencil lead is carefully sharpened. With the dividers it is possible to "step off" (measure off) the lengths of the desired ordinates without reading their actual values and to accomplish the addition by laying off the desired lengths, one after the other. To illustrate, let's consider the summation of the ordinates of the y_1 and y_2 curves of Fig. 7-4 at the abscissa point marked θ_1. To carry out the addition procedure:

1. Place one point of the dividers on the horizontal axis of Fig. 7-4a at the abscissa point marked θ_1.

2. Spread the dividers and place the second point of the dividers at the arrowhead end of the y_2 ordinate, shown marked in the a portion of the figure.

3. Maintain this y_2 spacing between the points of the dividers, and transfer this distance to the axis that will show the summation (y_3) curve. This is done by bringing the properly spaced dividers to the lower (b figure) horizontal axis and placing one point of the dividers on the horizontal axis at a corresponding θ_1 position. Using the gridwork of the graph paper as a guide, place the second point of the dividers above the axis on the same vertical calibration line as the first point at θ_1. If this point is now marked with a pencil, the ordinate y_2 will have been transferred to the b portion of the figure. It is shown marked in its proper location in Fig. 4-7b.

4. Now step off the ordinate value of the y_1 curve corresponding to the θ_1 abscissa, by placing one point of the dividers at the axis end of y_1 and the other point of the dividers at the curve end of this y_1 ordinate.

5. Transfer the y_1 ordinate to the b diagram and add it to the y_2 ordinate already marked. The addition is accomplished by placing one point of the y_1 spaced dividers at the end of the y_2 ordinate already marked in the b diagram. The other point of the dividers is placed

above the end of y_2 on the vertical calibration line containing y_2. Thus, we have "tacked on" the length of the y_1 ordinate to the end of the y_2 ordinate, and the total length of line from the horizontal axis at the θ_1 point to the end of the y_1 ordinate just placed represents the ordinate length of the new y_3 curve, since $y_3 = y_1 + y_2$.

This procedure can be carried out for all points between $\theta = 0$ and π, without variation except for the lengths of the ordinates being added at these two abscissa points. However, between π and 2π radians the ordinates of the y_1 curve are negative and those of the y_2 curve are positive. How is the graphical summation carried out when the ordinates being added are in opposite direction? To answer this question, let's consider the addition of the ordinates of the two curves of the a figure at the abscissa, θ_{11}. Basically, the procedure for the addition of ordinates is the same here as in the case when both ordinates are in the same direction. In each case it is necessary first to mark off one of the ordinates and secondly to start the second ordinate at the end of the first and measure its length *in the proper direction. Then, the sum of the two ordinates is the length of line from the beginning of the first ordinate to the end of the second.* Using this general procedure, to add the ordinates of the two curves at the θ_{11} point proceed as follows.

1. Space the dividers to conform to the length of ordinate y_1 shown at the θ_{11} position of Fig. 7-4a. (This is often stated more concisely by saying, "Step off the ordinate y_1 shown . . . .")

2. Transfer this y_1 distance to the proper position in the b diagram, as shown in the figure.

3. Step off y_2.

4. Transfer this ordinate to the b diagram by placing one divider point at the end of the (negatively directed) y_1 ordinate and the second divider point *above* (in the positive direction from) the first.

5. The ordinate y_3 is the short negatively directed vertical line starting at the horizontal

axis and ending where the divider point indicated the end of ordinate y_2. Thus, the ordinate y_3 is the sum of $y_1 + y_2$ and is negatively directed, since the larger of the two ordinate values being added is negative.[1]

Hence, we see that it is possible to carry out the entire summation process graphically without resorting to numerical additions and subtractions. We see further that this graphical addition applies regardless of whether we are dealing with positive ordinates or sums of positive and negative ordinates. You can readily extend the described procedure (1) to a case in which all the ordinates being added are negative and (2) to cases in which more than two curves are being added. This may require several positive and negative ordinates to be added at each abscissa point.

7.3. Effect of a graphical addition of waveshapes

Now that we are familiar with the procedure for adding waves graphically, the question arises, "What is the purpose of this operation?" What do we know now that we didn't before the addition was carried out? Investigation of the results of several typical additions of waveshapes will help answer these questions.

Let us first look very carefully at the addition depicted in Figs. 7-4a and b. We started with two parts, one a fixed, positive quantity, the second a true symmetrical sine wave. The sine wave is referred to as symmetrical, since the areas above and below the axis are identical. If a tiny mirror were placed on the horizontal axis at the half-wave position (π radians), then the negative portion of the wave would be the mirror image of the positive portion. Thus, we have a symmetrical waveshape and, to be more specific, we have *point symmetry*. How has the addition of the two components affected this? Does wave 1 of Fig. 7-4b look any different from the sine wave of Fig. 7-4a? The general shapes of the two curves may be the same, but the two curves

are not identical. Note first that the waveshape of the b figure shows a large area above the axis and a small area below the axis. If we consider the area above the axis as positive and that below as negative, the waveshape of the b figure shows a net *positive* area. The net area of the true sine wave (figure a) is 0.

From discussions in earlier chapters, we realize that the area under a curve may be significant. If, for example, the particular curve represents a plot of power vs. time, then the area under the curve represents energy. In an electrical application the area under the positive portion of the curve would represent the energy sent by the generator of the system to its load. The negative area would represent the energy sent back by the load to the generator. The net area is therefore the net energy supplied by the generator to the load in one complete period. We have seen by this addition that before the addition of a fixed quantity to the sinusoidal power-vs.-time curve, the net energy supplied is 0. After the addition of the fixed y_2 component, a very substantial amount of energy transfer takes place. This is but one example of what the area might represent, but since the area is usually significant the relationship between the amount of positive and negative areas bounded by the curve is important.

We now know that the addition of a positive fixed component to a sinusoid changes it from one of 0 net area to one of positive net area. Consequently, if we come across a waveshape for which the areas above and below the axis are not equal, we know that, if the waveshape can be broken down into component waveshapes, one of the components would be a fixed quantity. The fixed quantity would be positive if the net area of the waveshape is positive, and the fixed quantity would be negative if the net area under the waveshape is negative.

Before the addition of the fixed component, the varying waveshape of figure a showed point symmetry. Does this type of symmetry exist in the curve of figure b that includes the fixed component? What conclusion can you draw from this observation?

---

[1] This type of addition, in which we are as much concerned with the *direction* of the quantities being added as the *magnitude* of the quantities, is known as *vector addition*.

7.4. Adding odd harmonics

Figure 7-5 is another example of addition of ordinates of two curves. In this case the two component waveshapes being added (y_1 and y_2) are both sine waves, yet they are different from one another. What are the major differences between the sine waves y_1 and y_2? Their amplitudes (maximum ordinates) are different, and a different number of complete cycles are shown for each of the two sinusoids. The latter is the most significant distinction between the waveshapes. In the time that the y_1 waveshape completes one cycle, the y_2 waveshape completes three cycles. We can therefore say that the y_2 waveshape is three times as fast as the y_1, or that the frequency of y_2 is three times that of y_1. If we consider the y_1 waveshape as the *fundamental* (reference frequency) waveshape, then we can refer to the y_2 waveshape as the "third *harmonic*" (multiple). To restate our addition problem, therefore, we can say that we are interested in determining the effect of adding a third-harmonic component to a fundamental. When this type of terminology is used, it is understood that reference is to sinusoids. The method of addition, as previously described, is a graphical addition of ordinates accomplished with a pair of dividers and a pencil. The resultant waveshape is the y_3 curve shown in Fig. 7-5a, and before proceeding any further, you should verify at least five of the ordinates of the y_3 curve with a pair of dividers and a pencil.

Now let's look at the resultant waveshape critically to see what conclusions can be drawn from this type of addition. Each of the two component waveshapes, y_1 and y_2, shows point-mirror symmetry at the π-radian horizontal intercept. Does the resultant waveshape, y_3, show this type of symmetry? Yes, it does! The reflection of the positive half of the y_3 curve in a tiny mirror placed at the π-radian intercept is the negative half of this curve. For each of the two curves, y_1 and y_2, the area under the positive portion of the curve is exactly equal to the area under the negative half of the curve. Is this still true of the summation waveshape, y_3? Again the answer is, Yes. We have seen, therefore, that the addition of the third harmonic to a fundamental sine wave has an entirely different effect than the previous addition discussed. Here the resultant waveshape still shows point symmetry and still shows 0 net area. In this example, we used the third harmonic as a representative of all odd harmonics, third, fifth, seventh, etc. Their addition to the fundamental, or better, the addition of all the odd harmonics to the fundamental, would yield the same result.

What other property of the resultant waveshape can you notice that you would consider significant? Note that the effect of the addition is to produce a shape that shows a tendency to "square off." The "sides" of the resultant waveshape are steeper than those of either of the two components, and the upper portion of the resultant shows less drastic variation than do the two component waveshapes at their peaks. Indeed, if all the odd harmonics (out to infinity) were added together, the result would be the idealized square wave shown in Fig. 7-5b.

Reading our results backwards, so to speak, if we encounter a waveshape that shows square-wave characteristics, with a net area of 0, we know that the components of this wave are odd harmonics of the fundamental and that no fixed component is included.

7.5. Adding even harmonics

Analysis of graphs based on addition of waveshapes can be carried much further. However, our purpose here is to indicate, rather than to exhaust, the possibilities of obtaining information by graphical analysis. A few more examples will suffice to accomplish this purpose. Figure 7-6 shows the effect of adding even harmonics to a fundamental waveshape. Note that in Fig. 7-6a a second harmonic sine-wave is added to its fundamental. In Fig. 7-6b we can say that a second harmonic cosine is subtracted from the fundamental waveshape. However, for purposes of graphical analysis it is more convenient to consider the addition of a second harmonic *negative* cosine to the fundamental waveshape. It is recognized that the subtraction of a cosine term and the addition of a negative cosine term are two ways of

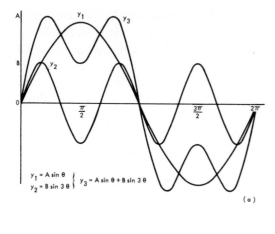

$y_1 = A \sin \theta$
$y_2 = B \sin 3\theta$ $\}$ $y_3 = A \sin \theta + B \sin 3\theta$

(a)

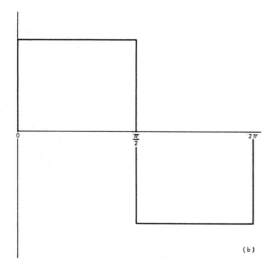

(b)

Fig. 7-5. Adding odd harmonics

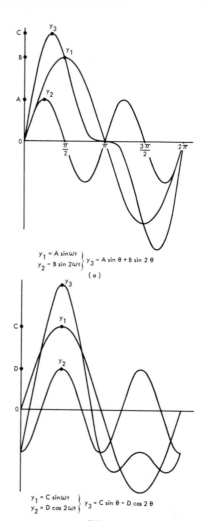

$y_1 = A \sin \omega t$
$y_2 = B \sin 2\omega t$ $\}$ $y_3 = A \sin \theta + B \sin 2\theta$

(a)

$y_1 = C \sin \omega t$
$y_2 = D \cos 2\omega t$ $\}$ $y_3 = C \sin \theta - D \cos 2\theta$

(b)

Fig. 7-6. Adding even harmonics

stating the same thing. Note that we are using the second harmonic as a representative of all the even harmonics. This approach is similar to that used in the previous paragraph, in which the third harmonic was used to represent all odd harmonics.

From the resultant waveshape (marked y_3 in each case), we see that even harmonic addition may or may not produce point symmetry in the resultant and that it may or may not produce the same effect on the positive and negative portions of the wave. Even in the *a* figure, where the positive and negative areas are similarly shaped, the two halves of the wave are not identical. The even harmonic

sine wave addition seems to have given a right-hand, left-hand character to the two halves of the resultant waveshape. Thus, even harmonic addition usually upsets symmetry, as compared with odd harmonic addition, which always maintains symmetry of a waveshape.

7.6. Other common waveshapes

Figure 7-7*a* shows the general shape of an entire group of waveshapes bearing the descriptive name "sawtooth." These waveshapes can be produced by adding harmonic components. The sawtooth waveshapes are obtained by the combination of all the harmonic components, even and odd. The value of such a

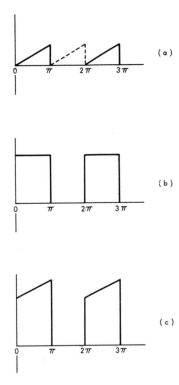

Fig. 7-7. Adding nonsinusoids

it is possible to eliminate alternate half-cycles to permit the variation to "lie dormant" for an interval. Since the sawtooth waveshape shown has more positive area than negative (no negative area exists in this example), we realize that the wave must also contain a positive, fixed component.

The waveshape of Fig. 7-7b is an example of the square-wave group referred to earlier in connection with Fig. 7-5. The term "square" refers only to the right angles appearing at the "corners" of the waveshape. Actually, the entire wave is more often rectangular in over-all shape than square. Bear in mind that the geometrical appearance of the width and height of the wave is determined by the scale chosen as much as by the values of the abscissa and ordinate values. The sudden increase, the constant value for an interval, and the sudden drop of the ideal square are its important properties. This waveshape is often used to start an operation suddenly, then to maintain that condition (because of the constant-value "top" of the wave), and finally to stop that operation suddenly. When used in this manner, it is referred to as a "gate" waveshape. The term "pulse" is used if one portion of the square wave is very narrow as compared with the intervals between portions, as shown in Fig. 7-8.

Figure 7-7c shows the pattern produced when the waves of Figs. 7-7a and b are added to produce a waveshape that contains the properties of both its components. For obvious

waveform becomes apparent when we recognize that it shows a linearly increasing ordinate value, that is, the increase occurs at a constant rate as in the true straight line. Unlike the straight line, however, the increase stops at a point and then a decrease occurs. In the example of Fig. 7-7a the decrease occurs suddenly, but other sawtooth waveshapes can show the decrease occurring at the same rate as the increase in ordinate or at a faster or slower rate. Furthermore, the decreasing ordinate can stop at 0 as shown in the diagram, or in other waveshapes it can go negative as far as desired.

The sawtooth waveshape is therefore an excellent control, or operating guide. In application the ordinates can be made to represent voltage, current, power, pressure, force, volume, or many other quantities. In each case the quantity increases to a desired point in a preset time and then decreases (rapidly or slowly) again to a desired level, 0, positive or negative. As indicated by the dotted second half-cycle of the sawtooth shown in the figure,

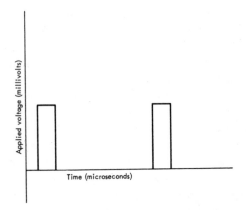

Fig. 7-8. Square wave as pulse

reasons, the resultant pattern of Fig. 7-7c is known as a "trapezoidal" waveshape. One common application of this type of waveshape is in the home television receiver. A trapezoidal voltage waveshape is required to cause the electron beam within the picture tube to move back and forth across the screen and "paint" the picture we see.

7.7. Fourier analysis

We have considered some of the effects of combining sinusoids and fixed components to produce waveshapes that differ in appearance from any of the component waveshapes and have discussed some of the properties of these resultant waveshapes. As pointed out earlier, we are concerned with combinations of sinusoids to yield the desired end result waveshape. Just why the sine wave is used as the reference wave for these discussions rather than, let us say, a circle, a parabola, a straight line, etc., will be clarified in a later paragraph. Suffice it to say for the present that in most electrical, mechanical, or combined systems, the basic component waveshape is the sinusoid. Therefore, if a method existed whereby an output waveshape from a device could be broken down into its sinusoidal components, then a system could be designed that would permit the use of this output waveshape in the desired manner. Conversely, if it is desired to produce a waveshape of a particular shape and character, then it would be very helpful to have a technique that would predict the sinusoidal components that will combine into the desired waveshape. Such a technique does exist, and it is known as "Fourier analysis."

To quote John R. Riggs, associate editor of *Electrical Manufacturing,*

Fourier analysis, one of the oldest mathematical-engineering tools, is usable as a design approach in the widest range of applications. In system and sub-system design, Fourier analysis permits the engineer to design or select devices for a particular transient performance solely on the basis of their steady-state sinusoidal performance. It is also useful in setting over-all system requirements and in predicting system behavior. Many control system engineers use aspects of Fourier analysis without recognizing the source of their methods.

This method of harmonic analysis of waves is based on the Fourier series developed in the early 1880s by the French mathematician-physicist Jean Baptiste Joseph Fourier. The series itself states that a periodic waveshape can be expressed as the sum of a fixed term and all the even and odd harmonics, sine terms and cosine terms, of different amplitudes. Putting this statement in mathematical shorthand, we have

$$y = A_1 \sin \theta + A_2 \sin 2\theta + A_3 \sin 3\theta$$
$$+ A_4 \sin 4\theta + \ldots + A_n \sin n\theta + B_0$$
$$+ B_1 \cos \theta + B_2 \cos 2\theta + B_3 \cos 3\theta$$
$$+ B_4 \cos 4\theta \ldots B_n \cos n\theta$$

where $y =$ composite waveshape

$\sin \theta =$ fundamental sine wave

$\sin 2\theta =$ second harmonic sine term

$\sin n\theta =$ sine term of harmonic number n, which may be as high as desired

$\cos \theta =$ fundamental cosine wave term

$\cos 2\theta =$ second harmonic cosine term

$\cos n\theta =$ cosine term of harmonic number as high as desired (but same as for sine harmonics)

A's $=$ different amplitudes of various sine terms and can be either positive or negative

B's $=$ different amplitudes of various cosine terms and can be either positive or negative

$B_0 =$ value of constant term and can be either positive or negative

The purpose of the analysis is to determine, first, which of the sine or cosine harmonic terms do not exist, that is, have coefficients equal to 0, and, second, the value of the A and B coefficients of the terms that do exist, including the B_0 term. The Fourier analysis can be conducted with either of two approaches. One is the analytical (mathematical) method that depends upon being able to write equations for different portions of the composite wave. The second is a graphical method, and it is this technique that concerns us here.

7.8. Graphical Fourier analysis

When a waveshape can be plotted or obtained by means of a recording device, whether mechanical, electrical, or electronic (as shown in Chapters 1 and 8) and knowledge exists of the value of the scale calibrations on which this graphical read-out is obtained, then a graphical Fourier analysis can be conducted. The analysis will yield the A and B values of the Fourier series. Thus, upon completion the amplitudes of each of the existing sine and cosine harmonic terms will be known, as well as the value of the fixed term. These components can either be written as a sum to form the Fourier equation of the composite wave, and the equation used in design considerations, or the components individually or in combination can be the basis of design decisions. The graphical analysis technique requires that a series of equally spaced ordinates be drawn and these ordinate values read and used as will be described. There is no limit to the number of equally spaced ordinates that can be drawn for the analysis. However, the accuracy of the result depends upon the number of ordinates drawn. The more ordinates used, the more accurate are the results. Ordinates measured every 30° suffice to yield an accurate enough result for most purposes. With a 30° spacing, a total of 12 ordinates can be erected within the 360°. Consequently, the method based on this subdivision is known as the "12-point method" of graphical Fourier analysis.

In order to carry out the 12-point method, proceed as follows:

1. Obtain the periodic curve to be analyzed from either a manual plot, oscillogram, mechanical plotter, or other device.

2. Subdivide the cycle of the waveshape into 12 equal divisions by erecting an ordinate to the curve every 30°, as shown in Fig. 7-9.

3. Designate each ordinate with an appropriate subscript as indicated in Table 7-1.

4. Measure and record the length of each ordinate, including both the magnitude and direction of the ordinates. Put the data thus

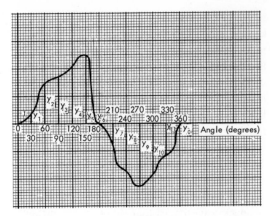

Fig. 7-9. 12-point graphical Fourier analysis

Table 7-1.

Length of ordinate	Abscissa
y_1	30°
y_2	60°
y_3	90°
y_4	120°
y_5	150°
y_6	180°
y_7	210°
y_8	240°
y_9	270°
y_{10}	300°
y_{11}	330°
y_{12}	360°

taken from the curve in tabular form, showing clearly the scale value of each of the 12 ordinates as well as the positive or negative direction of each.

5. Use these tabulated values to find the A and B coefficients of the Fourier series. The evaluation of the A and B coefficients is accomplished by substituting in the summation formulas given below. These formulas have been developed from the analytical Fourier analysis procedure and adapted for the graphical method. Each formula involves merely sums and differences of values obtained from the ordinates measured and the summation divided by 6. The B_0 term is divided by 12, as shown below. Since this is a 12-point analysis, a maximum of six A and six B terms can be evaluated in addition to the constant term. This means that when the final equation for

the composite waveshape is written from this analysis, it will contain at most six sine harmonic terms, six cosine harmonic terms, and a constant term. Should any of the A or B terms evaluate to 0, the end result will contain that many fewer terms.

6. The formulas for evaluating the A and B terms from the known ordinate values are as follows:

for B_0, the fixed quantity:

$$B_0 = \tfrac{1}{12} \, (y_1 + y_2 + y_3 + y_4 + y_5 + y_6 \\ + y_7 + y_8 + y_9 + y_{10} + y_{11} + y_{12})$$

for A_1, the coefficient of the fundamental sine term, $\sin \theta$:

$$A_1 = \tfrac{1}{6} \, [0.5 \, (y_1 - y_{11}) + 0.866 \, (y_2 - y_{10}) \\ + (y_3 - y_9) + 0.866 \, (y_4 - y_8) \\ + 0.5 \, (y_5 - y_7) \,]$$

for A_2, the coefficient of the second-harmonic sine term, $\sin 2\theta$:

$$A_2 = \tfrac{1}{6} \, [0.866 \, (y_1 - y_{11}) + 0.866 \, (y_2 \\ - y_{10}) - 0.866 \, (y_4 - y_8) \\ - 0.866 \, (y_5 - y_7) \,]$$

for A_3, the coefficient of the third-harmonic sine term, $\sin 3\theta$:

$$A_3 = \tfrac{1}{6} \, [\,(y_1 - y_{11}) - (y_3 - y_9) \\ + (y_5 - y_7) \,]$$

for A_4, the coefficient of the fourth-harmonic sine term, $\sin 4\theta$:

$$A_4 = \tfrac{1}{6} \, [0.866 \, (y_1 - y_{11}) - 0.866 \, (y_2 \\ - y_{10}) + 0.866 \, (y_4 - y_8) \\ - 0.866 \, (y_5 - y_7) \,]$$

for A_5, the coefficient of the fifth-harmonic sine term, $\sin 5\theta$:

$$A_5 = \tfrac{1}{6} \, [0.5 \, (y_1 - y_{11}) - 0.866 \, (y_2 \\ - y_{10}) + (y_3 - y_9) - 0.866 \, (y_4 \\ - y_8) + 0.5 \, (y_5 - y_7) \,]$$

for A_6, the coefficient of the sixth-harmonic sine term, $\sin 6\theta$:

$$A_6 = 0$$

for B_1, the coefficient of the fundamental cosine term, $\cos \theta$:

$$B_1 = \tfrac{1}{6} \, [y_0 + 0.866 \, (y_1 + y_{11}) \\ + 0.5 \, (y_2 + y_{10}) - 0.5 \, (y_4 + y_8) \\ - 0.866 \, (y_5 + y_7) - y_6]$$

for B_2, the coefficient of the second-harmonic cosine term, $\cos 2\theta$:

$$B_2 = \tfrac{1}{6} \, [y_0 + 0.5 \, (y_1 + y_{11}) \\ - 0.5 \, (y_2 + y_{10}) - (y_3 + y_9) \\ - 0.5 \, (y_4 + y_8) + 0.5 \, (y_5 + y_7) \\ + y_6]$$

for B_3, the coefficient of the third-harmonic cosine term, $\cos 3\theta$:

$$B_3 = \tfrac{1}{6} \, [y_0 - (y_2 + y_{10}) + (y_4 + y_8) \\ - y_6]$$

for B_4, the coefficient of the fourth-harmonic cosine term, $\cos 4\theta$:

$$B_4 = \tfrac{1}{6} \, [y_0 - 0.5 \, (y_1 + y_{11}) - 0.5 \, (y_2 \\ + y_{10}) + (y_3 + y_9) - 0.5 \, (y_4 \\ + y_8) - 0.5 \, (y_5 + y_7) + y_6]$$

for B_5, the coefficient of the fifth-harmonic cosine term, $\cos 5\theta$:

$$B_5 = \tfrac{1}{6} \, [y_0 - 0.866 \, (y_1 + y_{11}) \\ + 0.5 \, (y_2 + y_{10}) - 0.5 \, (y_4 + y_8) \\ + 0.866 \, (y_5 + y_7) - y_6]$$

for B_6, the coefficient of the sixth-harmonic cosine term, $\cos 6\theta$:

$$B_6 = \tfrac{1}{6} \, [y_0 - (y_1 + y_{11}) + (y_2 + y_{10}) \\ - (y_3 + y_9) + (y_4 + y_8) \\ - (y_5 + y_7) + y_6]$$

Because of the regularity of the formulas they can readily be expressed in tabular form. Tables 7-2 and 7-3 represent such a tabulation and can be used instead of the above formulas. The method for reading these tables becomes apparent when the numbers in the various columns are compared with the coefficients of the terms in parentheses in the above equations.

Table 7-2. Sine coefficients (A_k)

Col. I	A_1	A_2	A_3	A_4	A_5	A_6
y_0	0	0	0	0	0	0
$y_1 - y_{11}$	0.500	0.866	1.000	0.866	0.500	0
$y_2 - y_{10}$	0.866	0.866	0.000	−0.866	−0.866	0
$y_3 - y_9$	1.000	0.000	−1.000	0.000	1.000	0
$y_4 - y_8$	0.866	−0.866	0.000	0.866	−0.866	0
$y_5 - y_7$	0.500	−0.866	1.000	−0.866	0.500	0
y_6	0	0	0	0	0	0

A_k = sum of products of Column I and Column k divided by 6 (where k equals either 1, 2, 3, 4, 5, or 6).

(Courtesy RCA Institutes)

Table 7-3. Cosine coefficients (B_k)

Col. I	B_1	B_2	B_3	B_4	B_5	B_6	B_0
y_0	1.000	1.000	1.000	1.000	1.000	1.000	1.00
$y_1 + y_{11}$	0.866	0.500	0.000	−0.500	−0.866	−1.000	1.00
$y_2 + y_{10}$	0.500	−0.500	−1.000	−0.500	0.500	1.000	1.00
$y_3 + y_9$	0.000	−1.000	0.000	1.000	0.000	−1.000	1.00
$y_4 + y_8$	−0.500	−0.500	1.000	−0.500	−0.500	1.000	1.00
$y_5 + y_7$	−0.866	0.500	0.000	−0.500	0.866	−1.000	1.00
y_6	−1.000	1.000	−1.000	1.000	−1.000	1.000	1.00

B_k = sum of products of Column I and Column k divided by 6.
B_0 = sum of products of Column I and last column divided by 12.

(Courtesy RCA Institutes)

7.9. A typical curve, graphically analyzed

To illustrate the use of the above procedure and to show how straightforward and effective a method it is, let us carry out a graphical analysis of a simple curve, one that is often encountered.

One process of converting alternating current to direct current is known as "half-wave rectification." In this process, the negative half of sine wave is eliminated, and the resultant waveshape appears as shown in Fig. 7-10a. Thus, the problem is to analyze the 10-volt peak voltage waveshape of Fig. 7-10a and determine the fixed and harmonic components of the waveshape, then write the equation of the resultant waveshape and show a scale graph of each of the components. The steps of the solution are:

1. Draw the ordinates every 30° and tabulate their values. The existing ordinates are shown drawn in Fig. 7-10a and their values are tabulated at the bottom of this page.

2. Evaluate the A and B coefficients by using the formulas given in the preceding section and tabulate the results:

$$B_0 = \tfrac{1}{12}\,(5 + 8.66 + 10 + 8.66 + 5)$$
$$= 37.32/12$$
$$= 3.11 \text{ volts}$$

$$A_1 = \tfrac{1}{6}\,[0.5(5) + 0.866(8.66) + (10)$$
$$+ 0.866(8.66) + 0.5(5)] = 30/6$$
$$= 5 \text{ volts}$$

$$A_2 = \tfrac{1}{6}\,[0.866(5) + 0.866(8.66)$$
$$- 0.866(8.66) - 0.866(5)] = 0$$

$$A_3 = \tfrac{1}{6}\,[(5) - (10) + (5)]$$
$$= 0$$

Ordinate	y_1	y_2	y_3	y_4	y_5	y_6	y_7	y_8	y_9	y_{10}	y_{11}	y_0
Value (volts)	5	8.66	10	8.66	5	0	0	0	0	0	0	0

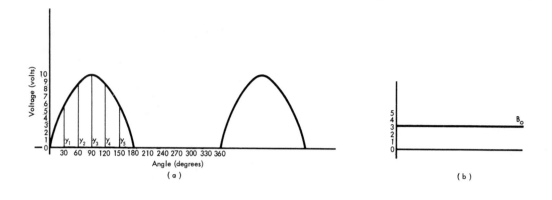

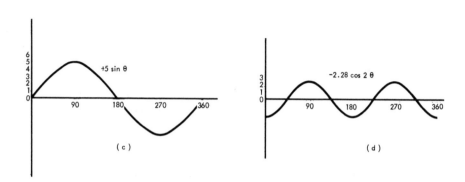

Fig. 7-10. Half-wave rectified sine wave and its major Fourier components

$A_4 = \frac{1}{6} [0.866(5) - 0.866(8.66)$
$\quad + 0.866(8.66) - 0.866(5)] = 0$

$A_5 = \frac{1}{6} [0.5(5) - 0.866(8.66) + (10)$
$\quad - 0.866(8.66) + 0.5(5)] = 0$

$A_6 = 0$

$B_1 = \frac{1}{6} [0 + 0.866(5) + 0.5(8.66)$
$\quad - 0.5(8.66) - 0.866(5) - 0] = 0$

$B_2 = \frac{1}{6} [0 + 0.5(5) - 0.5(8.66) - (10)$
$\quad -0.5(8.66) + 0.5(5) + 0]$
$\quad = \frac{1}{6} [-13.66]$
$\quad = -2.28 \text{ volts}$

$B_3 = \frac{1}{6} [0 - (8.66) + (8.66) - 0]$
$\quad = 0$

$B_4 = \frac{1}{6} [0 - 0.5(5) - 0.5(8.66) + (10)$
$\quad - 0.5 (8.66) - 0.5(5) + 0]$
$\quad = \frac{1}{6} [-3.66]$
$\quad = -0.61 \text{ volt}$

$B_5 = \frac{1}{6} [0 - 0.866(5) + 0.5(8.66)$
$\quad - 0.5(8.66) + 0.866(5) - 0] = 0$

$B_6 = \frac{1}{6} [0 - (5) + (8.66) - (10)$
$\quad + (8.66) - (5) + 0] = \frac{1}{6} [-2.68]$
$\quad = -0.446 \text{ volt}$

Coefficient	B_0	A_1	$A_2 {\rightarrow} A_6$	B_1	B_2	B_3	B_4	B_5	B_6
Value (volts)	3.11	5	0	0	−2.28	0	−0.61	0	−0.446

3. With the known coefficients, write the equation of the waveshape. Represent the waveshape by e:

$$e = 3.11 + 5 \sin \theta - 2.28 \cos 2\theta$$
$$- 0.61 \cos 4\theta - 0.446 \cos 6\theta$$

4. Show the components graphically. The first three terms of the waveshape equation are shown in Figs. 7-10b, c, and d, respectively. The next two terms are the fourth-harmonic and the sixth-harmonic components. These terms have amplitudes so small that an entirely different scale is required to show them. Therefore, unless these very small components are to be combined graphically with one or more of the others in the specific application, they need not be shown. Note from the equation that, as the number of the existing harmonic increases, the amplitude decreases. Although this is far from being a general rule, it occurs more often than not, in commonly seen waveshapes.

7.10. Linear and nonlinear devices

The question may very well suggest itself, "Why deal with nonsinusoids that have to be Fourier-analyzed?" If a system is to be devised from beginning to end, why not start, maintain, and finish with a true sinusoid? This would avoid much of the previously discussed work, and make the nonsinusoid the exception rather than the rule. Such an arrangement of affairs would truly be advantageous, but a short discussion of linear and nonlinear devices will make it clear why it is not a very practical approach.

First of all, what is a linear device?[2] *A linear device is one for which the shape of the output signal from the device is the same as the shape of the input signal to the device, although their amplitudes need not be the same.* It follows, therefore, that the definition of *a nonlinear device is one for which the shape of the output signal from the device is different*

from the shape of the input signal to the device. Another way of expressing these definitions is to state that a linear device causes no waveshape distortion, whereas a nonlinear device does cause waveshape distortion. Or, in the language of those interested in sound-range frequencies, a linear device shows (or has) "fidelity," whereas a nonlinear device does not exhibit "fidelity." But why is the word "linear" used in connection with wave-distorting or nondistorting properties of a device? What does "line" have to do with this discussion?

The answer to these questions can best be obtained by considering an example or two. Consider the straight line, *AQB*, of Fig. 7-11 to be the operating characteristic of a particular amplifying device.[3] This line is the *operating characteristic curve* because from this plot we can determine the amount of output from the device for known values of input signals. To permit us to follow through an example, the input quantity is taken to be voltage supplied, and the output quantity is taken to be the current produced. Thus, the independent axis (input signal axis) of the plot (Fig. 7-11) is calibrated in volts, and the dependent axis (output signal axis) is calibrated in milliamperes (10^{-3} amperes, abbreviated ma). Suppose now we have an input signal that varies with time; that is, the input voltage increases and decreases regularly with time. Not only does it vary with time, but it does so in the form of a perfect sine wave. To show this voltage variation with time, the input signal waveshape *abcde* is included in Fig. 7-11 in such a manner as to show the input voltage "swing" from a maximum of −2 volts down to a minimum of −8 volts. Note from the diagram that the time for one complete variation (cycle) of the input waveshape is 8 milliseconds, that is, 8 one-thousands of a second (8×10^{-3} sec, abbreviated 8 msec).

Our object is to determine graphically the shape of the output curve from the known shapes of the operating characteristic and the input signal waveshapes. Note again that the

---

[2] In this explanation of *linear*, no consideration is taken of the fixed (or d-c) component of a waveshape. Strict definitions of *linear* and *nonlinear* do include the effect of the device on the fixed component as well as on the shape of the input curve.

[3] An amplifying device is one that produces a large output variation for a relatively small input variation.

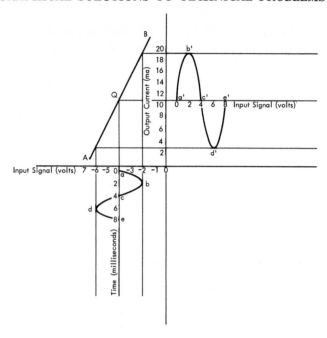

Fig. 7-11. Linear operating characteristic and its effect

operating characteristic, AQB, is a straight line, or that it is linear. To determine graphically the appearance of the output waveshape, it is necessary:

1. To project each point of the input waveshape up to the operating characteristic curve by means of a vertical projection line.

2. To continue this projection line horizontally from the characteristic curve to the vertical axis. This yields the amount of output for the specific value of input at which the projection line started.

3. Plot the values of output determined by the projection lines, on a time axis.

Let's follow through the three steps outlined above for several points of the given input sine wave of Fig. 7-11 in order to determine the shape of the output curve produced by this linear device. At time 0, the input voltage is seen to be at the —4 volt level. This point is designated in the diagram as point a. By following the —4-volt line up to the characteristic curve, AQB, and then over to the vertical (current) axis, we see that the a value of input voltage produces 11 ma of output current. Point a', at the 11-ma level, is thus the starting

point of the output waveshape and is plotted at an abscissa of 0 msec. Point b, on the input sine curve, occurs 2 msec later and is at a —2-volt input level. From the operating curve, AQB, this is seen to produce 19 ma of output current. Thus, point b' of the output waveshape is plotted at the 19-ma level and, like point b, at a 2-msec abscissa. Point c of the input waveshape is again at the —4-volt level and occurs at the 4-msec point in time. By following the projection lines from point c to the linear characteristic, AQB, and then to the vertical axis and beyond, we note that the corresponding output point is c', also plotted at the 4-msec point of its waveshape. The next input point to be considered is point d, which occurs at the 6-msec point of the input wave. The corresponding output point will therefore be plotted at the 6-msec abscissa of that wave. Point d is seen to be at the —6-volt input level and as such is shown to produce 3 ma of output current. Point d' is, therefore, at the 3-ma output level. At the 8-msec point the input wave is at point e and produces the output current level shown by point e' at the 8-msec point of the output waveshape.

A reasonably accurate output curve can be obtained by following this same procedure for an additional 10 points of the input waveshape to yield 10 more points of the output waveshape. The desired curve is then obtained by connecting the plotted output points with a smooth continuous curve. The output curve, $a'b'c'd'e'$ of Fig. 7-11, was obtained in this manner. How does the *shape* of this output curve compare to *shape* of the input curve? Both are true sinusoids, and therefore both have the same shape. Consequently, *the linear operating characteristic produces no distortion,* since the output waveshape is a faithful reproduction of the variation seen at the input to the device. Compare this result with that produced by the operating characteristic, *AQB,* of Fig. 7-12. Note that the input waveshape is again a true sine wave. The output waveshape was developed by the same procedure as before. Is this output waveshape a sine wave? Is it a sinusoid? The answer is, of course, No, the output is not a sine wave. We started with a true sine wave, fed it into a *nonlinear* device, and the output is a nonsinusoid. Another way of saying the same thing is that the nonlinear characteristic caused *distortion* of the input waveshape. On the basis of what we know of

Fourier analysis, what do we mean by distortion? What is truly the effect of the nonlinear operating characteristic of a device? We know from our previous discussion that this "distorted" waveshape can be broken down into its component sinusoidal harmonics plus a fixed component. Thus, *the effect of a nonlinear characteristic curve is seen to be the generation of harmonic components that do not exist in the input waveshape.* The sum of these harmonics yields the "distorted" output waveshape seen at the output of a nonlinear device.

Well, if this is the case, all that need be done to avoid distortion, or lack of fidelity, is to use only linear devices. This a is true statement, but one more readily stated than accomplished. In practice, no device is truly linear for all operating conditions. Nonlinearity of operating characteristics can be due to changes in temperature, pressure, current, voltage, humidity, speed, acceleration, or a host of other possible conditions. Most of these nonlinear devices have portions of their, operating characteristic curves that are linear. It is not often possible to utilize only the straight-line portion of the curve and nothing of the rest of the characteristic.

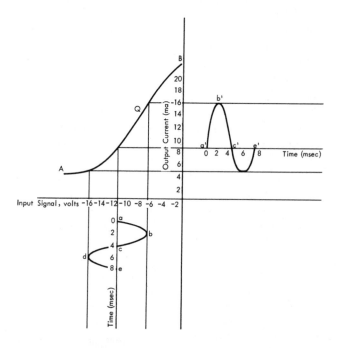

Fig. 7-12. Nonlinear operating characteristic and its effect

Thus, we see that it is necessary to deal with nonsinusoids that require Fourier analysis. The reason is that it is almost impossible to avoid a nonsinusoid, even if we start with a true sine wave at the input to a system or device.

7.11. Obtaining the operating characteristic curves

The graphical procedure discussed in the above section shows us how to determine the effect of a particular operating characteristic. But how do we obtain the operating characteristic curve for our particular conditions of operation? Actually there are as many different answers to that question as there are operating devices and systems throughout technology. However, in the vast majority of cases the most practical technique for obtaining a particular applicable operating characteristic is a graphical one. The type of operating characteristic curves shown in Figs. 7-11 and 7-12 apply to electron tubes. Since the method for obtaining the desired curve from a transistor is quite similar to that of an electron tube, and since almost every branch of technology is at least touched by these solid-state devices, let us consider the graphical method for obtaining an operating characteristic curve of a typical transistor for a particular condition of operation.

To avoid getting into areas that are outside the scope of our present discussion, suffice it to say that the "particular condition of operation" in the application being considered here is a "2,400-ohm resistive load" and that this load is represented graphically by the negatively sloped straight line shown in Fig. 7-13. The curves of this figure represent the behavior of the output (collector) circuit portion of this particular device and are normally supplied by the manufacturer of the device. They are therefore general, and the graphical procedure discussed here is necessary to obtain specific information from these curves that apply to a particular case.

The first step is to represent the particular case graphically. As already mentioned, this is accomplished by drawing the "load line"[4] directly onto the same set of axes used for the manufacturer's curves. Since the "load line" represents the special conditions of the application and the curves represent the general properties of the device being used, the intersections of these two graphically represented characteristics determines the operating curve of these devices used together. Figure 7-14 is the curve produced by plotting the points of intersection of the curves and line of Fig. 7-13. As such it is the operating characteristic curve that will determine the "fidelity" of the device; that is, the similarity in appearance of the output waveshape from the device to the input waveshape supplied to the device.

Judging this curve (Fig. 7-14) by the results of Figs. 7-11 and 7-12, would you say that this device will cause distortion or will it yield a true output sine wave for an input sine wave? This question is really the same as, "Is the operating characteristic curve of Fig. 7-14 nonlinear or linear?" Placing a straightedge beside this curve will show that it is practically a straight line. Therefore, the device repre-

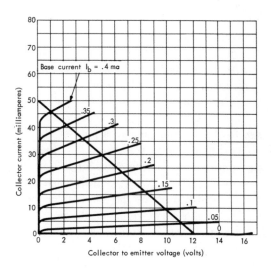

Fig. 7-13. Collector characteristics of transistor and 2,400-ohm load line

[4] It is not the purpose of this discussion to outline the procedure for drawing a "load line." The line is shown here merely as a graphical representation of the special operating conditions.

sented by this curve will produce some distortion of an input waveshape, but this distortion will be slight. If in operation the region of the curve between the first two plotted points, P_1 and P_2, and that between the last two plotted points, P_8 and P_9, are avoided, then for most purposes, we can say that this curve is linear.

As stated above, the points for this operating characteristic curve (known in the field of electronics as the "dynamic transfer" characteristic curve) are obtained from the intersections of Fig. 7-13. Note that the abscissa value for each of the plotted points of Fig. 7-14 comes from the value of "base current" shown on each of the manufacturer's curves of Fig. 7-13. The ordinate value for each of the plotted points of Fig. 7-14 is the ordinate of the point of intersection of the "load line" and the curves of Fig. 7-13. These coordinate values, as well as the numbers of the plotted points, are shown in Table 7-4.

7.12. The sine wave as the fundamental waveshape

In our preceding discussions two curves, or graph types, have been used more than any other as references, or bases of comparison. They are the straight line and the sine wave. The reason for using the straight line for reference is apparent from its simple shape. It is a curve readily plotted and read. However, these properties do not appear in the sine wave. It is not a curve that can be accurately plotted with two or three points, and it is not one that is necessarily simple to read. Certainly, the circle, which yields the sine curve, or any of the conic sections are more readily plotted and just as readily read as the sine curve. Why then is the sine curve so universally used as a reference? In other words, what important properties does it possess that make it so useful?

From our discussions in this chapter we have seen that it is often necessary to add and to subtract waveshapes. Addition of sine waves yields special results, since *if two or more sine waves of the same frequency are added or subtracted, the resultant waveshape is a sine wave.*

One of the applications discussed in Chapter 4, on significant waveshapes and their use, is simple harmonic motion. In that connection the rate of change of the slopes of several sinewaves is considered. It can be seen from Fig. 4-13 that *regardless of the sinusoid considered, the rate of change of its slope is another sinusoid.*[5] This is peculiar to exceedingly few waveshapes. In conjunction with the "sum and difference" property cited above, this advantage of the sine wave makes it the universal reference curve for discussions in electricity and electronics as well as for many other technologies.

7.13. Graphical solutions of simultaneous equations

In Chapter 3 we have considered information available from two graphs that are plotted on the same set of axes. In that connection the significance of the points of intersection of the three plots of Fig. 3-4 is examined. For example, point P_3 is the point where the straight-line plot of cars 1 and 3 intersect. Hence, the coordinates of this point tell us where and when the two cars meet. Since the coordinates of the point are (5, 150), we know that the cars meet after 5 hr of travel and 150 mi from the starting point.

---

[5] This property is often more generally expressed by the mathematician with the words *"the differentiation of a sinusoid yields a sinusoid."* Since the process known as "integration" is in effect antidifferentiation, then *integration of a sinusoid yields a sinusoid.* These properties are unique to the sinusoid.

Table 7-4. Coordinates for the Dynamic Transfer Characteristic

I_B (ma)	0	0.05	0.1	0.15	0.20	0.25	0.30	0.35	0.40
I_C (ma)	0	4	9	16	23	29	36	42	46
Plotted point	P_1	P_2	P_3	P_4	P_5	P_6	P_7	P_8	P_9

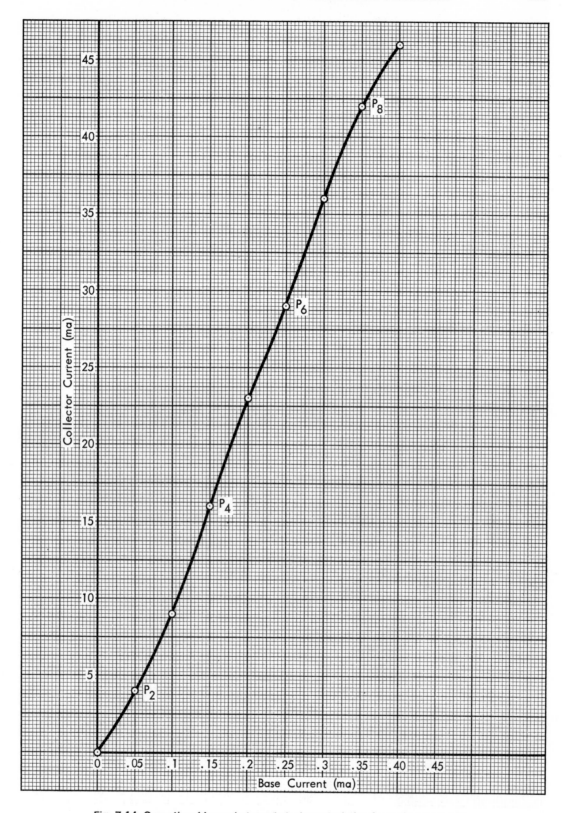

Fig. 7-14. Operating (dynamic transfer) characteristic of a typical transistor

Suppose now that the two lines are being plotted from their equations. The equation of the car 1 line is known to be $d = 30t$, and the equation of the car 3 line is $d = 50t - 100$.

By substituting the desired value of the independent quantity, t, into each equation, we will be able to determine the corresponding values of distance d. Thus, if in the equation of car 1 we let t equal 5 hr, we obtain $d = 30 \times 5$, or 150. Since d represents distance in miles, we have the coordinates for car 1 (5, 150). Carrying out the same procedure for car 3, we replace the t of the equation by 5 and obtain $d = 50(5) - 100$, which is $250 - 100$, or 150. Here again the coordinates of a point are determined to be (5, 150). In each case the value of t substituted in the equation is the abscissa of the point P_3 of intersection. In each case we note that this abscissa yields the same ordinate. In other words, it is possible to express the significance of the point (or points) of intersection of two curves by stating that the coordinates of the point of intersection are obtainable from the equation of each of the of the two curves. A phrasing often used for this statement is that the coordinates of the point (points) of intersection of two

curves *satisfies* the equation of both curves. In other words, we have a pair of values that, if substituted in the equations of the curves, will cause the value obtained on the left side of the equality sign to equal that on the right of the equality sign in each equation. *A set of values that thus satisfies a pair of equations is what is being sought when two equations are to be solved simultaneously.*

Figure 7-15 is an example of just such a solution. From our discussion of conic sections and their equations, we know that since the circle shown has its center at the origin and has a radius of 2 units, its equation is

$$x^2 + y^2 = 4$$

The line shown has a slope of $+3/1.7$, as read from the graph, and a vertical intercept of 2. Hence, its equation is

$$y = \frac{3}{1.7} x + 2$$

The coordinates of the two points of intersection of the two graphs, read to the accuracy of the plots, are $P_1(0, 2)$ and $P_2(-1.7, -1)$. Thus, these are the values that satisfy both equations at the same time, that is, simultane-

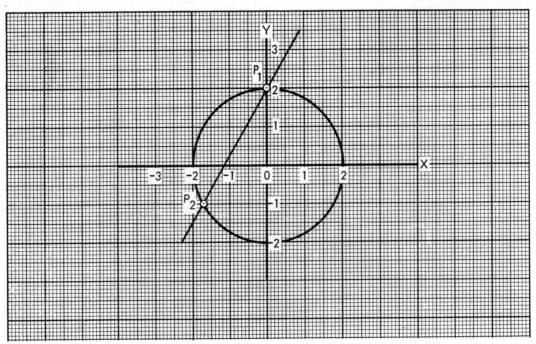

Fig. 7-15. Graphical simultaneous solution of two equations

ously; and these are the values that would be yielded by an "algebraic simultaneous solution" procedure carried out with these two equations. Let's check our graphical solutions by substituting the coordinate values of points P_1 and P_2 into the two equations. If in the equation of the circle

$$x^2 + y^2 = 4$$

we replace the x by 0, the abscissa of P_1, and replace the y by 2, the ordinate of P_1, we obtain

$$0 + 2^2 = 4$$
$$4 = 4$$

Obviously the coordinates of point P_1 *satisfy* the equation of the circle. Carrying out the same procedure with the coordinates of point P_2, we obtain

$$x^2 + y^2 = 4$$
$$(-1.7)^2 + (-1)^2 = 4$$
$$3 + 1 = 4$$
$$4 = 4$$

Thus, the coordinates of point P_2 also *satisfy* the equation of the circle. If these coordinate values are the simultaneous solution values for the two equations, these same pairs of coordinates will also satisfy the line equation. Making the substitution, we obtain

for point $P_1(0, 2)$:

$$y = \frac{3}{1.7} x + 2$$
$$2 = \frac{3}{1.7} (0) + 2$$
$$2 = 0 + 2$$
$$2 = 2$$

for point $P_2(-1.7, -1)$:

$$y = \frac{3}{1.7} x + 2$$
$$-1 = \frac{3}{1.7} (-1.7) + 2$$
$$-1 = -3 + 2$$
$$-1 = -1$$

As can be seen, the coordinates of the same

two points yield valid results for the line equation also. The two pairs of x, y values read from the points of intersection are therefore coordinates that satisfy the two equations simultaneously.

This method of simultaneous graphical solution need not be limited to two equations or curves. It is possible to have three or more curves intersect at a point. Under these conditions the coordinates of the point (or points) of intersection represent the simultaneous solution of the three equations. Figure 7-16 depicts such a condition. The equation of the circle shown is

$$x^2 + y^2 = 18$$

that of the parabola is

$$y^2 = 3x$$

and that of the straight line is

$$y = x$$

Although four points of intersection are shown on the graph, point P_1 is the only point where all three graphs come together. The coordinates of this point should therefore represent a simultaneous solution of the three equations. From the graph, the coordinates of the point are seen to be $(3, 3)$. A check of this solution can be made by substituting these values for x and y into the three equations to determine whether or not they satisfy the equations. Carrying out the substitutions, we obtain

for the circle:
$$x^2 + y^2 = 18$$
$$3^2 + 3^2 = 18$$
$$18 = 18$$

for the parabola:
$$y^2 = 3x$$
$$3^2 = 3(3)$$
$$9 = 9$$

for the straight line:
$$y = x$$
$$3 = 3$$

Thus, the coordinate values $x = 3, y = 3$ satisfy all three equations at the same time.

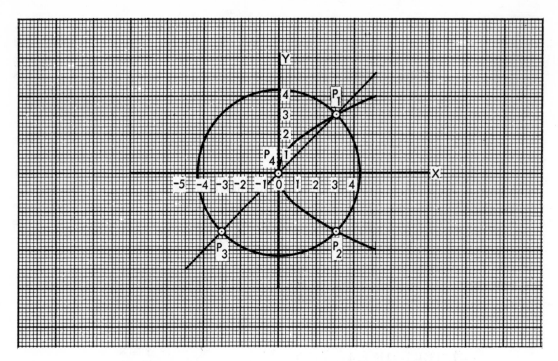

Fig. 7-16. Graphical simultaneous solution of three equations

The equivalent algebraic solution for these equations is a long one, since two of the equations are quadratic; that is, their variables are carried to the second power.

7.14. Additional graphical methods commonly used in technology

The material considered in the following several paragraphs represents a sampling of graphical techniques commonly met in technology. The sampling is sufficiently representative so that in conjunction with the other methods and techniques discussed thus far they can provide you with the basic ability to deal with technical data. The sampling referred to consists of determining area under a curve, conversion charts, special-purpose reference graphs, Lissajous patterns, normalized curves, and three-dimensional plots.

7.15. Area under a curve—the Trapezoidal Rule

From the discussions of the previous chapters we learned that important information is available from a graph by evaluating slopes, intercepts, coordinates of plotted points, and the area bounded by the plotted curve. Of these listed curve characteristics, area is the most difficult to measure accurately. And yet, we want this information because of its meaning in several applications. For example, the area under a velocity-versus-time plot represents distance and the area under a power-versus-time curve represents energy (as does the area bounded by a pressure–volume plot, Fig. 2-16).

As described in Chapter 3, the area under a plotted curve can be determined by geometry if the plot and other boundaries form a regular figure. Another method involves counting squares, and a third requires the use of a planimeter. However, still another method of area evaluation exists known as the Trapezoidal Rule.[6] This method is the most popular of all, if the area involved is not a regular figure like a triangle or rectangle. In effect, the trapezoidal rule reduces every area to a collection

[6] A trapezoid is a four-sided geometric figure with two sides parallel and two sides not parallel. The parallel sides are known as the "bases." The perpendicular distance between the bases is known as the height or altitude of the trapezoid.

of regular figures, regardless of the shape of the bounding curve. Basically, use of this rule involves

1. subdividing the area in question into several trapezoids

2. determining the area of each of the trapezoids

3. adding together the areas of the trapezoids. This sum is the value of the area in question.

This three-step breakdown of the trapezoidal rule is a very coarse one indeed. The advantages of this approach and the reason for its popularity will become apparent as we consider the details of this technique.

The curve of Fig. 7-17 represents the velocity-vs.-time plot of an object under the influence of several varying forces. Note that the velocity increases at first, reaches a maximum value, and then slowly decreases. This is so since to determine the area it is necessary to multiply together some vertical dimension, velocity in this case, and some horizontal dimension, time in this case. We know further that the product of velocity and time represents distance. Let's try to determine graphically the distance covered by this object from the 30-sec time point to the 70-sec point. The area in question is shown in Fig. 7-17 and is labeled ABCD. If this were a regular area such as a rectangle, triangle, or other, there would be little difficulty in evaluating the area. However, the upper boundary of the area is the arc of a curve, so that no simple formula for area can be used. Thus we apply the trapezoidal rule.

The first step in this procedure is to subdivide the area involved into several trapezoids. At this point you might ask several questions. First, why use trapezoids? Second, how many trapezoids should be used for this

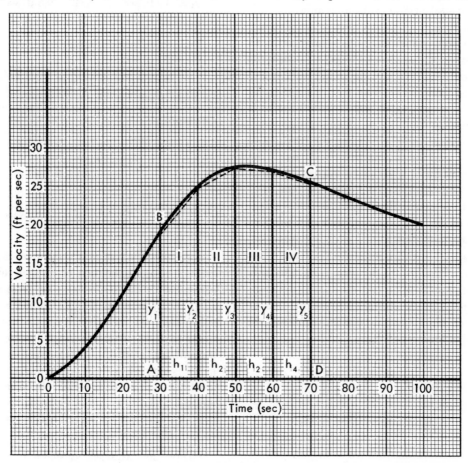

Fig. 7-17. Area under curve can be determined fairly accurately by Trapezoidal Rule

area? One reason for the use of a trapezoid is that it is a regular geometrical figure, the area of which is easily computed. The second reason can be seen by looking at Fig. 7-17. Note that each trapezoid is drawn so that one of its nonparallel sides very closely approximates the curve. These sides are shown drawn in broken line. Thus by use of several trapezoids we succeed in subdividing the area under the curve into several regular geometrical figures that very closely follow the curve. It is apparent from the diagram that only a very small error is involved if we assume that the sum of the areas of these four trapezoids is equal to the area bounded by the curve arc BC, the ordinate lines y_1 and y_5, and the portion of the horizontal axis between 30 and 70 sec. Note further that each of the four trapezoids have equal bases; that is, the lengths of lines h_1, h_2, h_3, and h_4 are all equal. This is done to simplify the calculation of the total area.

This brings us to the next question posed above. How many trapezoids should be used? The larger the number of trapezoids used, the greater the accuracy of the final result. It can be seen from the diagram that, if eight trapezoids were used, each with a base 5 sec wide (rather than the 10 sec used), the "broken-line" side of each figure would hug the curve more closely than the four trapezoids do now. The disadvantage of using more trapezoids is that more work is involved in finding the total area. Thus to determine the proper number of trapezoids to use it is necessary to weigh two factors, accuracy desired and work involved.

The second step in this procedure is the evaluation of the area of the trapezoids. The area of a trapezoid equals half the sum of the bases multiplied by the altitude. Thus, the area of each of the trapezoids can be expressed in equation form as follows:

$$\text{Area I} = \tfrac{1}{2}\,(y_1 + y_2)\,h_1$$
$$\text{Area II} = \tfrac{1}{2}\,(y_2 + y_3)\,h_2$$
$$\text{Area III} = \tfrac{1}{2}\,(y_3 + y_4)\,h_3$$
$$\text{Area IV} = \tfrac{1}{2}\,(y_4 + y_5)\,h_4$$

Since all of the h values are the same, the sum of these four areas, A_t, can be expressed as:

$$A_t = h\left(\frac{y_1}{2} + \frac{y_2}{2} + \frac{y_2}{2} + \frac{y_3}{2}\right.$$
$$\left. + \frac{y_3}{2} + \frac{y_4}{2} + \frac{y_4}{2} + \frac{y_5}{2}\right)$$

Note that each of the $y/2$ values appears twice, except the first and the last values, $y_1/2$ and $y_5/2$. As a result, the expression for total area becomes

$$A_t = h\left(\frac{y_1}{2} + y_2 + y_3 + y_4 + \frac{y_5}{2}\right)$$

In other words, to find the total area it is necessary merely to add up all the bases, plus half the first base, plus half the last base and to multiply the total by any one of the equal altitude values.

Let's apply the formula just developed to the area ABCD of Fig. 7-17. The values taken from the diagram are

$$y_1 = 19 \text{ ft/sec} \therefore{}^* \ y_1/2 = 9.5 \text{ ft/sec}$$
$$y_2 = 25 \text{ ft/sec}$$
$$y_3 = 27.5 \text{ ft/sec}$$
$$y_4 = 27 \text{ ft/sec}$$
$$y_5 = 25.5 \text{ ft/sec} \therefore \ y_5/2 = 12.75 \text{ ft/sec}$$
$$h = 10 \text{ sec}$$

Therefore
$$A_t = 10 \text{ sec } (9.5 + 25 + 27.5 + 27$$
$$+ 12.75) \text{ ft/sec}$$

Since the area represents distance,
$$A_t = \text{Distance} = 10\,\cancel{\text{sec}}\left(101.75\,\frac{\text{ft}}{\cancel{\text{sec}}}\right)$$
$$\text{Distance} = 1017.5 \text{ ft}$$

From this illustration it is apparent that this method of approximation of an area under a curve can be made almost as accurate as desired. As mentioned before, the more trapezoids used, the more accurate the result. In order to make the result absolutely accurate, without any error at all, the equation of the curve is needed. This is something not often available or even existent. However, the method utilizing a curve equation is not a graphical one and is thus not within the realm of this discussion.

---

    * Three dots arranged as shown ($\therefore$) mean *therefore*.

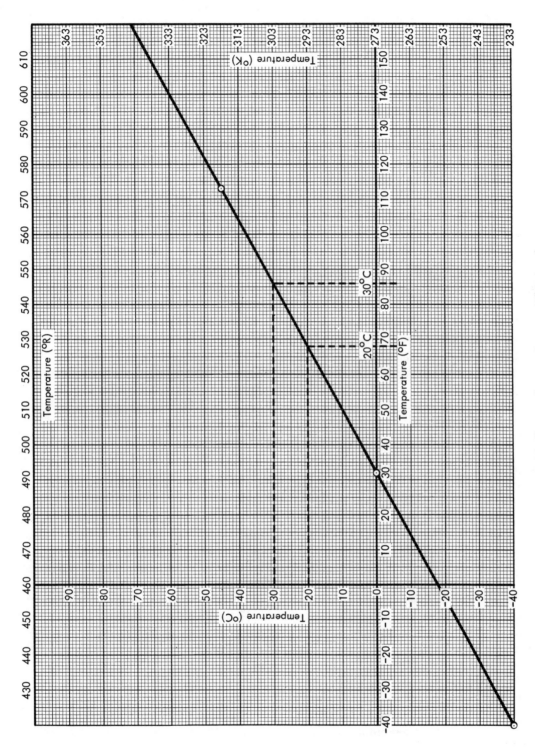

Fig. 7-18. Temperature scale conversion graph

7.16. Conversion graphs and charts

The temperature conversion chart of Fig. 7-18 is a prevalent example of conversion charts or graphs and represents nothing more than the plot of the equation that relates the quantities involved. In the example shown, the relating equation is

$$C = \frac{5}{9}\,(F - 32)$$

where $C =$ temperature reading on the Centigrade scale

$F =$ temperature reading on the Fahrenheit scale

Removing the parentheses from this equation makes it apparent that we are dealing with a straight line of slope 5/9 and a vertical intercept of $-160/9$ if C is calibrated along the vertical axis and F along the horizontal. Once the line is drawn, as in Fig. 7-18, any value of temperature on the Centigrade scale can readily be converted to its equivalent on the Fahrenheit scale, and vice versa. For example, starting with a temperature of 30°C, to find the Fahrenheit equivalent, follow the 30°C abscissa line from the vertical axis to the plotted line and from this point on the graph follow the ordinate line down to the horizontal Fahrenheit axis. The reading obtained is 86°F. Very often a conversion graph is adapted for use by nontechnical personnel by converting it to chart form. In order to convert from one temperature scale to another using Fig. 7-18, it is necessary to follow the horizontal and vertical grid lines from one axis to the graph and then to the second axis. Instead of this, one temperature scale can be shown on one side and the equivalent values in the second scale shown on the other side of a line. To show how this type of chart is developed from the conversion plot, let us consider the horizontal axis with its Fahrenheit scale as half of the conversion chart. The appropriate numbers of the Centigrade scale to be placed above the horizontal line are read from the plotted conversion graph. By following the broken abscissa and ordinate lines shown in Fig. 7-18, we see that 20°C should be placed above 68°F, and 30°C should be placed above 86°F. This

process can be continued until the desired number of equivalent values are located on the two sides of the line. Then the resultant conversion chart can be used in place of the conversion graph. Figure 7-18 also shows the Rankine and Kelvin scales, which are the absolute temperature equivalents of the Centigrade and Fahrenheit scales, respectively. The graph therefore permits ready conversion from any one of four temperature scales to any other with the use of one plotted curve. A conversion chart can also be developed to show the four-way conversion, but this would require four parallel rows of numbers, thereby defeating the attempt at simplification.

Figure 7-19 shows a second typical conversion graph. Ratios showing increases or decreases are commonly used as a means of comparison of data obtained from the input and output of a system or device. As a result, a unit of measurement of the ratio, the decibel, is commonly used (see review section of Chapter 5). In connection with voltage ratios, the definition of the decibel (abbreviated db) is given by the equation

$$\text{db} = 20 \log \frac{\text{voltage}_2}{\text{voltage}_1}$$

and in terms of power ratios the definition of the decibel is given by the equation

$$\text{db} = 10 \log \frac{\text{power}_2}{\text{power}_1}$$

In each case the subscript 1 refers to the reference value, and the subscript 2 refers to the quantity being compared with the reference. Here, as in the case of the temperature-scale conversion graph, it is possible to use the equations to convert from the ratio value to the equivalent value in decibels. Again however, conversion by use of the equation involves more time and effort than the same conversion by means of a graph. The form of the two equations immediately suggests the use of semilog paper, so that the ratios can be shown on the logarithmic axis and the equivalent decibel values on the linear axis. Comparison of the two equations shows that both can readily be shown on the same graph sheet and

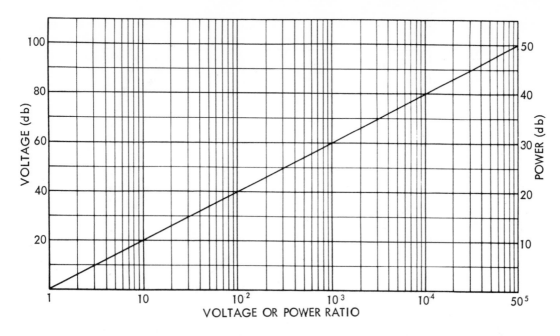

(Courtesy, Narda Microwave Corp.)

Fig. 7-19. Conversion of voltage and power ratio to decibels

with a common logarithmic axis. Separate vertical scales are necessary for the two decibel values, since the equations show the voltage decibel values to be twice the power decibel values for the same ratio. If the ratio values are considered the independent values, the graph paper is arranged to make the logarithmic axis horizontal and the linear axis vertical. The semilog paper causes the plot of the equation to appear as a straight line, a highly desirable shape for a conversion graph.

This conversion graph can also be made into a chart by the procedure described above for the temperature scales. However, since this type of conversion graph is used almost exclusively by technical personnel, the only advantage of the equivalent chart would be the space-saving it affords.

7.17. Reference curves for design purposes

A great deal of design work in technology is accomplished with the aid of charts and curves rather than formulas for two important reasons. The first is that the design equations often supply only an approximation of existing conditions. The curves, on the other hand, are obtained under actual operating conditions of a device. Second, in cases where complete equations do exist, they are often cumbersome, and their use is therefore very time-consuming. Thus, characteristic curves and reference curves are an important tool for the designer.

A set of characteristic curves is a family of plots obtained either manually or with an automatic plotting device. Step-by-step variations of conditions are introduced and a behavior curve plotted for each step. Figure 7-20 shows a family of "plate characteristic" curves for a specific electron tube. Each curve shows how the plate current of the tube will increase as the plate voltage increases. The quantity that is varied in steps is shown to be the grid voltage. Note that the grid voltage varies in steps of 7.5 volts from curve to curve but is fixed for any one curve. *A quantity that is maintained fixed for any one curve of a family of curves but is different for each curve of the family, is known as a parameter.* In this case, the grid voltage is the parameter. Curves of this type are used to determine whether the tube they describe is suitable for the range of operation the designer has in mind. By means

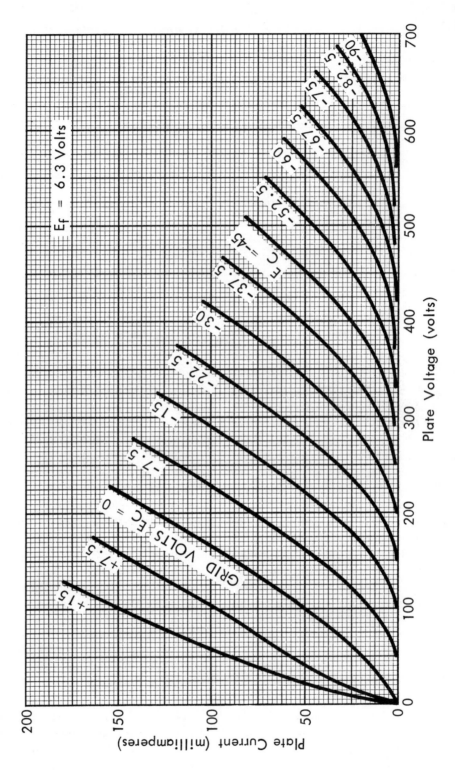

(Courtesy, Radio Corporation of America)

Fig. 7-20. Average plate characteristics of 6L6 electron tube—triode connection

of a load line (or curve) similar to that shown in Fig. 7-13, these characteristic curves yield the dynamic operating characteristic. This in turn tells us whether the device will introduce distortion. The slopes of the curves at different points and the spacing between the curves, as well as the corresponding ordinate and abscissa values of the points on the curves, are all important features of these characteristic curves.

Figure 7-21 is also a set of characteristic curves, but here the parameter is the material used. Note that the curve shown for each material is a plot of the thickness of that material required to stop completely beta-ray radiation[7] of different energy levels. Curves of this type are important in the design of shielding enclosures or surfaces.

Figure 7-22 is a set of reference curves or guide curves rather than a family of characteristic curves. These curves are not plotted manually or automatically but represent the plot of a formula with corrections introduced to compensate for special conditions. Note that these curves also have a parameter, which in the case shown is the efficiency of the heating system. Another similarity to the characteristic curves is that the set of reference curves of Fig. 7-22 applies to a particular type of building construction, much as the curves of Fig. 7-20 apply to a particular type of tube. Other types of building construction have a somewhat different set of curves applicable to them. From the wide range of values shown in Fig. 7-22 it is apparent that use of this reference plot can save many hours of calculations with formulas. Furthermore, the possibility of error in reading information from the curves is far less than the possibility of errors in calculations, since a glance at the curve being used gives the designer an idea of the range of values he is dealing with. No such guide, other than the experience of the designer, is available in formula solutions.

7.18. Lissajous patterns

The Lissajous pattern is a graphical means of determining the phase angle between two sinusoidal waveshapes of the same frequency or the frequency ratio of two sinusoids of different frequencies. Although the graphical technique for obtaining these patterns can be carried out manually, it is a tedious process, since two waveshapes have to be compared, each of which has to be very accurately drawn. As a result, the Lissajous patterns are usually produced on an oscilloscope. These electronic graphical recording devices are discussed in the following chapter. Suffice it to say here that a sinusoidal electrical voltage variation applied to the vertical "axis" of an oscilloscope will cause a spot of light to move vertically up and down along an imaginary Y axis on the screen of the oscilloscope. As shown in Fig. 7-23a, the position of the vertically moving spot at any one instant corresponds to the value of the "vertical deflection" voltage at that instant. Figure 7-23b depicts a similar condition, except that here the sinusoidal voltage is applied to the horizontal "axis" of the

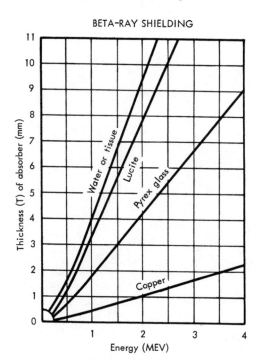

BETA-RAY SHIELDING

(Courtesy, N.B.S., U.S. Dept. of Commerce)
Fig. 7-21. Thickness of typical materials required to stop completely beta-rays of maximum energy

---

[7] "Beta particle" is the term used by the physicist instead of "electron."

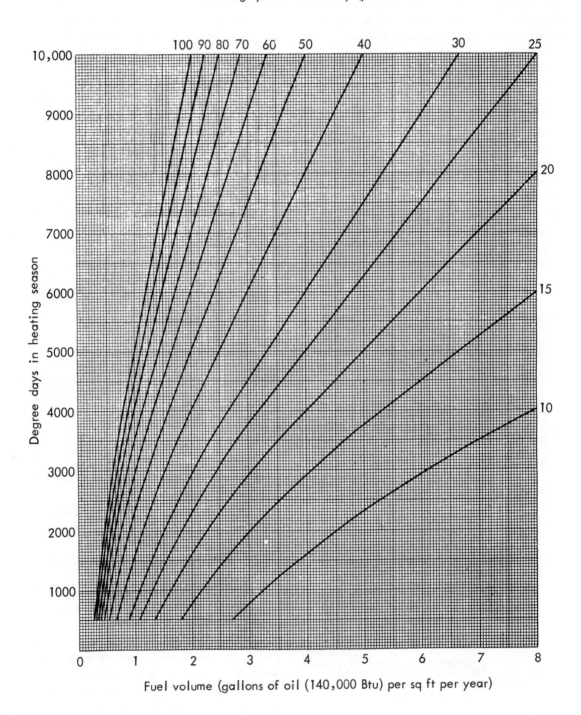

Fig. 7-22. Fuel requirements chart

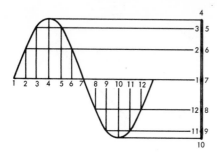

(a) Vertical deflection

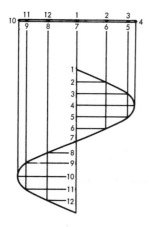

(b) Horizontal deflection

Fig. 7-23. Varying voltage applied to oscilloscope "axis" causes spot of light to trace out line on screen

oscilloscope and therefore causes deflection of the light spot along an imaginary X axis of the oscilloscope screen. Consequently, the use of this technique requires that it be possible to convert the sinusoidal variations to be compared into electrical voltages. When two sinusoidal variations of the same frequency and amplitude are applied simultaneously to the vertical and horizontal "axes" of the oscilloscope (commonly abbreviated 'scope), the spot of light is deflected at every instant by the vector sum of the two sine wave values at that instant. When the two sinusoids are in phase, the resultant pattern is a 45° straight line, as shown in Fig. 7-24. When the two sinusoids are out of phase by 90 deg, the resultant pattern

is a perfect circle, as shown in Fig. 7-25. Note that the previous statement does not specifically refer to a lead or a lag of 90 deg but only to a phase separation of 90 deg. The reason for this is that both a lead or a lag of the vertical axis curve with respect to the horizontal axis curve will yield a perfect circle. One other phase relationship between the two applied curves will yield a straight line, and this occurs when the two waveshapes are 180 deg out of phase. This condition is recognizable, since the straight line produced under this condition makes a 45-deg angle with the negative X-axis direction. All other phase-separation conditions produce ellipses of larger or smaller area.

To determine the phase angle between the two sinusoids when an ellipse is produced, measurements from the oscilloscope screen are necessary. The distances OA and OB shown in Fig. 7-26 are measured from the screen face. The phase angle between the two applied sinusoids is the angle whose sine equals the ratio of OA to OB. Expressing this in equation form, we have[8]

$$\sin \phi = OA/OB$$

where ϕ is the phase angle between the sine voltage applied to the vertical "axis" and to the horizontal "axis" of the oscilloscope.

When two sinusoids of different frequencies are applied to the two axes of an oscilloscope, Lissajous patterns are produced of the type shown in Figs. 7-27 and 7-28. If a stationary pattern of this type is obtained, it is possible to read from the figure the frequency ratio of the two applied sinusoids. Thus, if the frequency of one of the two applied sinusoids is unknown, it is possible to determine its frequency by comparing it with a wave of known frequency. To determine the ratio of the frequencies of the applied sinusoids, proceed as follows:

---

[8] This equation can also be written in the form, $\phi = \sin^{-1} OA/OB$ and is read "ϕ equals arc sin OA/OB," or "ϕ is the angle whose sine is OA/OB."

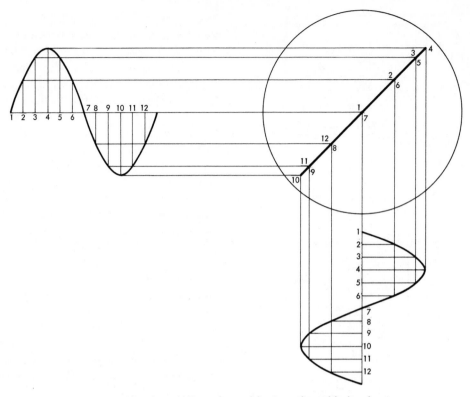

Fig. 7-24. Lissajous pattern formed by two sinusoids in phase

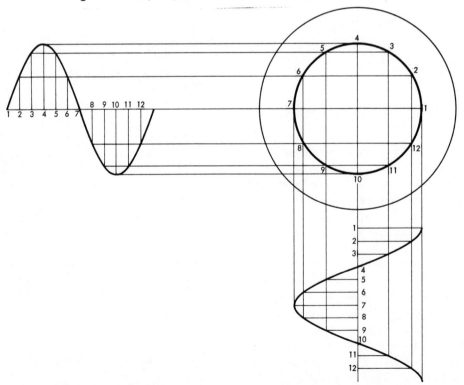

Fig. 7-25. Lissajous pattern formed by two sinusoids 90 deg out of phase

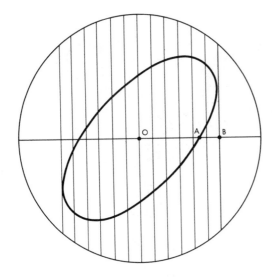

Fig. 7-26. Lissajous pattern formed by two sinusoids ϕ deg out of phase (sin ϕ = **OA/OB**)

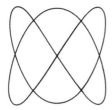

Fig. 7-27. Lissajous pattern formed by two sinusoids of different frequencies, 2 on horizontal axis and 3 on vertical axis

1. Obtain a stationary Lissajous pattern.

2. Locate the pattern on the oscilloscope so that one of the vertical grid lines of the oscilloscope tube face is tangent to the left side of the pattern. Determine the number of points of the pattern that touch this vertical tangent line. This number applies to the horizontal axis deflection frequency.

3. Locate the pattern on the oscilloscope so that one of the horizontal grid lines of the oscilloscope tube face is tangent to the top of the pattern. Determine the number of points of the pattern that touch this horizontal line. This number applies to the vertical deflection frequency.

4. Express the ratio of the two frequencies in terms of the numbers obtained, so that

$$\frac{\text{Horizontal deflection frequency}}{\text{Vertical deflection frequency}} = \frac{\text{number of points touching vertical tangent line}}{\text{number of points touching horizontal tangent line}}$$

By the above procedure we see that the ratios represented by the patterns of Figs. 7-27 and 7-28 are

$$f_H/f_V = 2/3$$

for the Fig. 7-27 pattern and

$$f_H/f_V = 1/2$$

for the Fig. 7-28 pattern.

7.19. Normalized curves

Very often data obtained from a given unit or system can best be analyzed and understood by comparing them to a given standard, reference, or normal. The comparison is usually accomplished by establishing a ratio of the given data to the reference, or normal, quantity. The value of this ratio is often known as the "relative value" and can be expressed in abbreviated form by stating that

$$\text{Relative value} = \frac{\text{datum[9] quantity}}{\text{normal quantity}}$$

If this relative value varies with time or with respect to another independent quantity, a plot can be made of the changing relative values vs. the independent quantity. Such a plot is known as a *normalized curve*. Since a normalized curve is a reference curve, that is, one in which the data are compared to a reference, it is often more useful than a plot of the raw data.

From our discussions in Chapter 5 we know that logarithmic graph paper is particularly applicable to the plotting of normalized curves, since a *fixed* ratio throughout will result in a straight-line plot. A changing ratio will result in a curve whose slope changes less rapidly than it would on linear paper, making it easier to read and to plot.

---

[9] Datum = singular; data = plural.

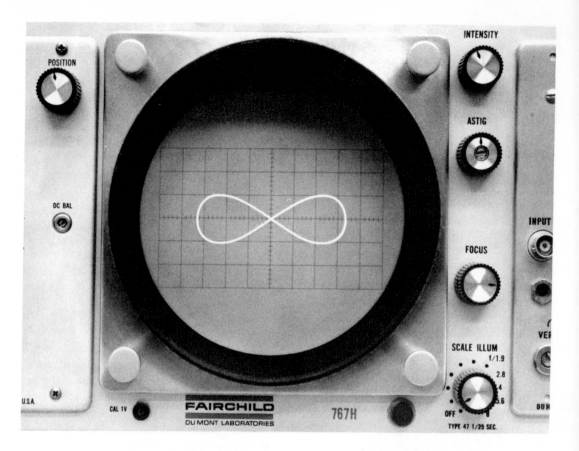

Fig. 7-28. Oscilloscope Lissajous pattern showing 2:1 frequency ratio between vertical axis and horizontal axis sine wave input

Table 7-5. National Census of the United States

Census year no.	Year	Population[a]	Population density (per square mile)	Normalized population (1880 reference)
1	1790	3,929,000	4.5	0.078
2	1800	5,309,000	6.1	0.106
3	1810	7,240,000	4.3	0.144
4	1820	9,639,000	5.6	0.179
5	1830	12,866,000	7.4	0.256
6	1840	17,070,000	9.8	0.339
7	1850	23,192,000	7.9	0.461
8	1860	31,443,000	10.6	0.628
9	1870	39,819,000	13.4	0.795
10	1880	50,156,000	16.9	1.00
11	1890	62,948,000	21.2	1.255
12	1900	75,995,000	25.6	1.515
13	1910	91,972,000	31.0	1.835
14	1920	105,711,000	35.6	2.105
15	1930	122,775,000	41.2	2.445
16	1940	131,669,000	44.2	2.625
17	1950	150,697,000	50.7	3.010
18	1960	178,464,000	60.0	3.555

[a] Values shown to the nearest 1,000.

As an example of the process of normalizing data and plotting the result, consider the population information shown in Table 7-5. If the population count of the 1880 census is used as a reference and all the others compared with it, the relative, or normalized, population figures of the last column are obtained. For example, the relative population figure for 1900 is obtained by comparing the 1900 population count with that of the selected reference. Thus,

Relative population for 1900

$$= \frac{\text{population of 1900}}{\text{population of 1880}}$$

$$= \frac{75,995,000 \text{ persons}}{50,156,000 \text{ persons}}$$

$$= 1.515$$

Note that the relative value is necessarily dimensionless, since the dimensions of the numerator term and denominator term are the same and, therefore, cancel out one another. The relative values are therefore often referred to as "pure numerics." In our example, 1880 is the reference for all the normalized values. Its ratio will thus be 1, as shown in Table 7-5.

A glance at the "Normalized population" column of Table 7-5 shows that the ratios computed vary from 0.078 to 3.555, a range of more than 45:1. Since the range of values is somewhat broad and since we are interested in showing rapidly how these normalized values compare with one another, the data of this column is shown plotted on the logarithmic axis of the semilog paper plot of Fig. 7-29. Since these values are plotted against time, the relative values are taken as the dependent quantities and the census years as the independent quantities. Note that for the first portion of the plot the relative values increase at roughly a constant rate, so that in the period from approximately 1800 to 1880 the population increased by a factor of 10. The rate of population increase is then seen to drop, so that in the next fifty years the population increases by a factor of 2.5. An inflectional point of the curve occurs at the fifteenth census year (1930), and the curve is seen to change from a downward concavity to an upward one, so

that a doubling again occurs within less than forty years. The portion of the curve between the last two plotted points is shown in broken line, since this region represents published predictions rather than actual count.

This type of curve is often used in technology to plot relative output levels or yields against an independent variable. Occasionally, the independent variable is also normalized or has a wide range of values. Under such conditions the horizontal axis may also be logarithmic, yielding a log-log plot. Relative values need not necessarily be plotted on a logarithmic axis, but the advantage of doing so is apparent from the example.

7.20. Three quantities varying at the same time

Consider a problem in which it is necessary to follow the variations of three quantities with respect to one another when they all vary at the same time. Our two-dimensional plotting systems fail us in a problem like this because they can handle only two variable quantities and not three. One solution to a three-variable problem is to hold one of the variables constant and to plot the other two. The process is repeated with the second variable held constant and then the third. If for the present we refer to the three variables as x, y, z, the first plot obtained by this procedure is a y-vs.-x plot with z held fixed, then a z-vs.-x plot with y held constant, and finally a y-vs.-z plot with x held constant. The result is a set of three planar curves, neither one of which supplies all the desired information, but taken together and read by an experienced technician in the field, they provide a true picture of the properties being measured.

One such problem existed in connection with electrocardiagrams "valuable for clinical diagnosis of a variety of cardiac disorders, to monitor normal heart activity and to monitor manned aerospace flights." Normally, electrocardiagrams are two-dimensional graphical displays that can be obtained in a top-to-bottom, left-to-right, and/or front-to-back direction. The following quotation from *Electromechanical Design* clearly defines the problem:

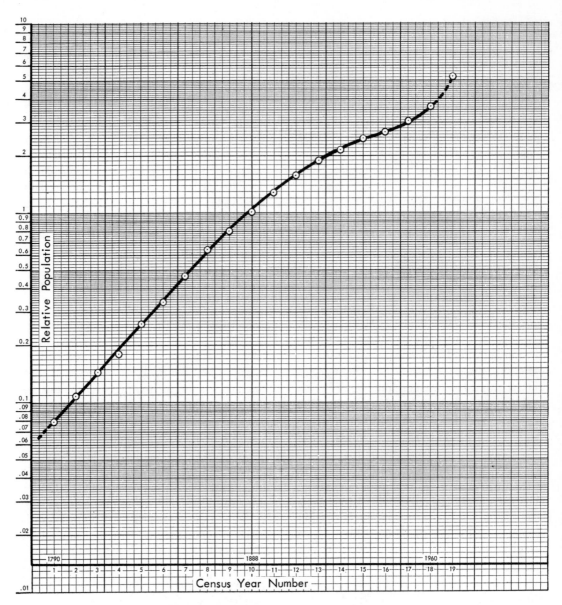

Fig. 7-29. Normalized curve of U.S. population

While a highly skilled diagnostician—with an excellent sense of spacial relations—might work directly from planar projections, such a display does not provide the immediacy of perception and ease of interpretation required for real-time monitoring.

The solution to this particular graphical problem, as developed for Lankenau Hospital in Philadelphia by ITT Federal Laboratories, is depicted in Fig. 7-30. The three-dimensional display shown is an automatically produced composite of the three planar curves.

This type of problem is by no means limited to the example described above, nor is the solution necessarily dependent upon a three-dimensional display automatically produced. Consider the three-dimensional plot of Fig. 7-31. Note that each of the individual curves shown is a two-dimensional plot of cross-section vs. energy and that each of these separate plots is physically arranged in order of ascending atomic weight. The resultant three-dimensional display shows how the three variable quanti-

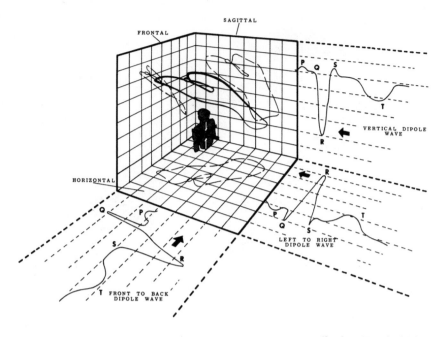

(Courtesy, ITT Federal Laboratories)
Fig. 7-30. Three-dimensional pattern associated with heart activity

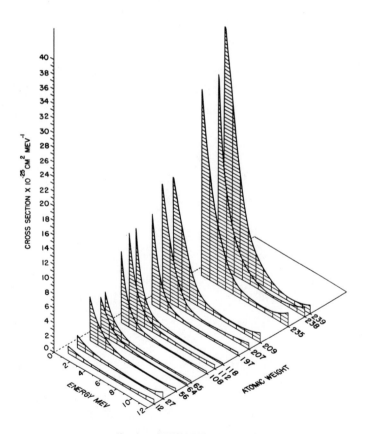

(Courtesy, PHYSICS TODAY, NUCLEONICS, and Los Almos Scientific Laboratory)
Fig. 7-31. Three-dimensional graphical display of spectrum of neutrons emitted in
interaction of neutrons with various elements

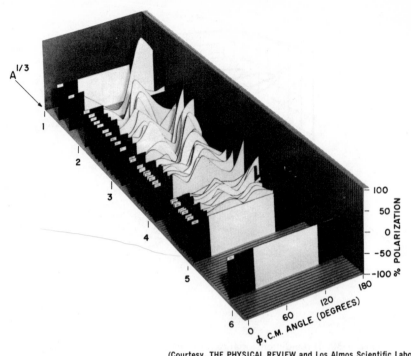

(Courtesy, THE PHYSICAL REVIEW and Los Almos Scientific Laboratory)

Fig. 7-32. Three-dimensional graphical display of angular dependence of polarizations resulting from elastic scattering of 10-MeV polarized protons by various neuclei

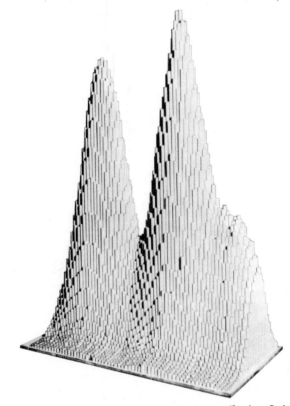

(Courtesy, Packard Instrument Co., Inc.)

Fig. 7-33. Three-dimensional graphical display produced with appropriately placed lucite rods

ties, cross section, energy, and atomic weight, relate to one another. This "manual" method of producing a three-dimensional surface display is depicted again in Fig. 7-32. A more elaborate system involves using rods of proper length representing the y dimensions, located in proper position in an x-y plane held horizontally. An example of this technique is shown in Fig. 7-33.

7.21. Plotting in three dimensions

The various techniques depicted in the preceding paragraph for producing three-dimensional curves and surfaces are very effectively used. However, if a single curve is required that shows how a set of three variables behave with respect to one another, the most direct approach is often a point-by-point plot of such a curve. This brings up the question, "How does one plot a point that has three coordinates?" In a two-dimensional plot each point had two locating values, the abscissa (x) denoting the perpendicular distance from the y axis and the ordinate (y) denoting the perpendicular distance from the x axis. Thus, the designation $P(x, y)$ is all that is necessary to indicate the location of the point P in a planar plot.

This same system, somewhat extended, is utilized in three-dimensional plotting. Here, three coordinates (x, y, z) are necessary to specify the exact location of point P in space, and their designations are taken from the X, Y, and Z axes of a three-dimensional system. Note, for example, the three-dimensional system of axes shown in Fig. 7-34a. In this figure only the positive direction of the three axes are shown. Note that the Y and X axes are in the same position as in a two-dimensional system. The Z axis is drawn at a convenient angle to the other two, but bear in mind that this is a means of representing three dimensions on a two-dimensional sheet of paper. In space, the Z axis is truly perpendicular to the X and to the Y axis, and it is so indicated on the diagram by the right-angle symbol. In a three-dimensional system,

$x =$ perpendicular distance from the YZ plane and is therefore measured in a direction parallel to the X axis

$y =$ perpendicular distance from the XZ plane and is therefore measured parallel to the Y axis

$z =$ perpendicular distance from the XY plane and is measured parallel to the Z axis

Now let us plot points on this coordinate system. The first point to be plotted is P_1 (3, 4, 2). Since the coordinates are given as (x, y, z), we know that the coordinates for this point are $x = 3, y = 4, z = 2$.

The order in which these coordinates are measured is not critical, as will be shown later, but for the sake of establishing a convenient arrangement, let us plot the x coordinate first. Thus, starting from the origin, measure 3 units along the positive X axis. This measurement is designated in the diagram by a heavy line, 3 units long, along the X axis. It is convenient to measure off the z coordinate next. To accomplish this, draw a line from the end of the x coordinate just plotted, parallel to the Z axis. Along this line measure off 2 Z-axis units. Again, this measurement is designated in Fig. 7-33a by a heavy line. The only remaining coordinate is the y value. From the end of the z-coordinate line just drawn, measure upward (parallel to the Y axis) a distance of 4 units as calibrated along the Y axis. Once again this operation is shown in Fig. 7-34a by a heavy line. The point P_1 appears at the end of this y coordinate line. It can be seen from the diagram that the three coordinate lines drawn are three sides of a "solid-rectangle"—correctly known as a "parallelopiped." The additional sides of this solid figure are shown drawn in broken lines. Note that the plotted point P_1 is a vertex of the parallelopiped and that it is the vertex diagonally opposite the origin. Consequently, an alternate method for plotting a point in a three-dimensional system is to construct the solid determined by the three coordinate values given. The point thus plotted is at the vertex of the solid figure that is diagonally opposite the origin. This method can well be used by beginning students in this area

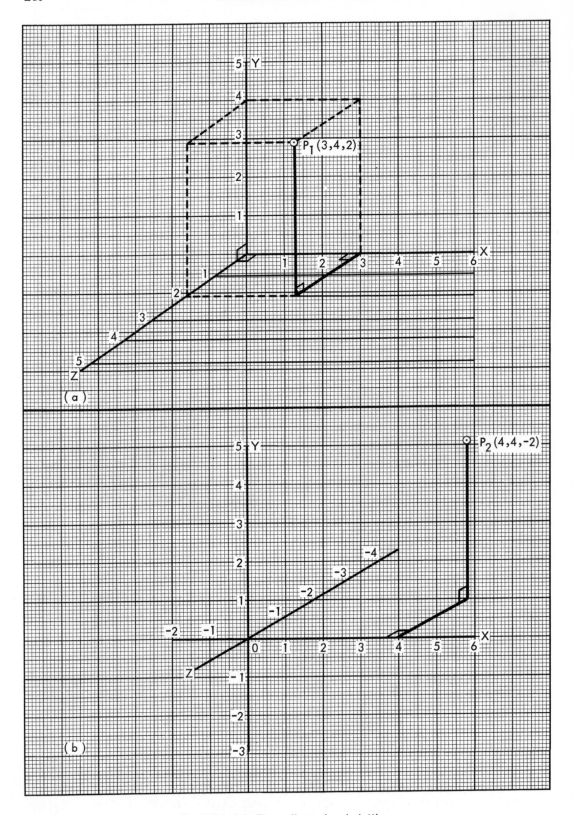

Fig. 7-34a & b. Three-dimensional plotting

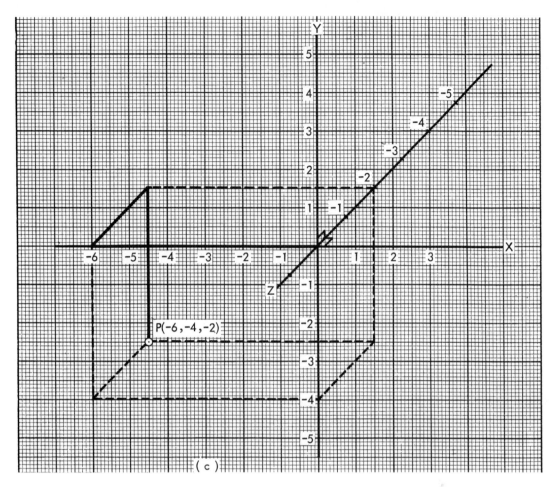

Fig. 7-34c. Three-dimensional plotting

until continued practice makes its use un-
necessary.

The following two parts of Fig. 7-34 show
one point plotted without the aid of the parallelopiped and one plotted with its aid. If you
follow carefully the general plotting procedure
outlined above for points P_2 and P_3, the means
used for locating these points will become apparent. A three-dimensional curve can be
plotted if equations are given that relate the
values so that a table of values can be developed.

7.22. Isometric paper and perspective paper

The isometric paper shown in Fig. 2-11 is
convenient for use in three-dimensional plotting, since a gridwork made up of 60-deg lines

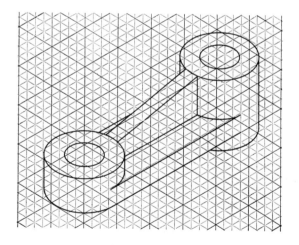

(Courtesy, Keuffel and Esser Co.)
Fig. 7-35. Use of isometric paper

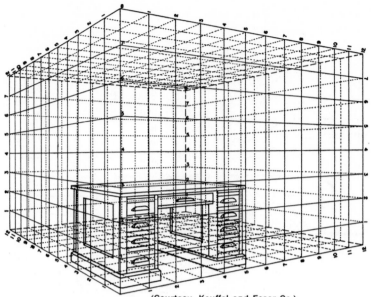

(Courtesy, Keuffel and Esser Co.)

Fig. 7-36. Use of perspective paper

is included. This paper was, however, originally designed to permit rapid transfer of information from a blueprint (orthographic) drawing to one that will show the part in three dimensions. This type of graph paper is therefore known as "isometric-orthographic" paper. An application of it is shown in Fig. 7-35.

Perspective paper, shown in Fig. 7-36, is a "three-dimensional" paper primarily used for sketching. Note that the three-dimensional effect is gained by having the grid lines converge toward a vanishing point. This paper is usually precalibrated to indicate the segments that represent equal distance.

REVIEW

Define concisely or otherwise explain the following terms:

7-1. Fundamental frequency

7-2. Harmonic

7-3. Square wave

7-4. Gate waveshape

7-5. Pulse waveshape

7-6. Trapezoidal waveshape

7-7. Sawtooth waveshape

7-8. Fourier analysis

7-9. Linear device

7-10. Nonlinear device

7-11. Amplifying device

7-12. Operating characteristic curve of a device

7-13. Effect of a nonlinear operating characteristic curve

7-14. Parameter

7-15. Lissajous pattern

7-16. Normalized curve

7-17. Parallelopiped

7-18. Name several significant properties of a plot that can yield useful information.

7-19. (a) A certain voltage varies linearly with time. At t (time) $= 0$, the voltage $= 0$; at $t = 0.05$ sec, the voltage $= 10$ volts. Draw this voltage-vs.-time graph. (b) On the same set of axes draw the voltage-vs.-time waveshape for $v = 5 \sin 377t$. If both of these voltage signals are applied to the input of a system, what does the composite input waveshape look like?

7-20. Refer to Fig. 7-4b. (a) Does the curve show point symmetry? (b) What conclusion is suggested by the fact that this curve was produced by adding a sine wave (that shows point symmetry) to a fixed component?

7-21. (a) What is the effect of adding together the fundamental sine waveshape and all its odd harmonic components? (b) How does this differ from the result obtained from the summation of the fundamental and its even harmonics?

7-22. Refer to Fig. 7-10a. (a) Sketch a waveshape that has two positive sine waveshaped curves similar to the one shown in the figure. (b) Carry out a graphical Fourier analysis of this waveshape. (c) Write the resultant equation. (d) Draw to scale the components of this waveshape. (e) Do you know of any system that produces such a waveshape?

7-23. Use the trapezoidal rule to determine the area bounded by the halfwave rectified curve of Fig. 7-10a.

7-24. Car 1, delivering a message, traveled at the rate of 20 miles per hour. Car 2, with instructions to overtake and stop the first car, started five hours later from the same point and traveled with a velocity of 40 miles per hour. In how many hours will the second car overtake the first? Solve this problem by showing a distance-vs.-time plot for each of the two cars on the same set of axes.

8 - GRAPHICAL RECORDERS

Variables that occur in all phases of science and technology today require precise, instantaneous, and usually permanent recording. These graphical records make the characteristics and functioning of the device or system being observed immediately available to the engineer, technician, analyst, or diagnostician. This type of graphical monitoring is possible for any variable that can be converted into an electrical voltage or current. Transducers exist today that accomplish this conversion for such quantities as force, pressure, temperature, speed, torque, stress, strain, acceleration, position, pitch, yaw, mechanical vibration, and a host of other mechanical quantities related to the fields of machines and vehicles of all descriptions: land, water, or airborne. Quantities in the medical, biological, chemical, and physical

fields are also convertible into electrical signals and graphically monitored. These include such common examples as electrocardiographs, pH readings, and radiation measurements. Figure 8-1 shows the two basic types of instrument used to provide this graphical "read-out" information, the oscilloscope on the right and the electromechanical graphical recorder on the left of the figure.

8.1. The oscilloscope

By far the most versatile instrument for producing a graphical display is the oscilloscope, a particular model of which is shown in Fig. 8-2. The 'scope (as it is commonly referred to) produces a beam of electrons (cathode ray) that strike a fluorescent screen and cause light to be given off at that point. (The operation

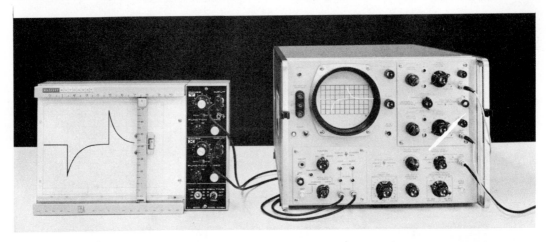

Fig. 8-1. Oscilloscope (right) and graphical recorder (left) provide displays of variables being monitored

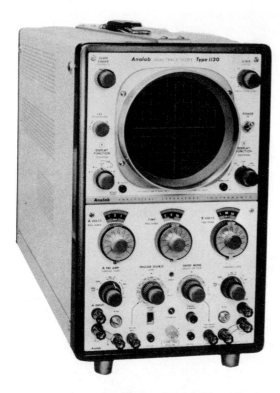

(Courtesy, Analab Instrument Corp.)

Fig. 8-2. Oscilloscopes are highly versatile instruments for producing graphical displays of electrical signals

of a television receiver is also based on this principle.) As shown in Fig. 8-2, the screen is usually provided with a calibrated cartesian coordinate grid-work to aid in the reading and analysis of the display. When an electrical signal is connected to the vertical-axis input terminal of the oscilloscope, it causes the electron beam to deflect vertically.[1] The amount of this vertical deflection varies in accordance with the instantaneous changes of the input electrical signal. Conventionally, the dependent quantity is connected to the vertical-axis terminal. When the independent variable, in the form of an electrical voltage, is connected to the horizontal-axis input terminals,[2] it causes

the electron beam to deflect right and left in accordance with the variations of the independent quantity. When both horizontal-axis and vertical-axis deflections occur simultaneously, the electron beam traces out a graph of y vs. x. Oscillograph displays are depicted in Chapters 1, 4, and 7. Since the "writing element" is a beam of electrons that has practically zero inertia, the oscilloscope can produce a faithful graphical trace of rapidly varying quantities.

When the independent variable is time, the horizontal beam deflection can be produced within the oscilloscope, and no horizontal input voltage need be applied. By setting the oscilloscope to operate at different "sweep frequencies,"[3] it is possible to cause the electron beam to move across the screen from left to right and to return to the left side in a wide variation of time intervals, from large fractions of a second down to microsecond "sweep" times.

Special-purpose oscilloscopes exist for particular problems. Dual-trace 'scopes are used to provide two different waveshapes, simultaneously displayed for purposes of comparison, as shown in Fig. 1-9. Figure 8-1 shows the display of a "charge and discharge" type of waveshape that quickly and accurately yields significant measurement information taken from electronic circuits and other possible sources. Figures 8-3 and 8-4 depict a special-purpose oscilloscope that can plot individual (digital) data points on the screen of a cathode-ray tube (CRT). Here again, the rapid accurate display possible with an electron beam is a tremendous asset.

8.2. Permanent oscillograms

One of the disadvantages of the oscilloscope is that the trace produced on the face of the CRT is not a permanent record. Very often such records are invaluable for purposes of comparison, for detailed study, and for keeping on file large quantities of information in its most abbreviated form. Special-purpose motion-picture film and single-frame cameras

---

[1] The vertical-axis input terminals are often designated Y or V. The 'scope model shown in Fig. 8-2 uses the designation A INPUT in the lower left-hand corner of the front panel.

[2] The horizontal input terminals are often designated X or H. The model shown in Fig. 8-2 uses B INPUT in the lower right-hand corner of the front face of the oscilloscope.

[3] The term "sweep" refers to the travel of the electron beam in the horizontal direction, across the screen of the oscilloscope.

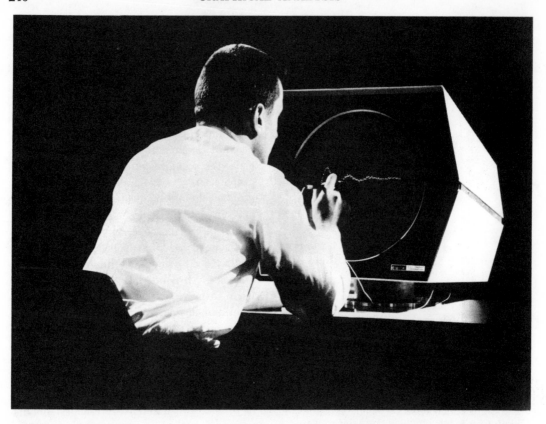

(Courtesy, Digital Equipment Corp.)

Fig. 8-3. Special-purpose oscilloscope plots individual (digital) data points

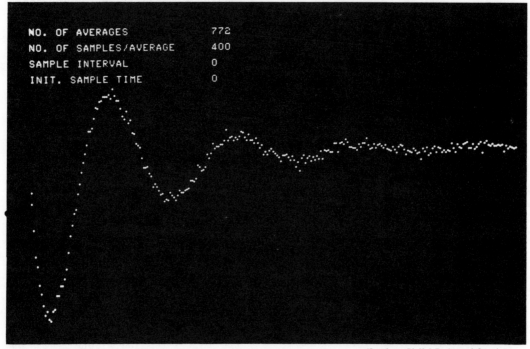

NO. OF AVERAGES   772
NO. OF SAMPLES/AVERAGE   400
SAMPLE INTERVAL   0
INIT. SAMPLE TIME   0

(Courtesy, Digital Equipment Corp.)

Fig. 8-4. Digital data displayed on cathode-ray tube (CRT)

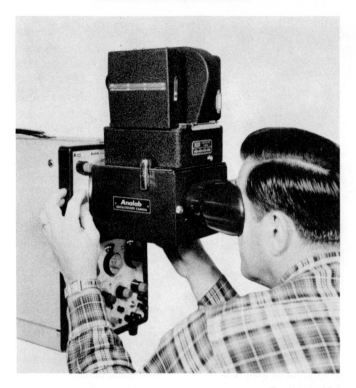

Fig. 8-5. Oscilloscope camera system for permanent trace recording on moving film

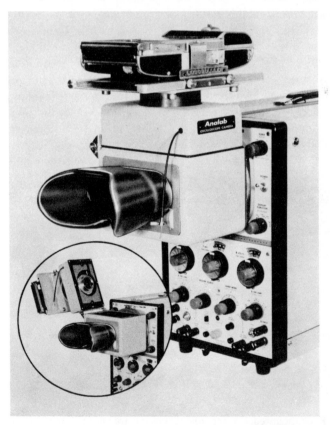

Fig. 8-6. Single-frame oscilloscope camera system

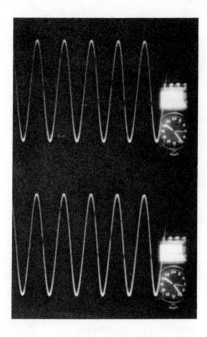

(Courtesy, Analab Instrument Corp.)
Fig. 8-7. Oscillograms are permanently recorded on film for purposes of comparison
and study

have been developed to answer this need, as
can be seen from Figs. 8-5, 8-6, and 8-7.

8.3. Electromechanical recorders

For over fifty years electromechanical
graphical recorders have been used to provide
a permanent record of the quantities being
measured. Since a mechanical system is involved in producing these plots its mass makes

it slower moving than the electron beam of a
cathode-ray oscilloscope. Various paper mark-
ing or "writing" techniques have been developed to supplement the direct-contact ink-fed
recorder pen in order to minimize this limita-
tion. Thus, recorders are available in which
the trace is produced by heat, by electrical
discharge, or by a light-beam writing device.
But even the last-mentioned writing technique
has considerably greater inertia than the electron beam.

However, in a wide variety of applications
graphical recorders have considerable advantages over the fast-moving oscilloscope.
Graphical recorders can produce a permanent
trace, or a multiplicity of traces, on standard-
size graph paper, or larger if necessary. This
expanded trace is more easily read because of
its larger size, finer graph gridwork calibration, and greater uniformity of trace line. (Can
you recognize a distinction between the two
traces shown in Fig. 8-1 that is due to the high
"writing" speed of the oscilloscope electron
beam?) Furthermore, where very low-speed
information is required, the oscilloscope is almost useless. Graphical recorders are readily
available, on the other hand, that will chart
slow-moving variations such as temperature or
humidity over a 24-hr period. Event recorders
plot ON-OFF information vs. time, thus providing a record of the time duration of a given
operation or occurence as well as the time
interval between such occurences. Here the

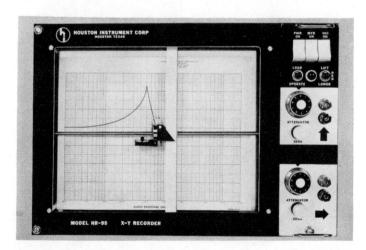

(Courtesy, Houston Instrument Co.)
Fig. 8-8. Rack-mounted X-Y recorder using ink tracing on standard graph paper

oscilloscope is not used at all. Thus, since different types of chart recorders have been developed for various areas of application, they are as a whole often more adaptable and more versatile than the cathode-ray oscilloscope.

8.4. *X-Y recorders*

An *X-Y* recorder is a device that will plot any dependent variable vs. an independent quantity as shown in Fig. 8-8. The variations of the dependent input signal cause the writing-pen assembly to move vertically up and down

(Courtesy, Electronic Associates, Inc.)

Fig. 8-9. High-speed X-Y plotting system with magnetic tape input

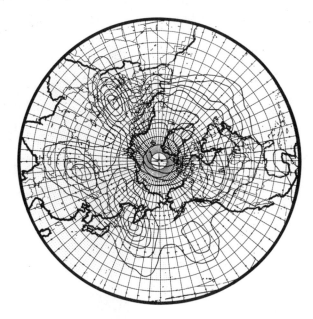

(Courtesy, Electronic Associates, Inc.)

Fig. 8-10. Typical isobar map of northern hemisphere plotted by EIA's 3410 Dataplotter in approximately two minutes

along its support bar, whereas the independent input signal to the recorder determines the horizontal, left-to-right travel of the pen assembly support. Families, or sets, of curves can also be plotted by introducing a parameter that will change the vertical variations for a repeat cycle of the horizontal quantity. Additional recording pens can be fitted to the recorder to produce multiple traces. Thus, the X-Y recorder is ideal for plotting tube and transistor characteristic families of curves as well as stress-vs.-strain curves, pressure-vs.-temperature plots, hysteresis loops, and any other plot where one quantity varies as a function of another. Use of this instrument eliminates manual measurements, plotting, and the inaccuracy inherent in drawing a curve from a limited number of plotted points. Furthermore, since it is an instantaneous recording device, its plot will show all variations, some of which may be too short-lived to be observed by manual measurement.

The recorder shown in Fig. 8-8 is designed primarily for mounting in an equipment rack so that it can measure and record test information as it is produced. Other, somewhat more elaborate X-Y plotting systems plot data previously fed into a magnetic tape by a computer. One such system is shown in Fig. 8-9, and an example of one type of plot obtainable from this plotting system is shown in Fig. 8-10. To quote the manufacturer, "Practical applications of this . . . plotting system include preparation of weather maps, stratigraphy, and subsurface structures plotting, plotting of geodetic survey work, preparation of highway cut-and-fill diagrams, and engineering design and test data display."

8.5. Y-vs.-time recorders

In this type of graphical recorder the independent variable is time. This "time base" is produced by moving the chart paper at a fixed rate, while the writing pen is actuated by the dependent input signal. The Y-vs.-time recorders are subdivided into two basic categories, rectilinear, or strip-chart recorders and polar, or circular, recorders.

In the rectilinear recorder the chart paper is moved linearly in the X direction, while the writing element moves perpendicular to the direction of paper travel to produce the dependent axis variation. Strip-chart recorders are further subdivided into low- and high-speed recorders. The "speed" of a recorder is determined by the ability of its writing element to respond quickly to variations in the input dependent signal. If a writing element response time is measured in seconds or large fractions of a second, the recorder is of the low-speed variety. If the writing element response time is measured in thousandths of a second (milliseconds), then we have a high-speed recorder. The variable being plotted vs. time determines the type of recorder required. Many recorders also incorporate special features that aid in the production or interpretation of the graphical record produced. Figure 8-11 shows a strip-chart recorder that produces two traces simultaneously. One trace is that of the dependent variable vs. time, and the second trace is known as the "integration trace," which represents a plot vs. time of the area under the signal trace. This additional trace provides quan-

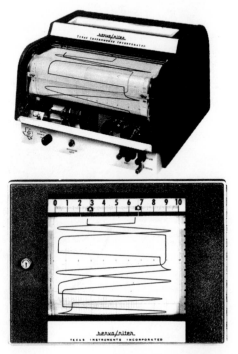

(Courtesy, Texas Instruments Inc.)
Fig. 8-11. Dual-trace strip-chart recorder

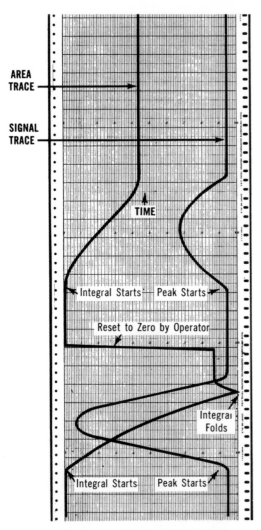

(Courtesy, Texas Instruments Inc.)
Fig. 8-12. Sample of output of integrator recorder

(Courtesy, Weksler Instrument Corp.)
Fig. 8-13. Low-speed circular chart recorder

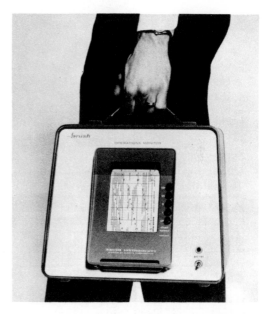

(Courtesy, Brush Instrument Div. of Clevite Corp.)
Fig. 8-14. Portable operations monitor

titative analysis information pertaining to the signal trace. Figure 8-12 shows a sample of the output of this integrating recorder.

Circular chart recorders are almost invariably low-speed recorders and are most useful when the variations to be monitored and recorded occur over a period of hours or even days. Figure 8-13 shows a miniaturized low-speed recorder of a type often used for monitoring temperature, pressure, or relative humidity changes. These recorders can be fitted with one or two pens and are obtainable with 24-hr-per-revolution or 7-day-per-revolution drives.

8.6. Event recorders

It is often necessary to monitor and record the start, stop, and operating time of specific machines, relays, circuit breakers, and other on-off devices. For such applications a special-

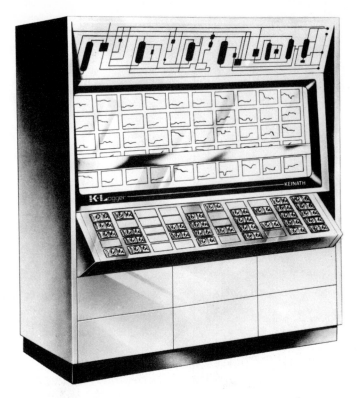

(Courtesy, Keinath Instrument Co.)

Fig. 8-15. Compact control center

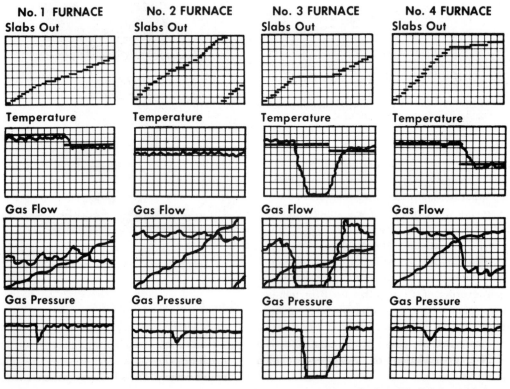

(Courtesy, Keinath Instrument Co.)

Fig. 8-16. Complete production story graphically presented

(Courtesy, Keinath Instrument Co.)

Fig. 8-17. Industrial control center based on graphical displays

purpose strip-chart recorder, commonly known as an "event recorder," is used. The pen deflection is usually actuated by the monitored device as it starts and stops operation by means of specially installed switches. Thus, a permanent record available for examination at any time is produced showing when the device went ON and OFF and how long an interval elapsed between successive occurences. Figure 8-14 shows a portable multi-trace event recorder used to monitor operating or non-operating time for machines and equipment. Another type of event recorder in the form of a bar-chart recorder is shown in Fig. 2-37.

8.7. Special-purpose recorders

Figures 8-15, 8-16, and 8-17 depict examples of the wide variety of special-purpose graphical recording systems designed to satisfy the needs of our technology, when key information graphically displayed is of utmost importance and significance.

Appendix A

GREEK ALPHABET

Letters		Names	Letters		Names	Letters		Names
A	α	Alpha	I	ι	Iota	P	ρ	Rho
B	β	Beta	K	κ	Kappa	Σ	σ	Sigma
Γ	γ	Gamma	Λ	λ	Lambda	T	τ	Tau
Δ	δ	Delta	M	μ	Mu	Υ	υ	Upsilon
E	ϵ	Epsilon	N	ν	Nu	Φ	ϕ	Phi
Z	ζ	Zeta	Ξ	ξ	Xi	X	χ	Chi
H	η	Eta	O	o	Omicron	Ψ	ψ	Psi
Θ	θ	Theta	Π	π	Pi	Ω	ω	Omega

Appendix B

VALUES OF THE TRIGONOMETRIC (CIRCULAR) FUNCTIONS

Angle	Sin	Cos	Tan	Angle	Sin	Cos	Tan
1°	.0175	.9998	.0175	46°	.7193	.6947	1.0355
2°	.0349	.9994	.0349	47°	.7314	.6820	1.0724
3°	.0523	.9986	.0524	48°	.7431	.6691	1.1106
4°	.0698	.9976	.0699	49°	.7547	.6561	1.1504
5°	.0872	.9962	.0875	50°	.7660	.6428	1.1918
6°	.1045	.9945	.1051	51°	.7771	.6293	1.2349
7°	.1219	.9925	.1228	52°	.7880	.6157	1.2799
8°	.1392	.9903	.1405	53°	.7986	.6018	1.3270
9°	.1564	.9877	.1584	54°	.8090	.5878	1.3764
10°	.1736	.9848	.1763	55°	.8192	.5736	1.4281
11°	.1908	.9816	.1944	56°	.8290	.5592	1.4826
12°	.2079	.9781	.2126	57°	.8387	.5446	1.5399
13°	.2250	.9744	.2309	58°	.8480	.5299	1.6003
14°	.2419	.9703	.2493	59°	.8572	.5150	1.6643
15°	.2588	.9659	.2679	60°	.8660	.5000	1.7321
16°	.2756	.9613	.2867	61°	.8746	.4848	1.8040
17°	.2924	.9563	.3057	62°	.8829	.4695	1.8807
18°	.3090	.9511	.3249	63°	.8910	.4540	1.9626
19°	.3256	.9455	.3443	64°	.8988	.4384	2.0503
20°	.3420	.9397	.3640	65°	.9063	.4226	2.1445
21°	.3584	.9336	.3839	66°	.9135	.4067	2.2460
22°	.3746	.9272	.4040	67°	.9205	.3907	2.3559
23°	.3907	.9205	.4245	68°	.9272	.3746	2.4751
24°	.4067	.9135	.4452	69°	.9336	.3584	2.6051
25°	.4226	.9063	.4663	70°	.9397	.3420	2.7475
26°	.4384	.8988	.4877	71°	.9455	.3256	2.9042
27°	.4540	.8910	.5095	72°	.9511	.3090	3.0777
28°	.4695	.8829	.5317	73°	.9563	.2924	3.2709
29°	.4848	.8746	.5543	74°	.9613	.2756	3.4874
30°	.5000	.8660	.5774	75°	.9659	.2588	3.7321
31°	.5150	.8572	.6009	76°	.9703	.2419	4.0108
32°	.5299	.8480	.6249	77°	.9744	.2250	4.3315
33°	.5446	.8387	.6494	78°	.9781	.2079	4.7046
34°	.5592	.8290	.6745	79°	.9816	.1908	5.1446
35°	.5736	.8192	.7002	80°	.9848	.1736	5.6713
36°	.5878	.8090	.7265	81°	.9877	.1564	6.3138
37°	.6018	.7986	.7536	82°	.9903	.1392	7.1154
38°	.6157	.7880	.7813	83°	.9925	.1219	8.1443
39°	.6293	.7771	.8098	84°	.9945	.1045	9.5144
40°	.6428	.7660	.8391	85°	.9962	.0872	11.4301
41°	.6561	.7547	.8693	86°	.9976	.0698	14.3007
42°	.6691	.7431	.9004	87°	.9986	.0523	19.0811
43°	.6820	.7314	.9325	88°	.9994	.0349	28.6363
44°	.6947	.7193	.9657	89°	.9998	.0175	57.2900
45°	.7071	.7071	1.0000	90°	1.0000	.0000	

Appendix C

ALTERNATE DEVELOPMENT OF THE TRIGONOMETRIC (CIRCULAR) FUNCTIONS

Most initial discussions of trigonometric functions relate these quantities to a right triangle. From the many examples throughout this volume and from other technical discussions, it is apparent that a triangle is seldom involved when dealing with a technical application of the trigonometric curves and values. Consequently, the discussion in Chapter 4 makes no reference to the relationship between the circular functions and the right triangle but deals strictly with these quantities as obtained from the projections of a rotating vector. It is the purpose of this appendix to show the common meeting ground of these two approaches to the circular functions.

If the radius, R of Fig. C-1 rotates from position OA to position OB, it sweeps out the angle θ shown. The vertical projection of the radius in the OB position is line CB and the horizontal projection of the radius in this position is line OC. Let's consider the length of the radius to be one unit. The actual size of this "one unit" is completely arbitrary. With this "unit radius" assumption how do the following two values compare to one another:

1. The ratio CB/OB
2. The length of line CB?

Certainly, they are the same, because the denominator of the ratio has a value of unity and the numerator is line CB. But CB is the vertical projection of the radius in the position shown. From Chapter 4 we know that the vertical projection represents the sine of the angle θ. Thus, we can express the sin θ either in terms of the ratio or the vertical projection of the rotating radius.

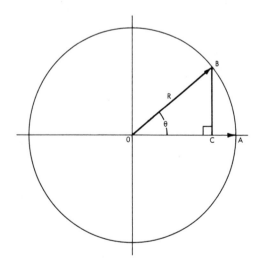

Fig. C-1. The projections of the rotating vector (**R**) produce a right triangle

Notice that the ratio of the above paragraph is written in terms of the letters used in Fig. C-1. Is it possible to express this ratio more generally to make it applicable to any diagram? It is possible if we note from the diagram that the radius (OB), its vertical projection (CB), and its horizontal projection (OC), form a right triangle. Radius OB is the hypotenuse of this triangle, line CB can be considered the leg (or side) of the triangle "opposite" the angle θ, and line OC can be considered the leg of the triangle "adjacent" to the angle θ. Now, instead of expressing the sine of the angle θ as the ratio of CB to OB, we can write

$$\sin \theta = \frac{\text{side opposite } \theta}{\text{hypotenuse}}$$

The value so obtained is valid for any angle θ.

We know from Chapter 4 that the horizontal projection of the rotating vector yields the cosine function. From Fig. C-1 we see that the value of the horizontal projection OC and the value of the ratio OC/OB are the same. If we write this ratio in the more general form, we obtain an expression for the cosine value of any angle, that is

$$\cos \theta = \frac{\text{side adjacent } \theta}{\text{hypotenuse}}$$

From what you know of the relationships between the six circular functions, use the general expressions for the sin θ and the cos θ to show that

$$\tan \theta = \frac{\text{side opposite } \theta}{\text{side adjacent } \theta}$$

$$\csc \theta = \frac{\text{hypotenuse}}{\text{side opposite } \theta}$$

$$\sec \theta = \frac{\text{hypotenuse}}{\text{side adjacent } \theta}$$

$$\operatorname{ctn} \theta = \frac{\text{side adjacent } \theta}{\text{side opposite } \theta}$$

Appendix D

VALUES OF THE HYPERBOLIC FUNCTIONS

x	Sinh x	Cosh x	Tanh x	Coth x
0.00	0.00000	1.00000	0.00000	∞
0.05	0.05002	1.00125	0.04996	20.017
0.10	0.10017	1.00500	0.09967	10.0333
0.15	0.15056	1.01127	0.14889	6.7166
0.20	0.20134	1.02007	0.19738	5.0665
0.25	0.25261	1.03141	0.24492	4.0830
0.30	0.30452	1.04534	0.29131	3.4327
0.35	0.35719	1.06188	0.33638	2.9729
0.40	0.41075	1.08107	0.37995	2.6319
0.45	0.46534	1.10297	0.42190	2.3702
0.50	0.52110	1.12763	0.46212	2.1640
0.55	0.57815	1.15510	0.50052	1.9979
0.60	0.63665	1.18547	0.53705	1.8620
0.65	0.69675	1.21879	0.57167	1.7493
0.70	0.75858	1.25517	0.60437	1.6546
0.75	0.82232	1.29468	0.63515	1.5744
0.80	0.88811	1.33743	0.66404	1.5059
0.85	0.95612	1.38353	0.69107	1.4470
0.90	1.02652	1.43309	0.71630	1.3961
0.95	1.09948	1.48623	0.73978	1.3517
1.00	1.17520	1.54308	0.76159	1.3130
1.05	1.25386	1.60379	0.78181	1.2791
1.10	1.33565	1.66852	0.80050	1.2492
1.15	1.42078	1.73741	0.81775	1.2229
1.20	1.50946	1.81066	0.83365	1.1995
1.25	1.60192	1.88842	0.84828	1.1789
1.30	1.69838	1.97091	0.86172	1.1605
1.35	1.79909	2.05833	0.87405	1.1441
1.40	1.90430	2.15090	0.88535	1.1295
1.45	2.01427	2.24884	0.89569	1.1165
1.50	2.12928	2.35241	0.90515	1.1048
1.55	2.24961	2.46186	0.91379	1.0943
1.60	2.37557	2.57746	0.92167	1.0850
1.65	2.50746	2.69951	0.92886	1.0766
1.70	2.64563	2.82832	0.93541	1.0691
1.75	2.79041	2.96419	0.94138	1.0623
1.80	2.94217	3.10747	0.94681	1.0562
1.85	3.10129	3.25853	0.95175	1.0507
1.90	3.26816	3.41773	0.95624	1.0458
1.95	3.44321	3.58548	0.96032	1.0413
2.00	3.62686	3.76220	0.96403	1.0373
2.05	3.81958	3.94832	0.96740	1.0337
2.10	4.02186	4.14431	0.97045	1.0304
2.15	4.23419	4.35067	0.97323	1.0275
2.20	4.45711	4.56791	0.97574	1.0249
2.25	4.69117	4.79657	0.97803	1.0225
2.30	4.93696	5.03722	0.98010	1.0203
2.35	5.19510	5.29047	0.98197	1.0184
2.40	5.46623	5.55695	0.98367	1.0166
2.45	5.75103	5.83732	0.98522	1.0150

VALUES OF THE HYPERBOLIC FUNCTIONS (cont.)

x	Sinh x	Cosh x	Tanh x	Coth x
2.50	6.05020	6.13229	0.98661	1.0136
2.55	6.36451	6.44259	0.98788	1.0123
2.60	6.69473	6.76901	0.98903	1.0111
2.65	7.04169	7.11234	0.99007	1.0100
2.70	7.40626	7.47347	0.99101	1.0091
2.75	7.78935	7.85328	0.99186	1.0082
2.80	8.19192	8.25273	0.99263	1.0074
2.85	8.61497	8.67281	0.99333	1.0067
2.90	9.05956	9.11458	0.99396	1.0061
2.95	9.52681	9.57915	0.99454	1.0055
3.00	10.01787	10.06766	0.99505	1.0050
3.5	16.5426	16.5728	0.99818	1.0018
4.0	27.2899	27.3082	0.99933	1.0007
4.5	45.0030	45.0141	0.99975	1.0002
5.0	74.2032	74.2099	0.99991	1.0001
5.5	122.34	122.35	0.99997	1.0000
6.0	201.71	201.72	0.99999	1.0000
6.5	332.57	332.57	1.0000	1.0000
7.0	548.32	548.32	1.0000	1.0000
7.5	904.02	904.02	1.0000	1.0000
8.0	1490.5	1490.5	1.0000	1.0000
8.5	2457.4	2457.4	1.0000	1.0000
9.0	4051.5	4051.5	1.0000	1.0000
9.5	6679.9	6679.9	1.0000	1.0000
10.0	11013.2	11013.2	1.0000	1.0000

Appendix E

COMMON LOGARITHMS OF NUMBERS*

N	0	1	2	3	4	5	6	7	8	9
10	0000	0043	0086	0128	0170	0212	0253	0294	0334	0374
11	0414	0453	0492	0531	0569	0607	0645	0682	0719	0755
12	0792	0828	0864	0899	0934	0969	1004	1038	1072	1106
13	1139	1173	1206	1239	1271	1303	1335	1367	1399	1430
14	1461	1492	1523	1553	1584	1614	1644	1673	1703	1732
15	1761	1790	1818	1847	1875	1903	1931	1959	1987	2014
16	2041	2068	2095	2122	2148	2175	2201	2227	2253	2279
17	2304	2330	2355	2380	2405	2430	2455	2480	2504	2529
18	2553	2577	2601	2625	2648	2672	2695	2718	2742	2765
19	2788	2810	2833	2856	2878	2900	2923	2945	2967	2989
20	3010	3032	3054	3075	3096	3118	3139	3160	3181	3201
21	3222	3243	3263	3284	3304	3324	3345	3365	3385	3404
22	3424	3444	3464	3483	3502	3522	3541	3560	3579	3598
23	3617	3636	3655	3674	3692	3711	3729	3747	3766	3784
24	3802	3820	3838	3856	3874	3892	3909	3927	3945	3962
25	3979	3997	4014	4031	4048	4065	4082	4099	4116	4133
26	4150	4166	4183	4200	4216	4232	4249	4265	4281	4298
27	4314	4330	4346	4362	4378	4393	4409	4425	4440	4456
28	4472	4487	4502	4518	4533	4548	4564	4579	4594	4609
29	4624	4639	4654	4669	4683	4698	4713	4728	4742	4757
30	4771	4786	4800	4814	4829	4843	4857	4871	4886	4900
31	4914	4928	4942	4955	4969	4983	4997	5011	5024	5038
32	5051	5065	5079	5092	5105	5119	5132	5145	5159	5172
33	5185	5198	5211	5224	5237	5250	5263	5276	5289	5302
34	5315	5328	5340	5353	5366	5378	5391	5403	5416	5428
35	5441	5453	5465	5478	5490	5502	5514	5527	5539	5551
36	5563	5575	5587	5599	5611	5623	5635	5647	5658	5670
37	5682	5694	5705	5717	5729	5740	5752	5763	5775	5786
38	5798	5809	5821	5832	5843	5855	5866	5877	5888	5899
39	5911	5922	5933	5944	5955	5966	5977	5988	5999	6010
40	6021	6031	6042	6053	6064	6075	6085	6096	6107	6117
41	6128	6138	6149	6160	6170	6180	6191	6201	6212	6222
42	6232	6243	6253	6263	6274	6284	6294	6304	6314	6325
43	6335	6345	6355	6365	6375	6385	6395	6405	6415	6425
44	6435	6444	6454	6464	6474	6484	6493	6503	6513	6522
45	6532	6542	6551	6561	6571	6580	6590	6599	6609	6618
46	6628	6637	6646	6656	6665	6675	6684	6693	6702	6712
47	6721	6730	6739	6749	6758	6767	6776	6785	6794	6803
48	6812	6821	6830	6839	6848	6857	6866	6875	6884	6893
49	6902	6911	6920	6928	6937	6946	6955	6964	6972	6981
50	6990	6998	7007	7016	7024	7033	7042	7050	7059	7067
51	7076	7084	7093	7101	7110	7118	7126	7135	7143	7152
52	7160	7168	7177	7185	7193	7202	7210	7218	7226	7235
53	7243	7251	7259	7267	7275	7284	7292	7300	7308	7316
54	7324	7332	7340	7348	7356	7364	7372	7380	7388	7396
N	0	1	2	3	4	5	6	7	8	9

* This table gives the mantissas of numbers with the decimal point omitted in each case. Characteristics are determined by inspection from the numbers.

COMMON LOGARITHMS OF NUMBERS (cont.)

N	0	1	2	3	4	5	6	7	8	9
55	7404	7412	7419	7427	7435	7443	7451	7459	7466	7474
56	7482	7490	7497	7505	7513	7520	7528	7536	7543	7551
57	7559	7566	7574	7582	7589	7597	7604	7612	7619	7627
58	7634	7642	7649	7657	7664	7672	7679	7686	7694	7701
59	7709	7716	7723	7731	7738	7745	7752	7760	7767	7774
60	7782	7789	7796	7803	7810	7818	7825	7832	7839	7846
61	7853	7860	7868	7875	7882	7889	7896	7903	7910	7917
62	7924	7931	7938	7945	7952	7959	7966	7973	7980	7987
63	7993	8000	8007	8014	8021	8028	8035	8041	8048	8055
64	8062	8069	8075	8082	8089	8096	8102	8109	8116	8122
65	8129	8136	8142	8149	8156	8162	8169	8176	8182	8189
66	8195	8202	8209	8215	8222	8228	8235	8241	8248	8254
67	8261	8267	8274	8280	8287	8293	8299	8306	8312	8319
68	8325	8331	8338	8344	8351	8357	8363	8370	8376	8382
69	8388	8395	8401	8407	8414	8420	8426	8432	8439	8445
70	8451	8457	8463	8470	8476	8482	8488	8494	8500	8506
71	8513	8519	8525	8531	8537	8543	8549	8555	8561	8567
72	8573	8579	8585	8591	8597	8603	8609	8615	8621	8627
73	8633	8639	8645	8651	8657	8663	8669	8675	8681	8686
74	8692	8698	8704	8710	8716	8722	8727	8733	8739	8745
75	8751	8756	8762	8768	8774	8779	8785	8791	8797	8802
76	8808	8814	8820	8825	8831	8837	8842	8848	8854	8859
77	8865	8871	8876	8882	8887	8893	8899	8904	8910	8915
78	8921	8927	8932	8938	8943	8949	8954	8960	8965	8971
79	8976	8982	8987	8993	8998	9004	9009	9015	9020	9025
80	9031	9036	9042	9047	9053	9058	9063	9069	9074	9079
81	9085	9090	9096	9101	9106	9112	9117	9122	9128	9133
82	9138	9143	9149	9154	9159	9165	9170	9175	9180	9186
83	9191	9196	9201	9206	9212	9217	9222	9227	9232	9238
84	9243	9248	9253	9258	9263	9269	9274	9279	9284	9289
85	9294	9299	9304	9309	9315	9320	9325	9330	9335	9340
86	9345	9350	9355	9360	9365	9370	9375	9380	9385	9390
87	9395	9400	9405	9410	9415	9420	9425	9430	9435	9440
88	9445	9450	9455	9460	9465	9469	9474	9479	9484	9489
89	9494	9499	9504	9509	9513	9518	9523	9528	9533	9538
90	9542	9547	9552	9557	9562	9566	9571	9576	9581	9586
91	9590	9595	9600	9605	9609	9614	9619	9624	9628	9633
92	9638	9643	9647	9652	9657	9661	9666	9671	9675	9680
93	9685	9689	9694	9699	9703	9708	9713	9717	9722	9727
94	9731	9736	9741	9745	9750	9754	9759	9763	9768	9773
95	9777	9782	9786	9791	9795	9800	9805	9809	9814	9818
96	9823	9827	9832	9836	9841	9845	9850	9854	9859	9863
97	9868	9872	9877	9881	9886	9890	9894	9899	9903	9908
98	9912	9917	9921	9926	9930	9934	9939	9943	9948	9952
99	9956	9961	9965	9969	9974	9978	9983	9987	9991	9996
N	0	1	2	3	4	5	6	7	8	9

Index